Zothique

"The Watcher of the Shadows" (1919) by Clark Ashton Smith

ZOTHIQUE

THE FINAL CYCLE

Clark Ashton Smith

Edited By Ronald S. Hilger

Hippocampus Press

New York

Published by Hippocampus Press
P.O. Box 641, New York, NY 10156.
www.hippocampuspress.com

Cover illustration and design © 2022 by Jason Van Hollander.
Title design on front cover by Daniel V. Sauer, dansauerdesign.com
Hippocampus Press logo designed by Anastasia Damianakos.

First Paperback Edition
1 3 5 7 9 8 6 4 2

ISBN 978-1-61498-376-7 (paperback)
ISBN 978-1-61498-372-9 (ebook)

For Donald Sidney-Fryer
Poet, Scholar, Mentor, and Friend

CONTENTS

A Far Older World
in the Far Future

In the cosmos imagined, or re-imagined, by Clark Ashton Smith—whether delineated in his memorable poetry or his prose—the one essential ingredient is beauty, nay, Beauty as posited by Plato and Plotinus. But the geography wherein this Beauty makes her appearance could not seem more diverse and variegated, and the tone is, more often than not, portentous, more like an oracle, or prophecy.

Whereas Ashton Smith could write charming stories that were generally rather brief—"The Willow Landscape" is a prime example—the sixteen tales he created as part of the Zothique cycle or sequence are almost all macabre or lethal. (When is Ashton Smith not macabre or lethal?) Death stalks these narratives as relentlessly as it does the dramas of Kit Marlowe and other dramatic poets of the period of the Elizabethan or Jacobean period, just as it did the everyday life of the late sixteen and early seventeenth centuries.

If the Averoigne stories appear superficially enchanting, death also stalks as much in that sequence as anywhere else in Smith's oeuvre. But evidently we do not notice this deathly presence as much as elsewhere given that Averoigne (probably derived from Auvergne, which dominates the Massif Central of southern France) is often ravishingly beautiful, the epitome or quintessence of green and greenery, of lush and lavish verdure.

What a contrast that makes with Zothique, the last continent of the planet Earth! The barren deserts are all that are left of once lush kingdoms and empires—especially as described in that characteristical-

9

ly portentous or ominous tone that Smith favors. The poet-author compels the serious reader to perceive his narratives with all due seriousness.

A few of the tales should be singled out by name. "Xeethra": one of the most poignant fables of emotional loss ever told. "The Dark Eidolon": a superlative thriller of necromancy and vengeance. "The Empire of the Necromancers": an utterly unique narrative if ever there was one. "The Voyage of King Euvoran": as the reader might guess, this tale is no lighthearted cruise; typically Smithian, it features one of the most ironic endings in all prose fiction anywhere.

Special mention must also be made of the system of metaphor and simile that accompanies each narrative as a kind of reflection or punctuation. Sometimes it is as close to the narrative as it could possibly be while still remaining distinct, in particular the ominous and eternally omni-poetic voice that presents the story, no less than the system of metaphor and simile.

About Zothique, that large land mass, Smith remains deadly serious, and he insists that the mood of the reader be as deadly serious as any of these sixteen tales. The author, it is obvious, means them as much more than lighthearted bagatelles. The poet-narrator, Smith himself, is always in dead, or deadly, earnest about what he relates. Smith is always the Specter at the Feast looking over our shoulder. Readers cannot escape him, nor can they but be intrigued or even charmed by all his death-related paraphernalia.

—DONALD SIDNEY-FRYER

Cape Cod, Massachusetts

INTRODUCTION

The Zothique cycle represents the largest and probably the most well-known series of thematically interrelated stories created by the California poet and weird fiction writer Clark Ashton Smith (1893–1961). At sixteen stories, plus *The Dead Will Cuckold You* (a play set in Zothique that Smith once described as his "masterpiece"), the series far surpasses both his Averoigne (eleven tales) and Hyperborea (ten tales) story-cycles. Smith conceived Zothique as a large continent which re-surfaces under a red and dying sun during the last days of humanity. The land is filled with a decadent and morbid atmosphere, where science and technology have been replaced by the resurgence of magic, sorcery, and necromancy, while the crumbling ruins of deserted cities are all that remain among vast tracts of uninhabited deserts. The elder gods have also returned to replace the more contemporary religions during these final days. Such gods as Thasaidon, Mordiggian, and Vergama have all re-emerged to witness the end of days and once again rule the remnants of the human race.

That Clark Ashton Smith hoped one day to see his Zothique tales collected in book form is evident from his correspondence, as in his letter to August Derleth of 29 August 1933.

> With the completion of two more tales, "Xeethra" and "The Madness of Chronomage," I will have a series totalling about 60,000 words, all dealing with the future continent of Zothique. These could be collected with a brief note as to suppositional geography and chronology. My Averoigne series also lacks about two more tales to bring it to book-size; and the Hyperborea and Atlantean suites are perhaps half-finished. Printed on good paper and decently bound, I think that all of these tales would show up as fine literature, in no wise inferior to Dunsany or Cabell.

Smith did not live to see his projected Zothique collection, but his concept of a far future world of magic and sorcery would fire the imaginations of many subsequent writers such as Jack Vance and his Dying Earth series and A. E. van Vogt and his Book of Ptath. Many other well-known writers such as Ray Bradbury, Harlan Ellison, and Fritz Leiber would credit Clark Ashton Smith as being a major inspiration in their decision to become fiction writers as well as an influence in their own writings.

The texts used in this collection all come from the restored versions published in the "Collected Fantasies" series by Night Shade books (2006–10), wherein heavily edited versions published in *Weird Tales* and other pulp magazines have been restored to their original states through comparison with the manuscripts Smith used when first submitting these tales for publication; much excised material as well as original titles and other elements have been restored. Smith often was forced to edit his tales for publication because various editors rejected the original versions, based on concerns with their poetic and descriptive style or mildly erotic content.

"Xeethra," one of Smith's most ironic tales of irretrievable loss, is preceded by "The Traveller," a prose poem first included in Smith's self-published poetry collection *Ebony and Crystal* (1922). It deals with a traveler who spends his entire life wandering in search of his former home and is manifestly the original concept behind the latter story.

"The Voyage of King Euvoran" is a tale originally set in Hyperborea, but after repeated rejections Smith decided to change the setting to the more popular Zothique. No manuscript for this original version has been found, but a listing of tales for a proposed collection of Hyperborean tales includes "Euvoran"; it is designated as item number three in *The Black Book of Clark Ashton Smith*. It is therefore not surprising that this tale is much more lighthearted in tone than his other Zothique tales, having an abundance of comical ironic content running throughout.

"The Last Hieroglyph" is another tale that Smith was forced to edit repeatedly in order to secure publication; however, in this case he would expand the tale rather than excise the presumably offensive atmospheric or poetic material. It was originally titled "In the Book of Vergama," and the one casualty of editing was the excision of the beginning pages, which formed a sort of prologue detailing the attributes and mythology behind the mysterious and godlike entity Vergama. That material has been restored in this volume and sets the stage for "The Last Hieroglyph."

There have been two other collections of Zothique tales previously published in English: *Zothique,* edited by Lin Carter for the Ballantine Adult Fantasy (1970), and *Tales of Zothique,* edited by Will Murray and Steve Behrends (Necronomicon Press, 1995); there are also other collections in Dutch, French, Italian, and Spanish. While *Tales of Zothique* is notable for its inclusion of *The Dead Will Cuckold You* and "In the Book of Vergama," only in the Ballantine edition did editor Lin Carter attempt to arrange the sequence according to internal evidence in order to present a more aesthetically pleasing chronology. In his epilogue, Carter goes to some length to explain the reasoning behind his arrangement of the Zothique series, and is for the most part successful in this. However, there are a few places wherein this collection diverges from Carter's sequence; as Will Murray points out in his introduction to *Tales of Zothique,* Carter apparently overlooks the introductory nature of "The Empire of the Necromancers." Given that this was the first Zothique tale written by Smith, it seems the perfect choice to begin the sequence. Smith also had a preference as to the ending of this series, as indicated by his letter to Robert Barlow of 21 May 1934: "I'm glad you liked 'Vergama.' I think I told you that I had amplified and embroidered the tale somewhat. It will form the concluding item of my Zothique series, if this series should ever appear between book covers." So, in deference to the wishes of the author himself, "The

Last Hieroglyph" concludes the volume and is prefaced by the excised "In the Book of Vergama" as originally conceived by Smith.

The map of Zothique was drawn by Tim Kirk, and while he has graciously allowed us to include it here, he cautions that it was drawn some forty years ago and seems rather juvenile to him now. I find it both well done and obviously much more detailed than the map used in the Ballantine edition. Carter's map is based on a sketch that was approved by Smith, but is quite limited and lacks the finer details Kirk has included and named, such as rivers, deserts, jungles, and most importantly, cities. Moreover, this map corresponds closely to the Smith-approved sketch, which is perhaps not surprising as he also consulted with noted Smith scholar Thomas G. L. Cockcroft on these finer points as described in Smith's various tales of Zothique.

The macabre and melancholy world of Zothique seems the perfect setting for Smith's distinctly decadent literary style and favorite atmospheric devices. Thick veins of irony and loss, decadence and hopelessness permeate these tales like some charnel nourishment, almost to the point of overwhelming the reader with doom and gloom. Do not despair, for there is beauty and wisdom to be found here as well, and yes, even love and hope may reside within the most noisome sepulchers of this ultimate continent. Welcome then, intrepid reader, to the common fate of mankind as Klarkash-Ton guides you through his visions of the final cycle of the Earth, and the last days of humanity, even as Charon ferried the newly deceased across the river Styx to fabulous realms and future incarnations.

—RONALD S. HILGER

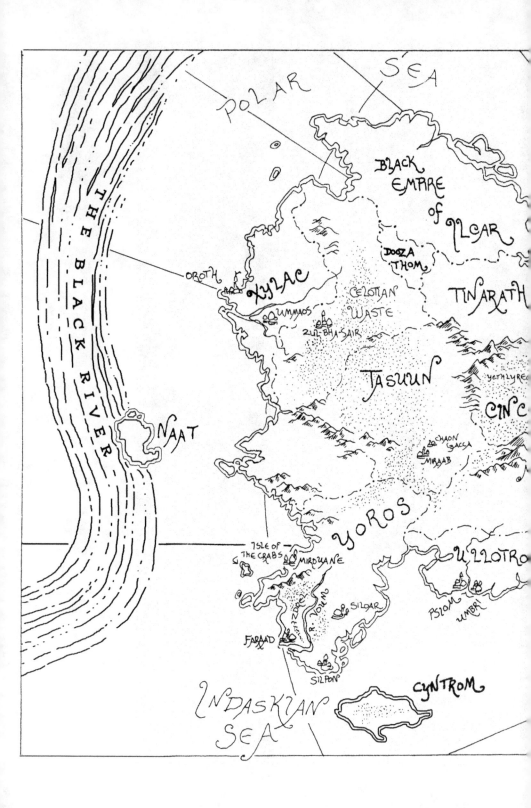

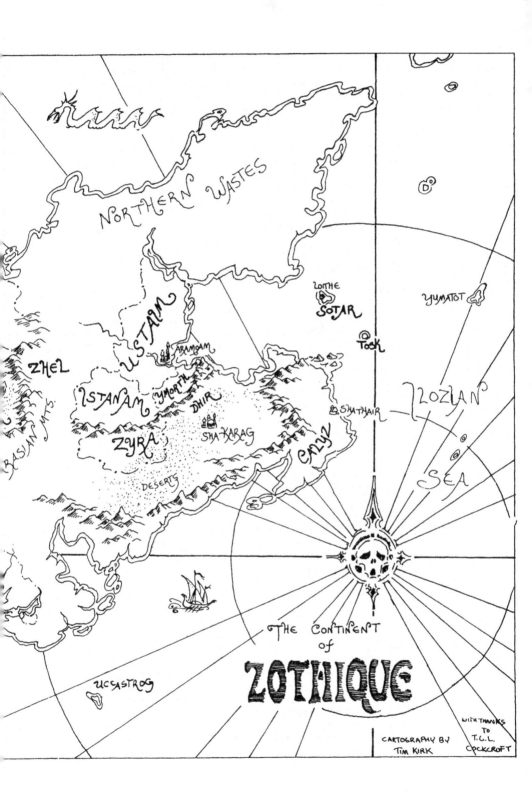

NORTHERN WASTES

ZHEL

USTAIM

ISTANAM

ARAMOAM

YMORTH

DHIR

ZYRA

SHA-KARAG

BASIAN MTS.

DESERTS

CALYZ

LOITHE

SOTAR

TASK

SHATHAIR

YUMATOT

IZOZLAN

SEA

UCCASTROG

THE CONTINENT
OF

ZOTHIQUE

CARTOGRAPHY BY
TIM KIRK

WITH THANKS
TO
T.C.L.
COCKCROFT

ZOTHIQUE

He who has trod the shadows of Zothique
And looked upon the coal-red sun oblique,
Henceforth returns to no anterior land,
But haunts a latter coast
Where cities crumble in the black sea-sand
And dead Gods drink the brine.

He who has known the gardens of Zothique
Where bleed the fruits torn by the simorgh's beak,
Savors no fruit of greener hemispheres:
In arbors uttermost,
In sunset cycles of the sombering years,
He sips an amaranth wine.

He who has loved the wild girls of Zothique
Shall come not back a gentler love to seek,
Nor know the vampire's from the lover's kiss:
For him the scarlet ghost
Of Lilith from time's last necropolis
Rears amorous and malign.

He who has sailed in galleys of Zothique
And seen the looming of strange spire and peak,
Must face again the sorcerer-sent typhoon,
And take the steerer's post
On far-poured oceans by the shifted moon
Or the re-shapen Sign.

THE EMPIRE OF THE NECROMANCERS

The legend of Mmatmuor and Sodosma shall arise only in the latter cycles of Earth, when the glad legends of the prime have been forgotten. Before the time of its telling, many epochs shall have passed away, and the seas shall have fallen in their beds, and new continents shall have come to birth. Perhaps, in that day, it will serve to beguile for a little the black weariness of a dying race, grown hopeless of all but oblivion. I tell the tale as men shall tell it in Zothique, the last continent, beneath a dim sun and sad heavens where the stars come out in terrible brightness before eventide.

I

Mmatmuor and Sodosma were necromancers who came from the dark isle of Naat, to practise their baleful arts in Tinarath, beyond the shrunken seas. But they did not prosper in Tinarath: for death was deemed a holy thing by the people of that grey country; and the nothingness of the tomb was not lightly to be desecrated; and the raising up of the dead by necromancy was held in abomination.

So, after a short interval, Mmatmuor and Sodosma were driven forth by the anger of the inhabitants, and were compelled to flee toward Cincor, a desert of the south, which was peopled only by the bones and mummies of a race that the pestilence had slain in former time.

The land into which they went lay drear and leprous and ashen below the huge, ember-colored sun. Its crumbling rocks and deathly solitudes of sand would have struck terror to the hearts of common men; and since they had been thrust out in that barren place without food or sustenance, the plight of the sorcerers might well have seemed a desperate one. But, smiling secretly, with the air of conquerors who tread the approaches of a long-coveted realm, Sodosma and Mmatmuor walked steadily on into Cincor.

Unbroken before them, through fields devoid of trees and grass, and across the channels of dried-up rivers, there ran the great highway by which travellers had gone formerly between Cincor and Tinarath. Here they met no living thing; but soon they came to the skeletons of a horse and its rider, lying full in the road, and wearing still the sumptuous harness and raiment which they had worn in the flesh. And Mmatmuor and Sodosma paused before the piteous bones, on which no shred of corruption remained; and they smiled evilly at each other.

"The steed shall be yours," said Mmatmuor, "since you are a little the elder of us two, and are thus entitled to precedence; and the rider shall serve us both and be the first to acknowledge fealty to us in Cincor."

Then, in the ashy sand by the wayside, they drew a threefold circle; and standing together at its center, they performed the abominable rites that compel the dead to arise from tranquil nothingness and obey henceforward, in all things, the dark will of the necromancer. Afterwards, they sprinkled a pinch of magic powder on the nostril-holes of the man and the horse; and the white bones, creaking mournfully, rose up from where they had lain and stood in readiness to serve their masters.

So, as had been agreed between them, Sodosma mounted the skeleton steed and took up the jewelled reins, and rode in an evil mockery of Death on his pale horse; while Mmatmuor trudged on beside him, leaning lightly on an ebon staff; and the skeleton of the man, with its rich raiment flapping loosely, followed behind the two like a servitor.

After a while, in the grey waste, they found the remnants of another horse and rider, which the jackals had spared and the sun had dried to the leanness of old mummies. These also they raised up from death; and Mmatmuor bestrode the withered charger; and the two magicians rode on in state, like errant emperors, with a lich and a skeleton to attend them. Other bones and charnel remnants of men and beasts, to which they came anon, were duly resurrected in like fashion; so that they gathered to themselves an ever-swelling train in their progress through Cincor.

Along the way, as they neared Yethlyreom, which had been the capital, they found numerous tombs and necropoli, inviolate still after many ages, and containing swathed mummies that had scarcely withered in death. All these they raised up and called from sepulchral night to do their bidding. Some they commanded to sow and till the desert fields and hoist water from the sunken wells; others they left at diverse tasks, such as the mummies had performed in life. The century-long silence was broken by the noise and tumult of myriad activities; and the lank liches of weavers toiled at their shuttles; and the corpses of plowmen followed their furrows behind carrion oxen.

Weary with their strange journey and their oft-repeated incantations, Mmatmuor and Sodosma saw before them at last, from a desert hill, the lofty spires and fair, unbroken domes of Yethlyreom, steeped in the darkening stagnant blood of ominous sunset.

"It is a goodly land," said Mmatmuor, "and you and I will share it between us, and hold dominion over all its dead, and be crowned as emperors on the morrow in Yethlyreom."

"Aye," replied Sodosma, "for there is none living to dispute us here; and those that we have summoned from the tomb shall move and breathe only at our dictation, and may not rebel against us."

So, in the blood-red twilight that thickened with purple, they entered Yethlyreom and rode on among the lofty, lampless mansions, and installed themselves with their grisly retinue in that stately and abandoned palace, where the dynasty of Nimboth emperors had reigned for two thousand years with dominion over Cincor.

In the dusty golden halls, they lit the empty lamps of onyx by means of their cunning sorcery, and supped on royal viands, provided from past years, which they evoked in like manner. Ancient and imperial wines were poured for them in moonstone cups by the fleshless hands of their servitors; and they drank and feasted and revelled in phantasmagoric pomp, deferring till the morrow the resurrection of those who lay dead in Yethlyreom.

They rose betimes, in the dark crimson dawn, from the opulent palace-beds in which they had slept; for much remained to be done. Everywhere in that forgotten city, they went busily to and fro, working their spells on the people that had died in the last year of the pest and had lain unburied. And having accomplished this, they passed beyond Yethlyreom into that other city of high tombs and mighty mausoleums, in which lay the Nimboth emperors and the more consequential citizens and nobles of Cincor.

Here, they bade their skeleton slaves to break in the sealed doors with hammers; and then, with their sinful, tyrannous incantations, they called forth the imperial mummies, even to the eldest of the dynasty, all of whom came walking stiffly, with lightless eyes, in rich swathings sewn with flame-bright jewels. And also later they brought forth to a semblance of life many generations of courtiers and dignitaries.

Moving in solemn pageant, with dark and haughty and hollow faces, the dead emperors and empresses of Cincor made obeisance to Mmatmuor and Sodosma, and attended them like a train of captives through all the streets of Yethlyreom. Afterwards, in the immense throne-room of the palace, the necromancers mounted the high double throne, where the rightful rulers had sate with their consorts. Amid the assembled emperors, in gorgeous and funereal state, they were invested with sovereignty by the sere hands of the mummy of Hestaiyon, earliest of the Nimboth line, who had ruled in half-mythic years. Then all the descendants of Hestaiyon, crowding the room in a great throng, acclaimed with toneless, echo-like voices the dominion of Mmatmuor and Sodosma.

Thus did the outcast necromancers find for themselves an empire and a subject people in the desolate, barren land where the men of

Tinarath had driven them forth to perish. Reigning supreme over all the dead of Cincor, by virtue of their malign magic, they exercised a baleful despotism. Tribute was borne to them by fleshless porters from outlying realms; and plague-eaten corpses, and tall mummies scented with mortuary balsams, went to and fro upon their errands in Yethlyreom, or heaped before their greedy eyes, from inexhaustible vaults, the cobweb-blackened gold and dusty gems of antique time.

Dead laborers made their palace-gardens to bloom with long-perished flowers; liches and skeletons toiled for them in the mines, or reared superb, fantastic towers to the dying sun. Chamberlains and princes of old time were their cupbearers; and stringed instruments were plucked for their delight by the slim hands of empresses with golden hair that had come forth untarnished from the night of the tomb. Those that were fairest, whom the plague and the worm had not ravaged overmuch, they took for their lemans and made to serve their necrophilic lust.

II

In all things, the people of Cincor performed the actions of life at the will of Mmatmuor and Sodosma. They spoke, they moved, they ate and drank as in life. They heard and saw and felt with a similitude of the senses that had been theirs before death; but their brains were enthralled by a dreadful necromancy. They recalled but dimly their former existence; and the state to which they had been summoned was empty and troublous and shadow-like. Their blood ran chill and sluggish, mingled with water of Lethe; and the vapors of Lethe clouded their eyes.

Dumbly they obeyed the dictates of their tyrannous lords, without rebellion or protest, but filled with a vague, illimitable weariness such as the dead must know, when having drunk of eternal sleep, they are called back once more to the bitterness of mortal being. They knew no passion or desire or delight, only the black languor of their awakening from Lethe, and a grey, ceaseless longing to return to that interrupted slumber.

Youngest and last of the Nimboth emperors was Illeiro, who had died in the first month of the plague, and had lain in his high-built mausoleum for two hundred years before the coming of the necromancers.

Raised up with his people and his fathers to attend the tyrants, Illeiro had resumed the emptiness of existence without question and had felt no surprise. He had accepted his own resurrection and that of his ancestors as one accepts the indignities and marvels of a dream. He knew that he had come back to a faded sun, to a hollow and spectral world, to an order of things in which his place was merely that of an obedient shadow. But at first he was troubled only, like the others, by a dim weariness and a pale hunger for the lost oblivion.

Drugged by the magic of his overlords, weak from the age-long nullity of death, he beheld like a somnambulist the enormities to which his fathers were subjected. Yet, somehow, after many days, a feeble spark awoke in the sodden twilight of his mind.

Like something lost and irretrievable, lying beyond prodigious gulfs, he recalled the pomp of his reign in Yethlyreom, and the golden pride and exultation that had been his in youth. And recalling it, he felt a vague stirring of revolt, a ghostly resentment against the magicians who had haled him forth to this calamitous mockery of life. Darkly he began to grieve for his fallen state, and the mournful plight of his ancestors and his people.

Day by day, as a cupbearer in the halls where he had ruled aforetime, Illeiro saw the doings of Mmatmuor and Sodosma. He saw their caprices of cruelty and lust, their growing drunkenness and gluttony. He watched them wallow in their necromantic luxury, and become lax with indolence, gross with indulgence. They neglected the study of their art, they forgot many of their spells. But still they ruled, mighty and formidable; and, lolling on couches of purple and rose, they planned to lead an army of the dead against Tinarath.

Dreaming of conquest, and of vaster necromancies, they grew fat and slothful as worms that have installed themselves in a charnel rich with corruption. And pace by pace with their laxness and tyranny, the fire of rebellion mounted in the shadowy heart of Illeiro, like a flame that struggles with Lethean damps. And slowly, with the waxing of his wrath, there returned to him something of the strength and firmness that had been his in life. Seeing the turpitude of the oppressors, and knowing the wrong that had been done to the helpless dead, he heard in his brain the clamor of stifled voices demanding vengeance.

Among his fathers, through the palace-halls of Yethlyreom, Illeiro moved silently at the bidding of the masters, or stood awaiting their command. He poured in their cups of onyx the amber vintages, brought by wizardry from hills beneath a younger sun; he submitted to their contumelies and insults. And night by night he watched them nod in their drunkenness, till they fell asleep, flushed and gross, amid their arrogated splendor.

There was little speech among the living dead; and son and father, daughter and mother, lover and beloved, went wearily to and fro without sign of recognition, making no comment on their evil lot. But at last, one midnight, when the tyrants lay in slumber, and the flames wavered in the necromantic lamps, Illeiro took counsel with Hestaiyon, his eldest ancestor, who had been famed as a great wizard in fable and was reputed to have known the secret lore of antiquity.

Hestaiyon stood apart from the others, in a corner of the shadowy hall. He was brown and withered in his crumbling mummy-cloths; and his lightless obsidian eyes appeared to gaze still upon nothingness. He seemed not to have heard the questions of Illeiro; but at length, in a dry, rustling whisper, he responded:

"I am old, and the night of the sepulcher was long, and I have forgotten much. Yet, groping backward across the void of death, it may be that I shall retrieve something of my former wisdom; and between us we shall devise a mode of deliverance." And Hestaiyon searched among the shreds of memory, as one who reaches into a place where the worm has been and the hidden archives of old time have rotted between their covers. Till at last he remembered, and said:

"I recall that I was once a mighty wizard; and among other things, I knew the spells of necromancy but employed them not, deeming their use and the raising up of the dead an abhorrent act. Also, I possessed other knowledge; and perhaps, among the remnants of that ancient lore, there is something which may serve to guide us now. For I recall a dim, dubitable prophecy, made in the primal years, at the founding of Yethlyreom and the empire of Cincor. The prophecy was, that an evil greater than death would befall the emperors and the people of Cincor in future times; and that the first and the last of the Nimboth dynasty, conferring together, would effect a mode of release and the lifting of the doom. The evil was not named in the prophecy; but it was said that the two emperors would learn the solution of their problem by the breaking of an ancient clay image that guards the nethermost vault below the imperial palace in Yethlyreom."

Then, having heard this prophecy from the faded lips of his forefather, Illeiro mused a while, and said:

"I remember now an afternoon in early youth, when searching idly through the unused vaults of our palace, as a boy might do, I came to the last vault and found therein a dusty, uncouth image of clay, whose form and countenance were strange to me. And, knowing not the prophecy, I turned away in disappointment, and went back as idly as I had come, to seek the moted sunlight."

Then, stealing away from their heedless kinfolk, and carrying jewelled lamps they had taken from the hall, Hestaiyon and Illeiro went downward by subterranean stairs beneath the palace; and, threading like implacable furtive shadows the maze of nighted corridors, they came at last to the lowest crypt.

Here, in the black dust and clotted cobwebs of an immemorial past, they found, as had been decreed, the clay image, whose rude features were those of a forgotten earthly god. And Illeiro shattered the image with a fragment of stone; and he and Hestaiyon took from its hollow center a great sword of unrusted steel, and a heavy key of untarnished bronze, and tablets of bright brass on which were inscribed the various things to be done, so that Cincor should be rid of the dark reign of the necromancers and the people should win back to oblivious death.

So, with the key of untarnished bronze, Illeiro unlocked, as the tablets had instructed him to do, a low and narrow door at the end of the nethermost vault, beyond the broken image; and he and Hestaiyon saw, as had been prophesied, the coiling steps of somber stone that led downward to an undiscovered abyss, where the sunken fires of earth still burned. And leaving Illeiro to ward the open door, Hestaiyon took up the sword of unrusted steel in his thin hand, and went back to the hall where the necromancers slept, lying a-sprawl on their couches of rose and purple, with the wan, bloodless dead about them in patient ranks.

Upheld by the ancient prophecy and the lore of the bright tablets, Hestaiyon lifted the great sword and struck off the head of Mmatmuor and the head of Sodosma, each with a single blow. Then, as had been directed, he quartered the remains with mighty strokes. And the necromancers gave up their unclean lives, and lay supine, without movement, adding a deeper red to the rose and a brighter hue to the sad purple of their couches.

Then, to his kin, who stood silent and listless, hardly knowing their liberation, the venerable mummy of Hestaiyon spoke in sere murmurs, but authoritatively, as a king who issues commands to his children. The dead emperors and empresses stirred, like autumn leaves in a sudden wind, and a whisper passed among them and went forth from the palace, to be communicated at length, by devious ways, to all the dead of Cincor.

All that night, and during the blood-dark day that followed, by wavering torches or the light of the failing sun, an endless army of plague-eaten liches, of tattered skeletons, poured in a ghastly torrent through the streets of Yethlyreom and along the palace-hall where Hestaiyon stood guard above the slain necromancers. Unpausing, with vague, fixed eyes, they went on like driven shadows, to seek the subterranean vaults below the palace, to pass through the open door where Illeiro waited in the last vault, and then to wend downward by a thousand thousand steps to the verge of that gulf in which boiled the ebbing fires of earth. There, from the verge, they flung themselves to a second death and the clean annihilation of the bottomless flames.

But, after all had gone to their release, Hestaiyon still remained, alone in the fading sunset, beside the cloven corpses of Mmatmuor and Sodosma. There, as the tablets had directed him to do, he made trial of those spells of elder necromancy which he had known in his former wisdom, and cursed the dismembered bodies with that perpetual life-in-death which Mmatmuor and Sodosma had sought to inflict upon the people of Cincor. And maledictions came from the pale lips, and the heads rolled horribly with glaring eyes, and the limbs and torsos writhed on their imperial couches amid clotted blood. Then, with no backward look, knowing that all was done as had been ordained and predicted from the first, the mummy of Hestaiyon left the necromancers to their doom, and went wearily through the nighted labyrinth of vaults to rejoin Illeiro.

So, in tranquil silence, with no further need of words, Illeiro and Hestaiyon passed through the open door of the nether vault, and Illeiro locked the door behind them with its key of untarnished bronze. And thence, by the coiling stairs, they wended their way to the verge of the sunken flames and were one with their kinsfolk and their people in the last, ultimate nothingness.

But of Mmatmuor and Sodosma, men say that their quartered bodies crawl to and fro to this day in Yethlyreom, finding no peace or respite from their doom of life-in-death, and seeking vainly through the black maze of nether vaults the door that was locked by Illeiro.

THE CORPSE AND THE SKELETON

Scene: The catacombs of the ancient city of Toomal. A new corpse has been deposited along-side a skeleton, which, from its mouldiness and worm-picked appearance, seems of considerable antiquity.

THE CORPSE
How now, old barebones! What word of the worm? Methinks you have known him well, in your time.

THE SKELETON
Aye, aye, and so will you: 'Tis a world of creditors, of which the tomb and the worm are the last; there is little left for the devil, when these have taken their due account. The vermin is a very Jew, and will have his last ounce of brain and marrow. He has spared me never a scrap of flesh, nor tatter of skin, against the mouldy breath of the cavern-wind, nor aught save the jaw-bone to stop the continual diddering of my teeth.

THE CORPSE
You speak so dismally: to change the theme, let us talk of our former lives.

THE SKELETON
Willingly, willingly, tho as for myself, I fear my memories have grown a trifle musty, from five hundred years, more or less, in an air that is rotten with the dead. However, for the dust which has settled among the bones of my throat, I bethink me that I was once a taverner, and a very wineskin at filling myself with my own vintages. Often-sith have I

thirsted for even a quart, in lieu of my former tunfuls. Time is a cheating merchant, he has given me this modicum of mould, in exchange for an ample corporosity. 'Tis a dull business, being dead, and without profit, for all the number of the traffickers.

THE CORPSE

Where, then, with all their multiform splendours, are the heavens of light and hells of fire, promised unto faith by the sybils and hierophants?

THE SKELETON

Ask of yonder cadaver, him whose corpulence diminishes momently, for the pampering of worms. He was once a priest, and spoke authentically of these matters, with all the delegated thunder of gods. As for myself, I have found nothing beyond this narrow charnel-vault, in whose lethal night are bred the vapours of pestilence, that wander forth to swell our number with the living, and rise from the rotten earth for an incense to the very sun.

THE CORPSE

It was the pestilence that sent me here from my marriage-bed. I was an optimate of Toomal, yet they have thrust me away to rot among the common rogues.

THE SKELETON

(Sympathetically, and in a tone less like the grating of bones than heretofore.) Too bad, too bad! Albeit I am long beyond the flesh myself, I commiserate you. The brides are bony, and the bedfellows cold, that you are like to find here, even tho you lie till the death-light glimmers within your eye-sockets for the sparkling of lust.

THE CORPSE

Find we, then, no recompense, no meed of wisdom holden unto death, nor the secrets buried from the sun, in the deep night of subterranes?

THE SKELETON

We have wisdom, if you like—a dull and dusty wisdom, and I would give it all for a good draught of Chian wine. Perchance 'tis something to know that bodies are made of dust and water, the last of which is evaporable, and the soul as the vapour thereof; for this is all our knowledge, in spite of much that is known and spoken of hierophant or philosopher. However, unlike the lore and wisdom of these, it may be crammed without discommodation into one skull.

NECROMANCY IN NAAT

Dead longing, sundered evermore from pain:
How dim and sweet the shadow-hearted love,
The happiness that perished lovers prove
In Naat, far beyond the sable main.
                        —*Song of the Galley-Slaves.*

Yadar, prince of a nomad people in the half-desert region known as Zyra, had followed throughout many kingdoms a clue that was often more elusive than broken gossamer. For thirteen moons he had sought Dalili, his betrothed, whom the slave traders of Sha-Karag, swift and cunning as desert falcons, had reft from the tribal encampment with nine other maidens while Yadar and his men were hunting the black gazelles of Zyra. Fierce was the grief of Yadar, and fiercer still his wrath, when he came back at eve to the ravaged tents. He had sworn then a great oath to find Dalili, whether in slave-mart or brothel or harem, whether dead or living, whether tomorrow or after the lapse of grey years.

The tracks of the slavers' camels ran plainly toward the iron gates of Sha-Karag, lying many leagues away in the west. Because of similar raidings, the nomads had long been at war with the people of that infamous market-place where women were the chief merchandise. Knowing that the high-walled city was impregnable to assault by his little band of followers, Yadar disguised himself as a rug-merchant; and accompanied by four of his men in like attire, with certain hoarded heirlooms of the tribe for a stock-in trade, he appeared before the shut gates and was admitted without challenge by the guards. Listening discretely to the gossip of the bazaars, he learned that the raiders had not remained in Sha-Karag; but, after selling most of their captives to local dealers, they had gone on without delay toward the great empires of the sunset, taking with them Dalili and her fairest companions. It was said that they hoped to sell Dalili to some opulent king or emperor who would pay a city's ransom for the wild, rare beauty of the outland princess.

Weary and perilous was the quest to which Yadar and his followers now dedicated themselves. Still disguised as rug-merchants, they joined a caravan that was departing on the route taken by the slavers. From realm to realm they followed a doubtful trail, sometimes led astray by vain rumors.

In Tinarath, hearing that a nomad girl of strange loveliness had lately been purchased by the king, they entered the palace harem on a night of storm, slaying the griffon-like monsters who warded its balconies, and braving the hideous pitfalls that had been set for intruders in the inner halls. They found the girl, who was not Dalili but another of the maidens reaved from Yadar's people; and swiftly, amid the bewildered hubbub of the awakening palace, they carried her away into the darkness and storm. She knew little of the fate of Dalili, saying that the princess had been parted from her in Tinarath and had gone with the slave-traders toward Zul-Bha-Sair: for the king of Tinarath had refused to pay the vast sum demanded for Dalili.

Now, when they were safely beyond the borders of Tinarath, Yadar sent the girl back toward Zyra with one of his tribesmen; and he and the others resumed their search and were brought near to death amid the springless dunes of the waste lying between Tinarath and Zul-Bha-Sair. And in Zul-Bha-Sair, Yadar learned that Dalili had been offered to the king who, caring not for a sun-dark beauty, had declined to buy her; and, after that, the princess and her captors had gone northward to an undeclared destination. But, before the nomads could follow, Yadar's companions were seized by a strange fever and died swiftly; and their bodies, according to custom, were claimed by the priesthood of a great temple-dwelling ghoul who was worshipped in that city. So Yadar went on alone, and after much random wandering, he came to Oroth, a western sea-port of the land of Xylac.

There, for the first time in several moons, he heard a rumor that might concern Dalili: for the people of Oroth were still gossiping about the departure of a rich galley bearing a lovely outland girl who had been bought by the emperor of Xylac and sent to the ruler of the far southern kingdom of Yoros as a gift concluding a treaty between these realms.

Yadar, who had almost yielded to despair, was now hopeful of finding his beloved: since, by the description the people had given, he thought that the girl was indeed none other than Dalili. Nothing remained of the precious weavings of the tribe which he had brought with him to sell as merchandise; but, through the sale of his camels, he procured money with which to engage his passage on a ship that was about to sail for Yoros.

The ship was a small merchant galley, laden with grain and wine, that was wont to coast up and down, hugging closely the winding western shores of the continent Zothique and venturing never beyond eyeshot of land. On a clear blue summer day it departed from Oroth with all auguries for a safe and tranquil voyage. But on the third morn after leaving port, a tremendous wind blew suddenly from the low-lying sandy shore they were then skirting; and with it, blotting the heavens and sea, there came a blackness as of night thickened with clouds. The sails and oars could win no headway against the gale, and the vessel was swept far out to sea, going with the blind tempest.

After two days, the wind fell from its ravening fury and was soon no more than a vague whisper; and the skies cleared, leaving a bright azure vault from horizon to horizon. But nowhere was there any land visible, only a waste of waters that still roared and tossed turbulently without wind, pouring ever westward in a cataracting tide that was too swift and strong for the galley to stem. And the galley was borne on irresistibly by that strange current, even as by the hurricane.

Yadar, who was the sole passenger, marvelled much at this thing; and he was struck by the pale terror on the faces of the captain and crew. And, looking again at the sea, he remarked a singular darkening of its waters, which assumed from moment to moment a hue as of old blood commingled with more and more of blackness: though above it the sun shone untarnished. So he made inquiry of the captain, a grey-beard from Yoros, named Agor, who had sailed the ocean for forty summers; and the captain answered, with many seafaring oaths:

"This I had apprehended when the storm bore us westwardly: for know now that we have fallen into the grip of that terrible ocean-stream which is called by mariners the Black River. Evermore the stream surges and swiftens toward the fabled place of the sun's outer-most setting, till it pours at last from the world's rim. Between us now and that final verge, there is no land, saving the evil land of Naat, which is called also the Isle of Necromancers. And I know not which were the worse fate, to be wrecked on that infamous isle or hurled into space with the waters falling eternally from earth's edge. From either place there is no return for living men such as we. And from the Isle of Naat none go forth except the ill sorcerers who people it, and the dead who are raised up and controlled by their sorcery. In magical ships that breast the full current of the Black River, the sorcerers sail at will to other strands; and beneath their necromancy, to fulfill their wicked errands, the dead men swim without pause for many days and nights whithersoever the masters may send them."

Yadar, who knew little of sorcerers and necromancy, was some-what incredulous concerning the matters whereof the captain spoke. But he saw that the blackening waters streamed always more wildly and torrentially toward the skyline, as if pouring adown some subma-rine slope of earth that steepened to the final rim; and verily there was small hope that the galley could regain its southward course. And he was troubled chiefly by the thought that he should never reach the kingdom of Yoros, where he had dreamt to find Dalili.

All that day the vessel was borne on without respite by the dark seas racing weirdly beneath an airless and immaculate heaven. It followed the silent orange sunset into a night filled with large, unquivering stars; and at length it was overtaken by the flying amber morn. But still there was no abating of the waters; and neither land nor cloud was discernible in the vastness about the galley.

Yadar held little converse with Agor and the crew, after questioning them vainly as to the reason of the ocean's blackness, which was a thing that no man understood. Despair was upon him; but, standing at the bulwark, he watched the sky and wave with an alertness born of his nomad life. Toward middle afternoon he descried far-off a strange vessel, rigged with funereal purple sails, that drove steadily on an eastering course against the mighty current. At this, he cried out in wonder, calling the captain's attention to the vessel; and the captain, with a muttering of outlandish oaths, told him that it was a ship belonging to the necromancers of Naat, whose malign magic was more cogent than the tide of the Black River.

Soon the purple sails were lost to vision; but a little later, Yadar perceived certain objects, queerly resembling human heads, that passed in the high-billowing water to the galley's leeward, as if swimming easily toward Zothique on the route of that necromantic ship. Deeming that no mortal living men could swim thus, and remembering that which the captain had told him concerning the dead swimmers who went forth from Naat, Yadar shivered a little with such trepidation as a brave man may feel in the presence of preternatural things; and he did not speak of the matter. And seemingly the head-like objects were not noticed by any of his companions.

Still the galley drove on, its oarsmen sitting idle at the oars, and the captain standing listless beside the untended helm.

Now, as the sun declined above that tumultuous ebon ocean, it seemed that a great bank of thunder-cloud arose from the west, long and low-lying at first, but surging rapidly skyward with mountainous domes and craggy battlements. Ever higher it loomed, revealing the menace as of piled cliffs and somber awful sea-capes; but its form changed not in the manner of clouds; and Yadar, watching it closely, knew it at last for an island bulking far aloft in the long-rayed sunset. From it, a chill effluence of evil came like a sighing breath; and a shadow was thrown for leagues, darkening still more the sable waters, as if with the fall of untimely night; and in the shadow, the foam-crests flashing upon hidden reefs were white as the bared teeth of Death. And Yadar needed not the shrill, frightened cries of his companions to tell him that this was the terrible Isle of Naat.

Direly the current swiftened, raging, as it raced onward for battle with the rock-fanged shore; and the voices of the mariners, praying loudly to their gods, were drowned by its clamor. Yadar, standing in the prow, gave only a silent prayer to the dim, fatal deity of his tribe; and his eyes searched the towering isle like those of a sea-flown hawk, seeing the bare horrific crags, and the spaces of sullen forest creeping seaward between the crags, and the white mounting of breakers on a shadowy strand. And he discerned, on the lofty downs behind the shore, the furtive scattered roofs of houses pale amid cypress-trees that clotted the gloom with funereal umbrage.

Shrouded, and ominous of bale was the island's aspect, and the heart of Yadar sank like a plummet in unsunned seas. As the galley drew nearer to land, he thought that he beheld people moving darkly, visible in the lapsing of surges on a low beach, and then hidden once more by foam and spindrift. Ere he saw them a second time, the galley was hurled with thunderous crashing and grinding on a reef covered by the torrent waters. The whole forepart of its prow and bottom were broken in, and being lifted from the reef by a great comber, it filled instantly and sank. And of those who had sailed from Oroth in the vessel, Yadar alone leapt free ere its foundering; but, since he was little skilled as a swimmer, he was drawn under quickly and was like to have drowned in the maelstroms of that evil sea.

His senses left him, and in his brain, like a lost sun returned from yesteryear, he beheld the face of Dalili; and with Dalili, in a bright phantasmagoria, there came the happy days that had been ere his bereavement. The visions passed, and he awoke struggling, with the bitterness of the sea in his mouth, and its loudness in his ears, and its rushing darkness all about him. And, as his senses quickened, he became aware of a form that swam close behind him, and arms that supported him amid the waters.

He lifted his head in the twilight, and saw dimly the pale neck and half-averted face of his rescuer, and the long black hair that floated from wave to wave. Touching the body at his side, he knew it for that of a woman. Mazed and wildered though he was by the sea's buffeting, a sense of something familiar stirred within him; and he thought that he had known somewhere, at some former time, a girl with like hair and similar curving of cheek; but he could not remember clearly. And, trying to remember, he touched the woman again, and felt in his fingers a strange coldness from her naked body. At this, he wondered a little, but forgot his wonder in the wildness of that sea through which he was borne by the swimmer.

Miraculous was the woman's strength and skill, for she rode easily the dreadful mounting and falling of the surges. Yadar, floating as in a cradle upon her arm, beheld the nearing shore from the billows' summits; and hardly it seemed that any swimmer, however able, could win alive through the ponderous cataracting of that surf on the stony strand. Dizzily, at the last, they were hurled upward, as if the surf would fling them against the highmost crag; but, as if checked by some enchantment, the wave fell with a slow, lazy undulation; and Yadar and his rescuer, released by its ebbing, lay unhurt on a shelfy beach.

Uttering no word, nor turning to look at Yadar, the woman rose swiftly to her feet; and, beckoning the nomad prince to follow, she moved away in the deathly blue dusk that had fallen upon Naat. Yadar, arising and following the woman, heard a strange and eerie chanting of

voices above the sea's tumult, and saw a fire that burned weirdly, with
the colors of driftwood, at some distance before him in the dusk.
Straightly, toward the fire and the voices, the woman walked in the
fashion of a somnambulist. And Yadar, with eyes grown used to that
doubtful twilight, saw that the fire blazed in the mouth of a low-
sunken cleft between crags that overloomed the beach; and behind the
fire, like tall, evilly posturing shadows, there stood the dark-clad figures
of those who chanted.

Now memory returned to him of that which the galley's captain
had said regarding the people of Naat and their necromantic practices;
and with the memory came misgiving. For the very sound of that
chanting, albeit in an unknown language, seemed to suspend the heart-
ward flowing of his veins, and to set the tomb's chillness in his marrow. And though he was little learned in such matters, the thought came
to him that the words uttered were of sorcerous import and power.

Going forward, the woman bowed low before the chanters, in
such fashion as a slave, and stood waiting submissively. The men, who
were three in number, continued their incantation without pausing,
and they seemed not to perceive the presence of Yadar as he entered
the firelight. Gaunt as starved herons they were, and great of stature,
with a common likeness, as of brothers; and sharply ridged were their
faces, where shadows inhabited their hollow cheeks, and their sunk
eyes were visible only by red sparks reflected within them from the
blaze. And their eyes, as they chanted, seemed to glare afar on the dar-
kling sea and on things hidden by dusk and distance. And Yadar, coming before them, was aware of swift horror and repugnance that made
his gorge rise as if he had encountered, in a place given wholly to
death, the powerful evil ripeness of corruption.

High leaped the fire as he neared it, with a writhing of tongues that
were like blue and green serpents coiling amid serpents of yellow. And
the light flickered brightly on the face and breasts of that woman who
had saved him from the Black River; and Yadar, beholding her clearly,

knew why she had stirred within him a dim remembrance: for she was none other than his lost love, Dalili!

Forgetting the presence of the dark chanters, and the ill renown of that isle to which the seas had brought him, he sprang forward to clasp his beloved, crying out her name in an agony of rapture. But she answered not his cry, and responded to his embrace only with a faint trembling. And Yadar, sorely perplexed and dismayed, was aware of the deathly coldness that crept into his fingers and smote through his very raiment from her flesh. Mortally pale and languid were the lips that he kissed, and it seemed that no breath emerged between them, nor was there any rising and falling of the wan bosom against his. In the wide, beautiful eyes that she turned to him, he found only a drowsy voidness, and such recognition as a sleeper gives when but half awakened, relapsing quickly into slumber thereafter.

"Art thou indeed Dalili?" he said. And she answered somnolently, in a toneless, indistinct voice, "I am Dalili."

To Yadar, baffled by mystery, chilled, forlorn and aching, it was as if she had spoken from a land farther away than all the weary leagues of his search throughout Zothique. Fearing to understand the change that had come upon her, he said tenderly:

"Surely thou knowest me, for I am thy lover, the Prince Yadar, who has sought thee through half the kingdoms of Earth, and has sailed afar for thy sake on the unshored sea." And she replied like one bemused by some heavy drug, in a soulless voice, as if echoing his words without true comprehension: "Surely I know thee." And to Yadar there was no comfort in her reply; and his concernment was not allayed by the parrotings with which she answered all his other loving speeches and queries.

He knew not that the three chanters had all ceased their incantation; and verily, he had forgotten their presence in his finding of Dalili. But as he stood holding the girl closely, the men came toward him, and one of them clutched his arm. And the man hailed him by name and addressed him, albeit uncouthly, in a language commonly spoken throughout many parts of Zothique, saying: "We bid thee welcome to the Isle of Naat, from which no living traveller may return."

Yadar, feeling a dread suspicion, interrogated the man fiercely: "What manner of beings are ye? And why is Dalili in this place? And what have ye done to her?"

"I am Vacharn, a necromancer," the man replied readily, "and these others with me are my sons, Vokal and Uldulla, who are also necromancers. We dwell in a house behind the crags, and are attended by the drowned people that our sorcery has called up from the sea to a semblance of life and animation. Among our servants is this girl, Dalili, together with the whole crew of that ship in which she sailed from Oroth. For, like the vessel in which thou camest later, the ship was blown far asea and was taken by the ineluctable Black River, and was wrecked finally on the reefs of Naat. And my sons and I, chanting that powerful formula which requires no use of circle or pentacle, summoned ashore the drowned company: even as we have now summoned the crew of that other vessel, from which thou alone wert saved alive by the necromantic swimmer at our command, for a certain purpose."

Vacharn ended, and stood peering into the dusk intently; and Yadar at that moment heard behind him a noise of slow footsteps coming upward across the shingle from the surf. Turning, he saw emerge from the livid twilight the old captain of that merchant galley in which he had voyaged so unwillingly to Naat; and behind the captain were the sailors and oarsmen. With the paces of sleep-walkers they approached the firelight, the sea-water dripping heavily from their raiment and hair, and drooling from their mouths. Some were sorely bruised, and others came stumbling or dragging with limbs broken by the rocks on which that torrential sea had flung them; and on all their faces was the ghastly look of men who have suffered the doom of drowning.

Stiffly, like automatons, they made obeisance in a body before

Vacharn and his sons, acknowledging thus their thralldom to those who had raised them from deep death. In their glassily staring eyes there was no recognition of Yadar, no awareness of outward things; and they spoke only in dull, rote-like recognition of certain obscure words addressed to them by the necromancers.

To Yadar, it was as if he too stood and moved like the living dead in a dark, hollow, half-conscious dream. Even thus, walking side by side with Dalili, and followed by those others, he was led by the enchanters through a dusky ravine that wound secretly toward the uplands of Naat. Obediently he went: but in his heart there was small joy at the finding of Dalili; and his love was companioned by a sick despair.

Vacharn lit the way with a brand of driftwood plucked from the fire; and Yadar beheld vaguely, by its flickering, the black and cruel precipices of a steepening gorge, and the dwarfish crooked pines that leaned malignantly from high ledges, as if to cast with wizard hands a malediction upon the wayfarers. Anon a bloated moon rose red as with sanies-mingled blood behind them, over the wild, racing sea; and, ere its orb had cleared to a death-like paleness, they emerged from the gorge on a stony fell where stood the house of the three necromancers.

Long and low-lying was the house, built of dark granite, with crouching wings half hidden amid the foliage of close-grown cypresses. Behind it a cliff beetled, overhanging it starkly; and above the cliff were somber slopes and ridges piled in the moonlight, rising afar toward the mountainous center of Naat.

To Yadar, it seemed that the mansion was a place pre-empted by death: for no lights burned in its portals and windows; and a silence came from it to meet the stillness of the wan heavens. But, when the necromancers neared the threshold, a word was spoken by Vacharn, echoing distantly in the inner halls and chambers; and as if in answer, lamps were illumined suddenly everywhere, filling the house as with monstrous yellow eyes; and people appeared instantly within the portals like bowing shadows. But the faces of these beings were blanched by the tomb's pallor, and some were mottled with green decay, or marked by the tortuous gnawing of maggots. . . .

Later, in a great hall of the house, Yadar was bidden to seat himself at a table where Vacharn and Vokal and Uldulla were wont to sit alone during their meals. The table stood on a sort of dais formed of gigantic flagstones; and below, in the main hall, the dead were gathered about other tables, numbering nearly twoscore; and among them sat the girl Dalili, looking never toward Yadar. He, though sorely sick at heart, would have joined her, unwilling to be parted from her side: but a deep languor was upon him, as if an unspoken spell had enthralled his limbs, and he could no longer move at his own volition but must obey in all things the will of Vacharn.

Dully he sat, observing with small wonder the grimness and taciturnity of his hosts, who, dwelling always with the silent dead, had apparently assumed no little part of their manner and similitude. And he saw more clearly than before the common likeness of the three: for all, it seemed, were as brothers of one birth rather than parent and sons; and all were like ageless things, being neither old nor young in the fashion of ordinary men. Yadar could distinguish Vacharn from his sons only by the darker hue of his garments, and the greater breadth of brow and shoulders; and he knew Vokal from Uldulla merely by a sharper pitch of voice and a deeper hollowing of the gaunt cheeks. And more and more was he aware of that weird evil which emanated from the three, powerful and abhorrent as an exhalation of hidden death.

In the thralldom that weighed upon him, he scarcely marvelled at the serving of the strange supper that followed: though meats were brought in by no palpable agency, and wines poured out as if by the air itself; and the passing of the bearers to and fro was betrayed only by a rustle of doubtfully dying footsteps, and a light chillness that came and went.

Mutely, with stiff gestures and movements, the dead began to eat at their laden tables. But the necromancers refrained from the victuals before them, in an attitude of waiting; and Vacharn, in explanation, said to the nomad: "There are still others who will sup with us to-night." And Yadar, for the first time, perceived that a vacant chair had been set beside the chair of Vacharn.

Then, from an inner doorway, there entered the hall with hasty strides a man of great thews and stature, naked, and brown almost to blackness. Savage of aspect was the man, and his eyes were dilated as if with rage or terror, and little flecks of foam were on his thick purple lips. And close behind him, lifting in menace their heavy, rusted scimitars, there came two liches, like guards who attend a prisoner.

"This man is a cannibal," said Vacharn. "Our servants have captured him for us in the forest beyond the mountains, which is peopled mainly by such savages." Then, with a dark irony couching behind the words, he added: "Only the strong and courageous are summoned living to this mansion, and are suffered to eat with my sons and me at our table. . . . Not idly, O Prince Yadar, wert thou chosen for this honor among all who sailed in the merchant galley from Oroth. Observe closely all that follows."

The giant savage had paused within the threshold, as if fearing the hall's occupants more than the wicked weapons of his guards. At a signal from Vacharn, one of the liches slashed his left shoulder with the rusty blade, and blood rilled copiously from a deep wound as the cannibal came forward beneath that prompting. Convulsively he trembled, in such wise as a frightened animal, looking wildly to either side for an avenue of escape; and only after a second prompting did he mount the dais and approach the necromancers' table. But, after certain hollow-sounding words had been uttered by Vacharn, the man seated himself, still trembling, in the chair beside the master, opposite to Yadar. And behind him, with high-raised weapons, there stationed themselves the ghastly guards, whose features were those of men a fortnight dead.

"There is still another guest," said Vacharn, "a guest who prefers to sup when others have supped. He will come at his own time."

Without further ceremony, he began to eat, and Yadar, though with little appetence, followed suit. Hardly did the prince perceive the savor of those viands with which his plate was piled; nor could he have sworn whether the vintages he drank were sour or dulcet. For his thoughts were divided between Dalili and the strangeness and horror about him. The utterances of Vacharn, and the presence of the cannibal, and the reason of his own presence at that table, were obscure to him; and he felt in all this the incumbence of an ill mystery. And, seeing that there was no longer a vacant place at the table, he was perplexed by the necromancer's reference to the coming of still another guest. As he ate and drank, it seemed that his senses were sharpened weirdly, so that he grew aware of eldritch shadows moving between the lamps, and heard the chill sibilance of whispers that checked his very blood. And there came to him, from the peopled hall, every odor that is exhaled by mortality between the recentness of death and the end of corruption.

Vacharn and his sons addressed themselves to the meal with the unconcern of those long habituated to such surroundings. But the cannibal, whose fear was still palpable in his features and members, ate only a few scant mouthfuls, and these at the direct prompting of Vacharn, who appeared very solicitous of his guest's appetite. Blood, in two heavy rills, ran unceasingly down his bosom from his wounded shoulders, and fell at last on the stone flags with an audible dripping. But of this, in his sore terror, he seemed unaware.

Finally, at the urging of Vacharn, who spoke to him in the cannibal's own language, he was persuaded to drink from a cup of wine that had long stood before him untasted. This wine, Yadar perceived, was not the same that had been served to the rest of the company, being of a violet color, dark as the nightshade's blossom, while the other wine was a poppy red. Hardly had the man tasted it, when he sank back in his chair with the appearance of one smitten helpless by palsy. The wine-cup, rilling the remnant of its contents, was still clutched in his rigid fingers; there was no movement, no trembling of his limbs; and his eyes were wide open and staring, as if consciousness still remained within him.

A dire suspicion sprang up in Yadar, and no longer could he eat the food and drink the wine of the necromancers. And much was he puzzled by the actions of Vacharn and Vokal and Uldulla, who, abstaining likewise, turned in their chairs and peered steadfastly at a certain portion of the floor behind Vacharn, between the table and the hall's inner end. Rising a little in his seat, Yadar looked down across the table and saw that all three were staring at a small hole in one of the flagstones, which he had not hitherto perceived. The hole was such as might be inhabited by some tiny animal: but Yadar could not surmise the nature of a beast that burrowed in solid granite.

Now, in a loud clear voice, Vacharn spoke the single word, "Esrit," as if calling the name of one that he wished to summon. Not long thereafter, two little sparks of fire appeared in the darkness of the hole, and from it sprang a creature having somewhat the size and likeness of a weasel, but even longer and thinner of body. The fur of the creature was a rusted black, and its paws were like tiny hairless hands; and its beaded eyes of flaming fulvous yellow seemed to hold the malign wisdom and malevolence of a demon. Swiftly, with writhing movements that gave it the air of a furred serpent, it ran forward beneath the chair occupied by the cannibal, and began to drink greedily the pool of blood that had dripped down on the floor from his wounds.

Then, while horror fastened upon the heart of Yadar, it leapt to the knees of the huge savage, and thence to his left shoulder, where the deepest wound had been inflicted. And there the thing applied itself to the still bleeding cut, from which it sucked in the fashion of a weasel; and the blood ceased to flow down on the man's body. And the man stirred not in his chair; but his eyes still widened, slowly, with a horrible glaring, till the balls were isled in livid white; and his lips fell slackly apart, showing teeth that were strong and pointed as those of a shark.

The necromancers had resumed their eating, with eyes attentive on the small bloodthirsty monster; and it came to Yadar that this was the other guest expected by Vacharn. Whether the thing was an actual weasel, or a sorcerer's familiar, he knew not: but anger followed upon his horror before the plight of the cannibal; and, drawing a sword he had carried through all his travels and voyagings, he sprang to his feet and would have tried to kill the monster. But Vacharn described in the air a peculiar sign with his forefinger; and it seemed that the prince's arm was suspended in mid-stroke, and his fingers became weak as those of a newborn babe, and the sword fell from his hand, ringing loudly on the dais. Thereafter, as if by the unspoken will of Vacharn, he was constrained to seat himself again at the table.

Insatiable, to all appearance, was the thirst of the weasel-like creature: for, after many minutes had gone by in that hall of abominations, it continued to suck the blood of the savage. And from moment to moment the man's mighty thews became strangely shrunken, and the bones and taut sinews showed starkly beneath the wrinkling folds of skin. His face was like the chapless face of death, his limbs were lean as those of an old mummy: but the thing that battened upon him had increased in girth only so much as a stoat increases by sucking the blood of some farmyard fowl.

By this token, Yadar knew that the thing was indeed a demon, and was no doubt the familiar of Vacharn. Entranced with terror, he sat regarding it, till the creature dropped from the dry skin and bones of the cannibal, and ran with an evil writhing and slithering to its hole in the flagstone.

Weird was the life that now began for Yadar in the house of the necromancers. Upon him there rested by day and night the malign thralldom that had overpowered him during that first supper, and he moved as one who could not wholly awake from some benumbing dream. It seemed that his volition was in some way controlled by those masters

of the living dead. But, more than this, he was held by the old enchantment of his love for Dalili: though the love had now turned to a
spell of despair.

He ate at the table of the necromancers, and slept in a chamber adjoining that of Vacharn: a chamber unlocked, and without tangible
bars to hinder his going. Dully he foresaw the fate designed for him:
since Vacharn spoke seldom except with grim ironies, referring to the
doom of the cannibal, and of the thirst of the weasel-like familiar, whose
name was Esrit. And he learned that Esrit had undertaken to serve
Vacharn for a certain term, receiving in guerdon thereof, at the full of
each moon, the blood of a living man chosen for redoubtable strength
and valor. And it was clear to Yadar that, in default of some miracle, or
sorcery beyond that of the necromancers, his days of life were limited
by the moon's period. For, other than himself and the masters, there
was no person in all that mansion who had not already passed through
the bitter gates of death, thereby becoming unacceptable to Esrit.

Lonely was the house, standing far apart from all neighbors. Other
necromancers dwelt on the shores of Naat, served mainly by the people they had evoked from drowning after shipwreck; but betwixt these
and the hosts of Yadar there was little intercourse. And beyond the wild
mountains that divided the isle, there dwelt only certain tribes of anthropophagi, who warred perpetually with each other in the black woods
of pine and cypress, but feared the necromancers and their thralls.

The dead were housed in deep catacomb-like caves of the cliff behind the mansion, lying all night in rows of stone coffins, and coming
forth in daily resurrection to do the tasks ordained by the masters.
Some were compelled to till the rocky gardens on a slope sequestered
from sea-wind; others tended the sable goats and cattle of the isle; and
still others were sent out as divers for pearls in the sea that raged and
ravened prodigiously, not to be dared by living swimmers, on the bleak
atolls and headlands horned with granite. Of such pearls, Vacharn had
amassed a mighty store through years exceeding the common span of

life. And sometimes, in a ship that sailed contrary to the Black River, he or one of his sons would voyage to Zothique with certain of the dead for crew, and would trade the pearls for such things as their magic was unable to raise up in Naat.

Strange it was to Yadar, to see the companions of his voyage passing to and fro with the other liches, recognizing him not, or greeting him only in mindless echo of his own salutations. And bitter it was, yet never without a dim, sorrowful sweetness, to behold Dalili and speak with her, trying vainly to revive the lost ardent love in a heart that had gone fathom-deep into oblivion and had not returned therefrom. And always, with a desolate yearning, he seemed to grope toward her across a gulf more terrible than the stemless tide that poured forever about the Isle of the Necromancers.

Dalili, who had swum from childhood in the sunken lakes of Zyra, was among those enforced to dive for pearls in that ebon water. Often Yadar would accompany her to the shore and await her return from the mad surges; and at whiles he was tempted to fling himself after her, and find, if such were possible, the peace of very death. This he would surely have done: but, amid the eerie wilderments of his plight, and the grey webs of sorcery woven about him, it seemed that his old strength and resolution were wholly lacking.

Now, night by night, the moon was sharpened above the craggy isle, and it became a heavy scythe and then a thin scimitar. And, after the interlunar dusk, it broadened from a frail saber to a sickle, and, digit by digit, swelled toward the gibbous orb and the plenilune. Yadar, supping with the sorcerers as it changed, was not unregardful of that burrow in the granite flag, from which the weasel-demon, Esrit, had slithered forth to suck the blood of the cannibal. But, beneath his extreme languor and lethargy, he hardly feared that verminous death which would dart upon him at the time of the moon's fullness.

* * *

One day, toward sunset-time, as the month drew to its end, Vokal and Uldulla approached the prince where he stood waiting on a rock-walled beach while Dalili dived after pearls far out in the torrent waters. Speaking no word, they beckoned to him with furtive signs; and Yadar, vaguely curious as to their intent, suffered them to lead him from the beach and by perilous paths that wound from crag to crag above the curving sea-shore. Ere the fall of darkness, they came suddenly to a small landlocked harbor whose existence had been heretofore unsuspected by the nomad. In that placid bay, beneath the deep umbrage of the isle, there rode a galley with somber purple sails, resembling the ship that Yadar had discerned moving steadily toward Zothique against the full tide of the Black River.

Yadar was much bewondered, nor could he divine why they had brought him to the hidden harbor, nor the import of their gestures as they pointed out the strange vessel. Then, in a hushed and covert whisper, as if fearing to be overheard in that remote place, Vokal said to him:

"If thou wilt aid my brother and me in the execution of a certain plan which we have conceived, thou shalt have the use of yonder galley in quitting Naat. And with thee, if such be thy desire, thou shalt take the girl Dalili whom thou lovest, together with certain of the dead mariners for oarsmen. Favored by the powerful gales which our enchantments will evoke for thee, thou shalt sail against the Black River and return to Zothique. . . . But if thou helpest us not, then shall the weasel Esrit suck thy blood, till the last, least member of thy body has been emptied thereof; and Dalili shall remain forever as the bondslave of Vacharn, toiling for his avarice by day in the dark waters . . . and perchance serving his lust by night."

At the promise of Vokal, Yadar felt something of hope and manhood revive within him, and it seemed that the baleful sorcery of Vacharn was lifted from his mind; and an indignation against Vacharn was awakened in him by Vokal's hintings. And he said quickly: "I will aid thee in thy plan, whatever it may be, if such aid is within my power to give."

Then, with many fearful glances about and behind him, Uldulla took up the furtive whispering.

"It is our thought that Vacharn has lived beyond the allotted term, and has imposed his authority upon us for an excessive length of years. We, his sons, grow old: and we deem it no more than rightful that we should inherit the stored treasures and the magical supremacy of our father ere age has wholly debarred us from their enjoyment. Therefore we seek thy help in the slaying of the necromancer."

Though Yadar was somewhat surprised, it came to him, after brief reflection that the killing of the necromancer should be held in all ways a righteous deed, and one to which he could lend himself without demeaning his valor or his manhood. So he said without demur: "I will aid thee."

Then, seeming greatly emboldened by Yadar's consent, Vokal spoke again in his turn, saying: "This thing must be accomplished ere tomorrow's eve, which will bring a full-rounded moon from the Black River upon Naat, and will call the weasel-demon Esrit from his burrow. And tomorrow's forenoon is the only time when we can take Vacharn unaware in his chamber. During those hours, as is his wont, he will peer entranced on a magic mirror that yields visions of the outer sea, and the ships sailing over the sea, and the lands lying beyond. And we must slay him before the mirror, striking swiftly and surely ere he awakens from his trance."

At the hour set for the deed, Vokal and Uldulla came to Yadar where he stood awaiting them in the mansion's outer hall. Each of the brothers bore in his right hand a long and coldly glittering scimitar; and Vokal also carried in his left a like weapon, which he offered to the prince, explaining that these scimitars had been tempered to a muttering of lethal runes, and inscribed afterward with unspeakable death-spells. Yadar, preferring his own sword, declined the wizard weapon; and, delaying no more, the three went hastily and with all possible stealth toward Vacharn's chamber.

The house was empty at that hour, for the dead had all gone forth to their labors; nor was there any whisper or shadow of those invisible beings, whether sprites of the air or mere phantoms, that waited upon Vacharn and served him in sundry ways. In silence and, as they thought, wholly unperceived, the three came to the portals of the chamber, where entrance was barred only by a black arras wrought with the Signs of night in silver, and bordered all about with a repetition of the fives names of the archfiend Thasaidon in scarlet thread. The brothers paused before the arras, as if fearing to lift it; but Yadar, unhesitating, held it aside and passed into the chamber; and the twain followed him quickly as if for shame of their poltroonery.

Large and high vaulted was the room, and lit by a dim window looking forth between unpruned cypresses toward the black sea. No flames arose from the myriad lamps to assist that baffled daylight; and shadows brimmed the place like a spectral fluid, through which the vessels of wizardry used by Vacharn, the great censers and alembics and braziers, seemed to quiver and move like animate things. A little past the room's center, his back to the doorway, Vacharn sat on an ebon trivet before the mirror of clairvoyance, which was wrought from electrum in the form of a huge delta, and was held obliquely aloft by a serpentining copper arm. The mirror flamed brightly in the shadow, as if lit by some splendor of unknown source; and the intruders were dazzled by glimpsings of its radiance as they went forward.

It seemed that Vacharn had indeed been overcome by the wonted trance, for he peered rigidly into the mirror, immobile as a seated mummy. The brothers held back, while Yadar, thinking them close behind him, stole toward the necromancer with lifted blade. As he drew nearer, he perceived that Vacharn held a great scimitar across his knees; and deeming that the sorcerer was perhaps forewarned, Yadar ran quickly up behind him and aimed a powerful stroke at his neck, meaning to hew off the head with that single blow. But, even while he aimed, his eyes were wholly blinded by the strange brightness of the mirror, as though a sun had blazed into them from its depth across the shoulder of Vacharn; and the blade swerved and bit slantingly into the collar-bone, so that the necromancer, though sorely wounded, was saved from decapitation.

Now it seemed likely that Vacharn had foreknown the attempt to slay him, and had thought to do battle with his assailers when they came, and kill the three without injury to himself, by virtue of his superiority in swordsmanship and in magic. But, sitting at the mirror in pretended trance, he had no doubt been overpowered against his will by the weird brilliancy; and was aroused from that mantic slumber only by the lethal biting of Yadar's sword through flesh and bone.

Fierce and swift as a wounded tiger, he leapt from the brazen trivet, swinging his scimitar aloft as he turned upon Yadar. The prince, still blinded, could neither strike again nor avoid the stroke of Vacharn; and the scimitar clove deeply into his right shoulder, and he fell mortally wounded and lay with his head upheld a little against the base of the snakish copper arm that supported the mirror.

Lying there, with his life ebbing slowly, he beheld how Vokal, who stood somewhat in advance of Uldulla, sprang forward as if with the desperation of one who sees imminent death, and hewed mightily into the neck of Vacharn ere the sorcerer could turn. The head, almost sundered from the body, toppled and hung by a strip of flesh and skin: yet Vacharn, reeling, did not fall or die at once, as any mortal man should have done: but, still animated by the wizard power within him, he ran about the chamber, striking great blows at the parricides. Blood gushed from his neck like a fountain as he ran; and his head swung to and fro like a monstrous pendulum on his breast. And all his blows went wild because he could no longer see to direct them, and his sons avoided him agilely, hewing into him oftentimes as he went past. And sometimes he stumbled over the fallen Yadar, or struck the mirror of electrum with his sword, making it ring like a deep bell. And some-

times the battle passed beyond sight of the dying prince, toward the
dim window that looked seaward; and he heard the strange crashings,
as if some of the magic furniture were shattered by the strokes of the
warlock; and there were loud breathings from the sons of Vacharn,
and the dull sound of blows that went home as they still pursued their
father. And anon the fight returned before Yadar, and he watched it
with dimming eyes.

Dire beyond telling was that combat, and Vokal and Uldulla pant-
ed like spent runners ere the end. But, after a while, the power seemed
to fail in Vacharn with the draining of his life-blood. He staggered
from side to side as he ran, and his paces halted, and his blows became
enfeebled. His raiment hung upon him in blood-soaked rags from the
slashings of his sons, and certain of his members were half sundered,
and his whole body was hacked and overscored like an executioner's
block. At last, with a dexterous blow, Vokal severed the thin strip by
which the head still depended; and the head dropped and rolled with
many reboundings about the floor.

Then, with a wild tottering, as if still fain to stand erect, the body
of Vacharn toppled down and lay thrashing like a great, headless fowl,
heaving itself up and dropping back again, incessantly. Never, with all
its rearings, did the body quite regain its feet: but the scimitar was still
held firmly in the right hand, and the corpse laid blindly about it, striking from the floor with sidelong slashes, or slicing down as it rose half-
way to a standing posture. And the head still rolled, unresting, about
the chamber, and maledictions came from its mouth in a pipy voice no
louder than that of a child.

At this, Yadar saw that Vokal and Uldulla drew back, as if somewhat aghast; and they turned toward the door, manifestly intending to
quit the room. But before Vokal, going first, had lifted the portal-arras,
there slithered beneath its folds the long, black, snakish body of the
weasel-familiar, Esrit. And the familiar launched itself in air, reaching
at one bound the throat of Vokal; and it clung there with teeth fas-

tened in his flesh, sucking his blood steadily, while he staggered about the room and strove in vain to tear it away with maddened fingers.

Uldulla, it seemed, would have made some attempt to kill the creature; for he cried out, adjuring Vokal to stand firm, and raised his sword as if waiting for a chance to strike at the weasel-thing. But Vokal seemed to hear him not, or was too frenzied to obey his adjuration. And at that instant the head of Vacharn, in its rolling, bounded against Uldulla's feet; and the head, snarling ferociously, caught the hem of his robe with its teeth and hung there as he sprang back in panic fright. And though he sliced wildly at the head with his scimitar, the teeth refused to relinquish their hold. So he dropped his garment, and leaving it there with the still pendant head of his father, he fled naked from the chamber. And even as Uldulla fled, the life departed from Yadar, and he saw and heard no more. . . .

Dimly, from the depths of oblivion, Yadar beheld the flaring of remote lights, and heard the chanting of a far voice. It seemed that he swam upward from black seas toward the voice and the lights, and he saw as if through a thin, watery film the face of Uldulla standing above him, and the fuming of strange vessels in the chamber of Vacharn. And it seemed that Uldulla said to him: "Arise from death, and be obedient in all things to me the master."

So, in answer to the unholy rites and incantations of necromancy, Yadar arose to such life as was possible for a resurrected lich. And he walked again, with the black gore of his wound in a great clot on his shoulder and breast, and made reply to Uldulla in the fashion of the living dead. Vaguely, and as matters of no import, he remembered something of his death and the circumstances preceding it; and vainly, with filmed eyes, in the wrecked chamber, he looked for the sundered head and body of Vacharn, and for Vokal and the weasel-demon.

Then it seemed that Uldulla said to him: "Follow me;" and he went forth with the necromancer into the light of the red, swollen moon that had soared from the Black River upon Naat. There, on the fell before the mansion, was a vast heap of ashes where coals glowed and glared like living eyes in the moonshine. Uldulla stood in contemplation before the heap; and Yadar stood beside him, knowing not that he gazed on the burnt-out pyre of Vacharn and Vokal, which the dead slaves had built and fired at Uldulla's direction.

Then, with shrill, eerie wailings, a mighty wind came suddenly from the sea, and lifting all the ashes and sparks in a great, swirling cloud, it swept them upon Yadar and the necromancer. The twain could hardly stand against that wind, and their hair and beards and garments were filled with the leavings of the pyre, and both were blinded thereby. Then the wind went on, sweeping the cloud of ashes over the mansion and into its doorways and windows; and through all its apartments. And for many days thereafter, little swirls of ash rose up like phantoms under the feet of those who passed along the halls; and though there was a daily plying of besoms by the dead at Uldulla's injunction, it seemed that the place was never again wholly clean of those ashes. . . .

Regarding Uldulla, there remains little enough to be told: for his lordship over the dead was a brief thing. Abiding always alone, except for those liches who attended him, and the ashes that still haunted the mansion, he became possessed by a weird melancholy that turned quickly toward madness. No longer could he conceive the aims and objects of life; and the languor of death rose up around him like a black, stealthy sea, full of soft murmurs and shadow-like arms that were fain to draw him doomward. Soon he came to envy the dead, and to deem their lot desirable above any other. So, carrying that scimitar he had used at the slaying of Vacharn, he went into his father's chamber, which he had not entered since the raising up of Prince Yadar. There, beside the sun-bright mirror of divinations, he disembowelled himself, and fell amid the dust and the cobwebs that had gathered heavily over all. And, since there was no other necromancer to bring him back even to a semblance of life, he lay rotting and undisturbed forever after.

But in the gardens of Vacharn the dead people still labored, heedless of Uldulla's passing; and they still kept the goats and cattle, and dived for pearls in the dark, torrent main, even as before.

And Yadar, who had been called from nothingness to a dim, crepuscular state of being, dwelt and toiled with the other liches. He remembered but vaguely the various events that were antecedent to his death; and the fiery days of his youth in Zyra were less than ashes. The promise made to him by the sons of Vacharn, and his hope of escaping with Dalili, had now lost their meaning; and he knew the death of Uldulla only as the vanishing of a shadow. Yet, with a ghostly yearning, he was still drawn to Dalili; and he followed her during the day, and felt a ghostly comfort in her nearness; and through the night-time he lay beside her, and she was a dim sweetness in his shadowy dreams. The quick despair that had racked him aforetime, and the long torments of desire and separation, were as things faded and forgot; and he shared with Dalili a shadowy love and a dim contentment.

THE TRAVELLER

Stranger, where goest thou, in the sad raiment of a pilgrim, with shattered sandals retaining the dust and mire of so many devious ways? With thy brow that alien suns have darkened, and thy hair made white from the cold rime of alien moons? Wanderest thou in search of the cities greater than Rome, with walls of opal and crystal, and fanes more white than the summer clouds, or the foam of hyperboreal seas? Or farest thou to the lands unpeopled and unexplored, to the sunless deserts lit by the baleful and calamitous beacons of volcanoes? Or seekest thou an extremer shore, where the red and monstrous lilies are like a royal pageant, pausing with innumerable flambeaux held aloft on the verge of the waveless waters?"

"Nay, it is none of these that I seek, but forevermore I seek the city and the land of my former home: In the quest thereof I have wandered from the first, immemorial years of my youth till now, and have mingled the dust of many realms, of many highways, in my garments' hem. I have seen the cities greater than Rome, and the fanes more white than the clouds of summer; the lands unpeopled and unexplored, and the land that is thronged by the red and monstrous lilies. Even the far, aerial walls of the cities of mirage, and the saffron meadows of sunset I have seen, but nevermore the city and land of my former home."

"Where lieth the land of thine home? And by what name shall we know it, and distinguish the rumour thereof, among the rumours of many lands?"

"Alas! I know not where it lieth; nor in the broad, black scrolls of geographers, and the charts of old seamen who have sailed to the marge of the seventh sea, is the place thereof recorded. And its name I have never learned, howbeit I have learned the name of empires lying beneath stars to us invisible. In many languages have I spoken, in barbarous tongues unknown to Babel; and I have heard the speech of many men, even of them that inhabit the strange isles of the sea of fire and the sea of snow. Thunder, and lutes, and battle-drums, the fine unceasing querulousness of gnats, and the stupendous moaning of the simoon; lyres of ebony damascened with crystal, bells of malachite with golden clappers; the song of exotic birds that sigh like women or sob like fountains; whispers and shoutings of fire, the multitudinous mutter of cities asleep, the manifold tumult of cities at dawn, and the slow and weary murmur of desert-wandering streams–all, all have I heard, but never, in any place, from any tongue, a sound or syllable that resembled in the least in the name I would learn."

Xeethra

Subtle and manifold are the nets of the Demon, who
followeth his chosen from birth to death and from death to
birth, throughout many lives.

—The Testaments of Carnamagos.

Long had the wasting summer pastured its suns, like fiery red stallions, on the dun hills that crouched before the Mykrasian Mountains in wild easternmost Cincor. The peak-fed torrents were become
tenuous threads or far-sundered, fallen pools; the granite boulders
were shaled by the heat; the bare earth was cracked and creviced; and
the low, meager grasses were seared even to the roots.

So it occurred that the boy Xeethra, tending the black and piebald
goats of his uncle Pornos, was obliged to follow his charges farther
each day on the combes and hill-tops. In an afternoon of late summer
he came to a deep, craggy valley which he had never before visited.
Here a cool and shadowy tarn was watered by hidden well-springs; and
the ledgy slopes about the tarn were mantled with herbage and bushes
that had not wholly lost their vernal greenness.

Surprised and enchanted, the young goatherd followed his caper-
ing flock into this sheltered paradise. There was small likelihood that
the goats of Pornos would stray afield from such goodly pasturage; so
Xeethra did not trouble himself to watch them any longer. Entranced
by his surroundings, he began to explore the valley, after quenching his
thirst at the clear waters that sparkled like golden wine.

To him, the place seemed a veritable garden-pleasance. Everywhere there were new charms to beguile him onward: flowers that the

fell suns had spared, tiny and pale as the stars of evening; spicy ferns like fretted jade, growing in the moist shadows of boulders; and even a few edible orange berries, lingering past their season in this favorable reclusion.

Forgetting the distance he had already come, and the wrath of Pornos if the flock should return late for the milking, he wandered deeper among the winding crags that protected the valley. On every hand the rocks grew sterner and wilder; the valley straitened; and he stood presently at its end, where a rugged wall forbade further progress. Here, however, he found something that allured him even more than the flowers, the ferns, and the berries.

Before him, in the base of the sheer wall, he perceived the mysterious yawning of a cavern. It seemed that the rock must have opened only a little while before his coming: for the lines of cleavage were clearly marked, and the cracks made in the surrounding surface were unclaimed by the moss that grew plentifully elsewhere. From the cavern's creviced lip there sprang a stunted tree, with its newly broken roots hanging in air; and the stubborn taproot was in the rock at Xeethra's feet, where, it was plain, the tree had formerly stood.

Wondering and curious, the boy peered into the inviting gloom of the cavern, from which, unaccountably, a soft balmy air now began to blow, touching his face like a perfumed sigh. There were strange odors in the air such as he had never known except in nocturnal dreams, suggesting the pungency of temple incense, the languor and luxury of opiate blossoms. They disturbed the senses of Xeethra; and, at the same time, they seduced him with their promise of unbeholden marvellous things. It seemed that the cavern was the portal of some undiscovered world—and the portal had opened expressly to permit his entrance. Being of a nature both venturesome and visionary, he was undeterred by the fears that others might have felt in his place. Overpowered by a great curiosity, he soon entered the cave, carrying for torch a dry, resinous bough that had fallen from the tree in the cliff.

Beyond the mouth he was swallowed by a rough-arched passage
that pitched downward like the gorge of some monstrous dragon. The
torch's flame blew back, flaring and smoking in the warm aromatic
wind that strengthened from unknown depths. The cave steepened
perilously; but Xeethra continued his exploration, climbing down by
the stair-like coigns and projections of the stone.

Like a dreamer in a dream, he was wholly absorbed by the mystery
on which he had stumbled; and at no time did he recall his abandoned
duty. He lost all reckoning of the time consumed in his descent. Then
suddenly, his torch was extinguished by a hot gust that blew upon him
like the expelled breath of some prankish demon.

The enthralling spell was shattered for an instant, as he tottered in
darkness and sought to secure his footing on the dangerous incline. He
felt the assailment of a black panic; but, ere he could relume the
blown-out torch, he saw that the night around him was not complete,
but was tempered by a wan, golden glimmering from the depths below. Forgetting his alarm in a new wonder, he descended toward the
mysterious light.

At the bottom of the long incline, Xeethra passed through a low
cavern-mouth and emerged into sun-bright radiance. Dazzled and bewildered, he thought for a little while that his subterranean wanderings
had brought him back to the outer air in some unsuspected land lying
among the Mykrasian hills. Yet surely the region before him was no
part of summer-stricken Cincor: for he saw neither hills nor mountains
nor the black sapphire heavens from which the aging but despotic sun
glared down with implacable drouth on the many kingdoms of
Zothique.

Instead, he seemed to stand on the threshold of a fertile plain that
lapsed illimitably into golden distance under the measureless arch of a
golden vault. Far-off, through the misty radiance, he beheld the dim
towering of unidentifiable masses that might have been spires and
domes and ramparts. A level meadow lay at his feet, covered with

close-grown curling sward that had the greenness of verdigris; and the sward, at intervals, was studded with strange blossoms appearing to turn and move like living eyes beneath the regard of the young goat-herd. Near at hand, beyond the meadow, was an orchard-like grove of tall, amply spreading trees, amid whose lush leafage he descried the burning of numberless dark-red fruits. The plain, to all seeming, was empty of human life; and no birds flew in the fiery air or perched on the laden boughs. There was no sound other than the sibilant sighing of leaves in the perfume-burdened wind: a sound that had an elusive, troublous undertone such as might be made by the hissing of many small hidden serpents.

To the boy from the parched hill-country, this cavern-portalled realm was an Eden of untasted delights, alluring him with the promise of its fruited boughs and verdurous ground. But, for a little while, he was stayed by the strangeness of it all, and by the sense of weird and preternatural vitality which informed the whole landscape. Flakes of fire appeared to descend and melt in the rippling air; the grasses coiled with verminous writhings; the flowery eyes returned his regard intently; the trees palpitated as if a sanguine ichor flowed within them in lieu of sap; and the undernote of adder-like hissings amid the foliage grew louder and sharper.

In spite of all that was mysterious in his surroundings, Xeethra was deterred only by the thought that a region so fair and fertile must belong to some jealous owner who would resent his intrusion. He scanned the unpeopled plain with much circumspection. Then, deeming himself secure from observation, he yielded to the craving that had been roused within him by the red, luxuriant fruit.

The turf was elastic beneath him, like a living substance, as he ran forward to the nearest trees. Bowed with their shining globes, the branches drooped around him. He plucked several of the largest fruits and stored them thriftily in the bosom of his threadbare tunic. Then, unable to resist his appetence any longer, he lifted one of the fruits to his mouth. The rind broke easily under his teeth, and it seemed that a royal wine, sweet and puissant, was poured into his mouth from an overbrimming cup. He felt in his throat and bosom a swift warmth that almost suffocated him; and a strange fever sang in his ears and wildered his senses. It passed quickly, and he was startled from his bemusement by the sound of voices falling as if from an airy height above the trees.

He knew instantly that the voices were not those of men. They filled his ears with a rolling as of baleful drums, heavy with ominous echoes; yet it seemed that they spoke in articulate words, albeit of a strange language. Looking up between the thick boughs, he beheld a sight that inspired him with terror. Two beings of colossean stature, tall as the watch-towers of the mountain people, stood waist-high above the near tree-tops. It was as if they had appeared by sorcery from the green ground or the gold heavens: for surely the clumps of vegetation, dwarfed into bushes by their bulk, could never have concealed them from Xeethra's discernment.

The figures were completely clad in black armor, lusterless and gloomy, such as demons might wear in the service of Thasaidon, lord of the bottomless underworlds. Xeethra felt sure that they had seen him; and perhaps their unintelligible converse concerned his presence. He trembled, thinking now that he had trespassed on the gardens of genii. More and more he was terrified by the aspect of the giant shapes; for he could discern no features beneath the frontlets of the dark helms that were bowed toward him: but eyelike spots of yellow-ish-red fire, restless as marsh-lights, shifted to and fro in void shadow where the faces should have been.

It seemed to Xeethra that the rich foliage could afford no shelter from the scrutiny of these beings, the guardians of the land on which he had so rashly intruded. He was overwhelmed by a consciousness of guilt: the sibilant leaves, the drum-like voices of the giants, the eye-shaped flowers—all appeared to accuse him of trespass and thievery.

At the same time he was perplexed by a queer and unwonted vagueness in regard to his own identity: somehow it was not Xeethra the goatherd . . . but another . . . who had found the bright garden-realm and had eaten the blood-dark fruit. This alien self was without name or formulable memory; but there was a flickering of confused lights, a murmur of indistinguishable voices, amid the stirred shadows of his mind. Again he felt the weird warmth, the swift-mounting fever, that had followed the devouring of the fruit.

From all this, he was aroused by a livid flash of light that clove downward toward him across the branches. Whether a bolt of levin had issued from the clear vault, or whether one of the armored beings had brandished a great sword, he was never quite sure afterwards. The light seared his vision, he recoiled in uncontrollable fright, and found himself running, half blind, across the open turf. Through whirling bolts of color he saw before him, in a sheer, topless cliff, the cavern-mouth through which he had come. Behind him he heard a long rumbling as of summer thunder . . . or the laughter of colossi.

Without pausing to retrieve the still-burning brand he had left at the entrance, Xeethra plunged incontinently into the dark cave. Through Stygian murk he managed to grope his way upward on the perilous incline. Reeling, stumbling, bruising himself at every turn, he came at last to the outer exit, in the hidden valley behind the hills of Cincor.

To his consternation, twilight had fallen during his absence in the world beyond the cave. Stars crowded above the grim crags that walled the valley; and the skies of burnt-out purple were gored by the sharp horn of an ivory moon. Still fearing the pursuit of the giant guardians, and apprehending also the wrath of his uncle Pornos, Xeethra hastened back to the little tarn, collected his flock, and drove it homeward through the long, gloomy miles.

During that journey, it seemed that a fever burned and died within him at intervals, bringing strange fancies. He forgot his fear of Pornos,

forgot, indeed, that he was Xeethra, the humble and disregarded goatherd. He was returning to another abode than the squalid hut of Pornos, built of clay and brushwood. In a high-domed city, gates of
burnished metal would open for him, and fiery-colored banners would
stream on the perfumed air; and silver trumpets and the voices of
blonde odalisques and black chamberlains would greet him as king in a
thousand-columned hall. The ancient pomp of royalty, familiar as air
and light, would surround him, and he, the King Amero, who had
newly come to the throne, would rule as his fathers had ruled over all
the kingdom of Calyz by the orient sea. Into his capital, on shaggy
camels, the fierce southern tribesmen would bring a levy of date-wine
and desert sapphires; and galleys from isles beyond the morning would
burden his wharves with their semi-annual tribute of spices and
strange-dyed fabrics . . . .

Such were the wild fantasies that thronged the mind of Xeethra,
surging and fading like pictures of delirium. Clearer than the memories
of his daily life, the madness came and went; and once again he was
the nephew of Pornos, returning belated with the flock, and full of
confused apprehension and wonder.

Like a downward-thrusting blade, the red moon had fixed itself in
the somber hills when Xeethra reached the rough wooden pen in
which Pornos kept his goats. Even as Xeethra had expected, the old
man was waiting at the gate, bearing in one hand a clay lantern and in
the other a staff of briar-wood. He began to curse the boy with half-
senile vehemence, waving the staff, and threatening to beat him for his
tardiness.

Xeethra did not flinch before the staff. Again, in his fancy, he was
Amero, the young king of Calyz. Bewildered and astonished, he saw
before him by the light of the shaken lantern a foul and rancid-
smelling ancient whom he could not remember. Hardly could he understand the speech of Pornos; the man's anger puzzled but did not
frighten him; and his nostrils, as if accustomed only to delicate per-

fumes, were offended by the goatish stench. As if for the first time, he heard the bleating of the tired flock, and gazed in wild surprise at the wattled pen and the hut beyond.

"Is it for this," cried Pornos, "that I have reared my sister's orphan at great expense? Accursed moon-calf! thankless whelp! If you have lost a milch-goat or a single kid, I shall flay you from thigh to shoulder."

Deeming that the silence of the youth was due to mere obstinacy, Pornos began to beat him with the staff. At the first blow, the bright cloud lifted from Xeethra's mind. Dodging the briar-wood with agility, he tried to tell Pornos of the new pasture he had found hidden among the barren hills. At this the old man suspended his blows, and Xeethra went on to tell of the strange cave that had conducted him to an unguessed garden-land. To support his story, he reached within his tunic for the blood-red apples he had stolen; but, to his confoundment, the fruits were gone, and he knew not whether he had lost them in the dark, or whether, perhaps, they had vanished by virtue of some indwelling necromancy.

Pornos, interrupting the boy with frequent scoldings, heard him at first with open unbelief. But he grew silent as the youth went on; and when the story was done, he cried out in a trembling voice:

"Ill was this day, for you have wandered among enchantments. Verily, there is no tarn such as you have described amid the hills; nor, at this season, has any herder found such pasturage. These things were illusions, designed to lead you astray; and the cave, I wot, was no honest cave but an entrance into hell. I have heard my fathers tell that the gardens of Thasaidon, king of the seven underworlds, lie near to the earth's surface in this region; and caves have opened ere this, like a portal, and the sons of men, trespassing unaware on the gardens, have been tempted by the fruit and have eaten it. But madness comes thereof and much sorrow and long damnation: for the Demon, they say, forgetting not one stolen apple, will exact his price in the end. Woe! woe! the goat-milk will be soured for a whole moon by the grass of such wizard pasture; and, after all the food and care you have cost me, I must find another stripling to ward the flocks."

Once more, as he listened, the burning cloud of delirium returned upon Xeethra.

"Old man, I know you not," he said perplexedly. Then, using soft words of a courtly speech but half-intelligible to Pornos: "It would seem that I have gone astray. Prithee, where lies the kingdom of Calyz? I am king thereof, being newly crowned in the high city of Shathair, over which my fathers have ruled for a thousand years."

"Ai! Ai!" wailed Pornos. "The boy is daft. These notions have come through the eating of the Demon's apple. Cease your maundering, and help me to milk the goats. You are none other than the child of my sister Askli, who was delivered these nineteen years agone after her husband, Outhoth, had died of a dysentery. Askli lived not long, and I, Pornos, have reared you as a son, and the goats have mothered you."

"I must find my kingdom," persisted Xeethra. "I am lost in darkness, amid uncouth things, and how I have wandered here I cannot remember. Old man, I would have you give me food and lodging for the night. In the dawn I shall journey toward Shathair, by the orient main."

Pornos, shaking and muttering, lifted his clay lantern to the boy's face. It seemed that a stranger stood before him, in whose wide and wondering eyes the flame of golden lamps was somehow reflected. There was no wildness in Xeethra's demeanor, but merely a sort of gentle pride and remoteness; and he wore his threadbare tunic with a strange grace. Surely, however, he was demented; for his manner and speech were past understanding. Pornos, mumbling under his breath, but no longer urging the boy to assist him, turned to the milking . . . .

Xeethra woke betimes in the white dawn, and peered with amazement at the mud-plastered walls of the hovel in which he had dwelt since birth. All was alien and baffling to him; and especially was he troubled by his rough garments and by the sun-swart tawniness of his skin: for such were hardly proper to the young King Amero, whom he believed himself to be. His circumstances were wholly inexplicable; and he felt an urgency to depart at once on his homeward journey.

He rose quietly from the litter of dry grasses that had served him for a bed. Pornos, lying in a far corner, still slept the sleep of age and senescence; and Xeethra was careful not to awaken him. He was both puzzled and repelled by this unsavory ancient, who had fed him on the previous evening with coarse millet-bread and the strong milk and cheese of goats, and had given him the hospitality of a fetid hut. He had paid little heed to the mumblings and objurgations of Pornos; but it was plain that the old man doubted his claims to royal rank, and, moreover, was possessed of peculiar delusions regarding his identity.

Leaving the hovel, Xeethra followed an eastward-winding footpath amid the stony hills. He knew not whither the path would lead: but reasoned that Calyz, being the easternmost realm of the continent Zothique, was situated somewhere below the rising sun. Before him, in vision, the verdant vales of his kingdom hovered like a fair mirage, and the swelling domes of Shathair were as morning cumuli piled in the orient. These things, he deemed, were memories of yesterday. He could not recall the circumstances of his departure and his absence; but surely the land over which he ruled was not remote.

The path turned among lessening ridges, and Xeethra came to the small village of Cith, to whose inhabitants he was known. The place was alien to him now, seeming no more than a cirque of low, filthy hovels that reeked and festered under the sun. The people gathered about him, calling him by name, and staring and laughing oafishly when he inquired the road to Calyz. No one, it appeared, had ever heard of this kingdom or of the city of Shathair. Noting a strangeness in Xeethra's demeanor, and deeming that his queries were those of a madman, the people began to mock him. Children pelted him with dry clods and pebbles; and thus he was driven from Cith, following an eastern road that ran from Cincor into the neighboring lowlands of the country of Zhel.

Sustained only by the vision of his lost kingdom, the youth wandered for many moons throughout Zothique. People derided him when he spoke of his kingship and made inquiry concerning Calyz; but many, thinking madness a sacred thing, offered him shelter and sustenance. Amid the far-stretching fruitful vineyards of Zhel, and into Istanam of the myriad cities; over the high-winding passes of Ymorth, where snow tarried at the autumn's beginning; and across the salt-pale desert of Dhir, and through the python-haunted jungles of Ongath, Xeethra followed that bright imperial dream which had now become his only memory. Always eastward he went, travelling sometimes with caravans whose members hoped that a madman's company would bring them good fortune; but oftener he went as a solitary wayfarer.

At whiles, for a brief space, his dream deserted him, and he was only the simple goatherd, lost in foreign realms, and homesick for the barren hills of Cincor. Then, once more, he remembered his kingship, and the opulent gardens of Shathair and the proud palaces, and the names and faces of them that had served him following the death of his father, King Eldamaque, and his own succession to the throne. More often than other memories, there came to him the thought of a vernal evening, when he had walked alone on an eastward terrace of the palace, breathing the perfumes of languid flowers mingled with sharp sea-balsams, and watching the mighty star Canopus, which had climbed midway between the low skyline and the zenith. There he had stood, feeling a mystic joy and an obscure pain, while the night assumed a profounder purple, and the lesser stars came out thronging around Canopus.

At midwinter, in the far city of Sha-Karag, Xeethra met certain sellers of amulets from Ustaim, who smiled oddly when he asked if they could direct him to Calyz. Winking among themselves when he spoke of his royal rank, the merchants told him that Calyz was situated several hundred leagues beyond Sha-Karag, below the orient sun.

"Hail, O King," they said with mock ceremony. "Long and merrily may you reign in Shathair, over all the peoples of Calyz."

Very joyful was Xeethra, hearing word of his lost kingdom for the first time. And he did not heed the laughter and whispering that passed among the merchants of Ustaim as he left them.

Tarrying no longer in Sha-Karag, he journeyed on with all possible haste. In his thin rags he dared the heavy rains of winter; and he passed perilously over the salt marshes of an inland sea, and across the stony wilderness lying beyond, wherein no people dwelt but a clashing and tumult as of unseen armies was heard by the traveller. Through this he came with safety to the land of certain half-barbarous tribesmen, who treated him with kindness but could not understand his speech. Afterwards he arrived in the four cities of Athoad, whose inhabitants informed him, with a curious derision in their manner, that Calyz was still a full month's journey to the east.

Now, as he went on, Xeethra began to marvel because he met no travellers from his own country. He recalled that merchants were wont to traffic between Calyz and the vicinal regions; and dimly he remembered hearing of the cities of Athoad as far outland places. Everywhere men eyed him strangely when he asked for news of his kingdom; and some laughed openly, and others, in tones of irony, wished him well of his journeying.

When the first moon of spring was a frail crescent at eve, he knew that he neared his destination. For Canopus burned high in the eastern heavens, mounting gloriously amid the smaller stars even as he had once seen it from his palace-terrace in Shathair.

His heart leapt with the gladness of homecoming; but much he marvelled at the wildness and sterility of the region through which he passed. It seemed that there were no travellers coming and going from Calyz; and he met only a few nomads, who fled at his approach like the creatures of the waste. The highway was overgrown with grasses and cacti, and was rutted only by the winter rains. Beside it, anon, he came to a stone terminus carved in the form of a rampant lion, that had marked the western boundary of Calyz. The lion's features had crumbled away, and his paws and body were lichened, and it seemed that long ages of desolation had gone over him. A chill dismay was born in Xeethra's heart: for only yesteryear, if his memory served him rightly, he had ridden past the lion with his father Eldamaque, hunting hyenas, and had remarked then the newness of the carving.

Now, from the high ridge of the border, he gazed down upon Calyz, which had lain like a long verdant scroll beside the sea. To his wonderment and consternation, the wide fields were sere as if with autumn; the rivers were thin threads that wasted themselves in sand; the hills were gaunt as the ribs of unceremented mummies; and there was no greenery other than the scant herbage which a desert bears in spring. Far off, by the purple main, he thought that he beheld the shining of the marble domes of Shathair; and, fearing that some blight of hostile sorcery had fallen upon his kingdom, he hastened toward the city.

Everywhere, as he wandered heartsick through the vernal day, he found that the desert had established its empire. Void were the fields, unpeopled the villages. The cots had tumbled into midden-like heaps of ruin; and it seemed that a thousand seasons of drouth had withered the fruitful orchards, leaving only a few black and decaying stumps.

In the late afternoon he entered Shathair, which had been the white mistress of the orient sea. The streets and the harbor were alike empty, and silence sat on the broken housetops and the ruining walls. The great bronze obelisks were greened with antiquity; the massy marmorean temples of the gods of Calyz leaned and slanted to their fall.

Tardily, as one who fears to confirm an expected thing, Xeethra came to the palace of the monarchs. Not as he recalled it, a glory of soaring marble half veiled by flowering almonds and trees of spice and high-pulsing fountains; but, in stark dilapidation amid blasted gardens, the palace awaited him, while the brief, illusory rose of sunset faded upon its dome, leaving them wan as mausoleums.

How long the place had lain desolate, he could not know. Confusion filled him, and he was whelmed by utter loss and despair. It seemed that none remained to greet him amid the ruins; but, nearing the portals of the west wing, he saw, as it were, a fluttering of shadows that appeared to detach themselves from the gloom beneath the portico; and certain dubious beings, clothed in rotten tatters, came sidling and crawling before him on the cracked pavement. Pieces of their raiment dropped from them as they moved; and about them was an unnamed horror of filth, of squalor and disease. When they neared him, Xeethra saw that most of them were lacking in some member or feature, and that all were marked by the gnawing of leprosy.

His gorge rose within him, and he could not speak. But the lepers hailed him with hoarse cries and hollow croakings, as if deeming him another outcast who had come to join them in their abode amid the ruins.

"Who are ye that dwell in my palace of Shathair?" he inquired at length. "Behold! I am King Amero, the son of Eldamaque, and I have returned from a far land to resume the throne of Calyz."

At this, a loathsome cackling and tittering arose among the lepers. "We alone are the kings of Calyz," one of them told the youth. "The land has been a desert for centuries, and the city of Shathair had long lain unpeopled save by such as we, who were driven out from other places. Young man, you are welcome to share the realm with us: for another king, more or less, is a small matter here."

Then, with obscene cachinnations, the lepers jeered at Xeethra and derided him; and he, standing amid the dark fragments of his dream, could find no words to answer them. However, one of the oldest lepers, well-nigh limbless and faceless, shared not in the mirth of his fellows, but seemed to ponder and reflect; and he said at last to Xeethra, in a voice issuing thickly from the black pit of his gaping mouth:

"I have heard something of the history of Calyz, and the names of Amero and Eldamaque are familiar to me. In bygone ages certain of the rulers were named thus; but I know not which of them was the son and which the father. Haply both are now entombed, with the rest of their dynasty, in the deep-lying vaults beneath the palace."

Now, in the greying twilight, other lepers emerged from the shadowy ruin and gathered about Xeethra. Hearing that he laid claim to the kingship of the desert realm, certain of their number went away and returned presently, bearing vessels filled with rank water and mouldy victuals, which they proffered to Xeethra, bowing low with a mummery as of chamberlains serving a monarch.

Xeethra turned from them in loathing, though he was famished and athirst. He fled through the ashen gardens, among the dry fountain-mouths and dusty plots. Behind him he heard the hideous mirth of the lepers; but the sound grew fainter, and it seemed that they did not follow him. Rounding the vast palace in his flight, he met no more of these creatures. The portals of the south wing and the east wing were dark and empty, but he did not care to enter them, knowing that desolation and things worse than desolation were the sole tenants.

Wholly distraught and despairing, he came to the eastern wing and paused in the gloom. Dully, and with a sense of dreamlike estrangement, he became aware that he stood on that very terrace above the sea, which he had remembered so often during his journey. Bare were the ancient flower-beds; the trees had rotted away in their sunken basins; and the great flags of the pavement were runneled and broken. But the veils of twilight were tender upon the ruin; and the sea sighed as of yore under a purple shrouding; and the mighty star Canopus climbed in the east, with the lesser stars still faint around him.

Bitter was the heart of Xeethra, thinking himself a dreamer beguiled by some idle dream. He shrank from the high splendor of Canopus, as if from a flame too bright to bear; but, ere he could turn away, it seemed that a column of shadow, darker than the night and thicker than any cloud, rose upward before him from the terrace and blotted out the effulgent star. Out of the solid stone the shadow grew, towering tall and colossal; and it took on the outlines of a mailed warrior; and it seemed that the warrior looked down upon Xeethra from a great height with eyes that shone and shifted like fireballs in the darkness of his face under the lowering helmet.

Confusedly, as one who recalls an old dream, Xeethra remembered a boy who had herded goats upon summer-stricken hills; and who, one day, had found a cavern that opened portal-like on a garden-land of strangeness and marvel. Wandering there, the boy had eaten a blood-dark fruit and had fled in terror before the black-armored giants who warded the garden. Again he was that boy; and still he was the King Amero, who had sought for his lost realm through many regions; and, finding it in the end, had found only the abomination of desolation.

Now, as the trepidation of the goatherd, guilty of theft and trespass, warred in his soul with the pride of the king, he heard a voice that rolled through the heavens like thunder from a high cloud in the spring night.

"I am the emissary of Thasaidon, who sends me in due course to all who have passed the nether portals and have tasted the fruit of His garden. No man, having eaten the fruit, shall remain thereafter as he was before; but to some the fruit brings oblivion, and to others, memory. Know, then, that in another birth, ages agone, you were indeed the young King Amero. The memory, being strong upon you, has effaced the remembrance of your present life, and has driven you forth to seek your ancient kingdom."

"If this be true, then doubly am I bereft," said Xeethra, bowing sorrowfully before the shadow. "For, being Amero, I am throneless and realmless; and, being Xeethra, I cannot forget my former royalty and regain the content which I knew as a simple goatherd."

"Hearken, for there is another way," said the shadow, its voice muted like the murmur of a far ocean. "Thasaidon is the master of all sorceries, and a giver of magic gifts to those who serve Him and acknowledge Him as their lord. Pledge your allegiance, promise your soul to Him; and in fee thereof, the Demon will surely reward you. If it be your wish, He can wake again the buried past with His necromancy. Again, as King Amero, you shall reign over Calyz; and all things shall be as they were in the perished years; and the dead faces and the fields now desert shall bloom again; and not one petal shall be wanting from your gardens, nor one block or segment of mosaic from the high-builded glory of Shathair."

"I accept the bond," said Xeethra. "I plight my fealty to Thasaidon, and I promise my soul to Him if He, in return, will give me back my kingdom."

"There is more to be said," resumed the shadow. "Not wholly have you remembered your other life, but merely those years that correspond to your present youth. Living again as Amero, perhaps you will regret your royalty in time; and if such regret should overcome you, leading you to forget a monarch's duty, then the whole necromancy shall end and vanish like vapor."

"So be it," said Xeethra. "This too I accept as part of the bargain."

When the words ended, he beheld no longer the shadow towering against Canopus. The star flamed with a pristine splendor, as if no cloud had ever dimmed it; and, without sense of change or transition, he who watched the star was none other than King Amero; and the goatherd Xeethra, and the Emissary, and the pledge given to Thasaidon, were as things that had never been. The ruin that had come upon Shathair was no more than the dream of some mad prophet; for in the nostrils of Amero the perfume of languorous flowers mingled with salt sea-balsams; and in his ears the grave murmur of ocean was pierced by the amorous plaint of lyres and a shrill laughter of slave-girls from the palace behind him. He heard the myriad noises of the nocturnal city, where his people feasted and made jubilee; and, turning from the star with a mystic pain and an obscure joy in his heart,

Amero beheld the effulgent portals and windows of his fathers' house, and the far-mounting light from a thousand flambeaux that paled the stars in mid-heaven as they passed over Shathair.

It is written in the old chronicles that King Amero reigned for many prosperous years. Peace and abundance were upon all the realm of Calyz; the drouth came not from the desert, nor violent gales from the main; and tribute was sent at the ordained seasons to Amero from the subject isles and outlying lands. And Amero was well content, dwelling superbly in rich-arrased halls, feasting and drinking royally, and hearing the praise of his lute-players and his chamberlains and his lemans.

When his life was a little past the meridian years, there came at whiles to Amero something of that satiety which lies in wait for the minions of fortune. At such times he turned from the cloying pleasures of the court and found delight in blossoms and leaves and the verses of olden poets. Thus was satiety held at bay; and, since the duties of the realm rested lightly upon him, Amero still found his kingship a goodly thing.

Then, in a latter autumn, it seemed that the stars looked disastrously upon Calyz. Murrain and blight and pestilence rode abroad as if on the wings of unseen dragons. The coast of the kingdom was beset and sorely harried by pirate galleys. Upon the west, the caravans coming and going through Calyz were assailed by redoubtable bands of robbers; and certain fierce desert peoples made war on the villages lying near to the southern border. The land was filled with turmoil and death, with lamentation and many miseries.

Deep was Amero's concern, hearing the distressful complaints that were brought before him daily. Being but little skilled in kingcraft, and wholly untried by the ordeals of dominion, he sought counsel of his courtlings but was ill advised by them. The troubles of the realm multiplied upon him; uncurbed by authority, the wild peoples of the waste grew bolder, and the pirates gathered like vultures of the sea. Famine and drouth divided his realm with the plague; and it seemed to Amero, in his sore perplexity, that such matters were beyond all medication; and his crown was become a too onerous burden.

Striving to forget his own impotence and the woeful plight of his kingdom, he gave himself to long nights of debauch. But the wine refused its oblivion, and the kisses of his lemans no longer stirred him to rapture. He sought other divertissements, calling before him strange maskers and mummers and buffoons, and assembling outlandish singers, and the players of uncouth instruments. Daily he made proclamation of a high reward to any that could bemuse him from his cares.

Wild songs and sorcerous ballads of yore were sung to him by immortal minstrels; the black girls of the north, with amber-dappled limbs, danced before him their weird lascivious measures; the blowers of the horns of chimeras played a mad and secret tune; and savage drummers pounded a troublous music on drums made from the skin of cannibals; while men clothed with the scales and pelts of half-mythic monsters ramped or crawled grotesquely through the halls of the palace. But all these were vain to beguile the king from his grievous musings.

One afternoon, as he sat heavily in his hall of audience, there came to him a player of pipes who was clad in tattered homespun. The eyes of the man were bright as newly stirred embers, and his face was burned to a cindery blackness, as if by the ardor of outland suns. Hailing Amero with small servility, he announced himself as a goatherd who had come to Shathair from a region of valleys and mountains lying sequestered beyond the bourn of sunset.

"O King, I know the melodies of oblivion," he said, "and I would play for you, though I desire not the reward you have offered. If haply I succeed in diverting you, I shall take my own guerdon in due time."

"Play, then," said Amero, feeling a faint interest rise within him at the bold speech of the piper.

Forthwith, on his pipes of reed, the black goatherd began a music that was like the falling and rippling of water in quiet vales, and the passing of wind over lonely hill-tops. Subtly the pipes told of freedom and peace and forgetfulness lying beyond the sevenfold purple of outland horizons. Dulcetly they sang of a place where the years came not with an iron trampling, but were soft of tread as a zephyr shod with flower petals. There the world's turmoil and troubling were lost upon measureless leagues of silence, and the burdens of empire were blown away like thistledown. There the goatherd, tending his flock on solitary fells, was possessed of tranquility sweeter than the power of monarchs.

As he listened to the piper, a sorcery crept upon the mind of Amero. The weariness of kingship, the cares and perplexities, were as dream-bubbles lapsing in some Lethean tide. He beheld before him, in sun-bright verdure and stillness, the enchanted vales evoked by the music; and he himself was the goatherd, following grassy paths, or lying oblivious of the vulture hours by the margin of lulled waters.

Hardly he knew that the low piping had ceased. But the vision darkened, and he who had dreamt of a goatherd's peace was again a troubled king.

"Play on!" he cried to the black piper. "Name your own guerdon—and play."

The eyes of the goatherd burned like embers in a dark place at evening. "Not till the passing of ages and the falling of kingdoms shall I require of you my reward," he said enigmatically. "Howbeit, I shall play for you once more."

So, through the afternoon, King Amero was beguiled by that sorcerous piping which told ever of a far land of ease and forgetfulness. With each playing it seemed that the spell grew stronger upon him; and more and more was his royalty a hateful thing; and the very grandeur of his palace oppressed and stifled him. No longer could he endure the heavily jewelled yoke of duty; and madly he envied the carefree lot of the goatherd.

At twilight he dismissed the ministrants who attended him, and held speech alone with the piper.

"Lead me to this land of yours," he said, "where I too may dwell as a simple herder."

Clad in mufti, so that his people might not recognize him, the king stole from the palace through an unguarded postern, accompanied by the piper. Night, like a formless monster with the crescent moon for its lowered horn, was crouching beyond the town; but in the streets the invading shadows were thrust back by a flaming of myriad cressets. Amero and his guide were unchallenged by any man as they went toward the outer darkness. And the king repented not his forsaken throne: though he saw in the city a continual passing of biers laden with the victims of the plague; and faces gaunt with famine rose up from the shadows as if to accuse him of recreancy. These he heeded not: for his eyes were filled with the dream of a green silent valley, in a land lost beyond the turbid flowing of time with its wreckage and tumult.

Now, as Amero followed the black piper, there descended upon him a sudden dimness; and he faltered in weird doubt and bewilderment. The street-lights flickered before him, and swiftly they expired in the gloom. The loud murmuring of the city fell away in a vast silence; and, like the shifting of some disordered dream, it seemed that the tall houses crumbled stilly and were gone even as shadows, and the stars shone over broken walls. Confusion filled the thoughts and the senses of Amero; and in his heart was a black chill of unutterable desolation; and he seemed to himself as one who had known the lapse of long empty years, and the loss of high splendor; and who stood now amid the extremity of age and decay. In his nostrils was a dry mustiness such as the night draws from olden ruin; and it came to him, as a thing foreknown and now remembered obscurely, that the desert was lord in his proud capital of Shathair.

"Where have you led me?" cried Amero to the piper.

For all reply, he heard a laughter that was like the peal of derisive thunder. The muffled shape of the goatherd towered colossally in the gloom, changing, growing, till its outlines were transformed to those of a giant warrior in sable armor. Strange memories thronged the mind of Amero, and he seemed to recall darkly something of another life. . . Somehow, somewhere, for a time, he had been the goatherd of his dreams, content and forgetful . . . somehow, somewhere, he had entered a strange bright garden and had eaten a blood-dark fruit. . . .

Then, in a flaring as of infernal levin, he remembered all, and knew the mighty shadow that towered above him like a Terminus reared in hell. Beneath his feet was the cracked pavement of the seaward terrace; and the stars above the Emissary were those that precede Canopus; but Canopus himself was blotted out by the Demon's shoulder. Somewhere in the dusty darkness, a leper laughed and coughed thickly, prowling about the ruined palace in which had once dwelt the kings of Calyz. All things were even as they had been before the making of that bargain through which a perished kingdom had been raised up by the powers of hell.

Anguish choked the heart of Xeethra as if with the ashes of burnt-out pyres and the shards of heaped ruin. Subtly and manifoldly had the Demon tempted him to his loss. Whether these things had been dream or necromancy or verity he knew not with sureness; nor whether they had happened once or had happened often. In the end there was only dust and dearth; and he, the doubly accurst, must remember and repent forevermore all that he had forfeited.

He cried out to the emissary: "I have lost the bargain that I made with Thasaidon. Take now my soul and bear it before Him where he sits aloft on His throne of ever-burning brass; for I would fulfill my bond to the uttermost."

"There is no need to take your soul," said the Emissary, with an ominous rumble as of departing storm in the desolate night. "Remain here with the lepers, or return to Pornos and his goats, as you will: it matters little. At all times and in all places your soul shall be part of the dark empire of Thasaidon."

THE MASTER OF THE CRABS

I remember that I grumbled a little when Mior Lumivix awakened me. The past evening had been a tedious one with its unpleasant familiar vigil, during which I had nodded often. From sunfall till the setting of Scorpio, which occurred well after midnight at that season, it had been my duty to tend the gradual inspissation of a decoction of scarabs, much favored by Mior Lumivix in the compounding of his most requested love-potions. He had warned me often that this liquor must be thickened neither too slowly nor too rapidly, by maintaining an even fire in the athanor, and had cursed me more than once for spoiling it. Therefore I did not yield to my drowsiness till the decoction was safely decanted and strained thrice through the sieve of perforated shark-skin.

Taciturn beyond his wont, the Master had retired early to his chamber. I knew that something troubled him; but was too tired for overmuch conjecture, and had not dared to question him.

It seemed that I had not slept for more than the period of a few pulse-beats—and here was the Master thrusting the yellow-slotted eye of his lantern into my face and dragging me from the pallet. I knew that I should not sleep again that night: for the Master wore his one-horned hat, and his cloak was girdled tightly about him, with the ancient arthame depending from the girdle in its shagreen sheath that time and the hands of many magicians had blackened.

"Abortion fathered by a sloth!" he cried. "Suckling of a sow that has eaten mandragora! Would you slumber till doomsday? We must hurry: I have learned that Sarcand has procured the chart of Omvor and has gone forth alone to the wharves. No doubt he means to embark in quest of the temple-treasure. We must follow quickly for much time has already been lost."

I rose now without further demur and dressed myself expeditiously, knowing well the urgency of this matter. Sarcand, who had but lately come to the city of Mirouane, had already made himself the most formidable of all my master's competitors. It was said that he was native to Naat, amid the somber western ocean, having been begotten by a sorcerer of that isle on a woman of the black cannibals who dwell beyond its middle mountains. He combined his mother's savage nature with the dark necromantic craft of his father; and, moreover, had acquired much dubious knowledge and repute in his travels through orient kingdoms before settling in Mirouane.

The fabulous chart of Omvor, dating from lost ages, was a thing that many generations of wizards had dreamt to find. Omvor, an ancient pirate still renowned, had performed successfully a feat of impious rashness. Sailing up a closely guarded estuary by night with his small crew disguised as priests in stolen temple-barges, he had looted the fane of the Moon-God in Faraad and had carried away many of its virgins, together with gems, gold, altar-vessels, talismans, phylacteries and books of eldritch elder magic. These books were the gravest loss of all, since even the priests had never dared to copy them. They were unique and irreplaceable, containing the erudition of buried aeons.

Omvor's feat had given rise to many legends. He and his crew and the ravished virgins, in two small brigantines, had vanished ultimately amid the western seas. It was believed that they had been caught by the Black River, that terrible ocean-stream which pours with an irresistible swiftening beyond Naat to the world's end. But before that final voyage, Omvor had lightened his vessels of the looted treasure and had made a chart on which the location of its hiding-place was indicated. This chart he had given to a former comrade who had grown too old for voyaging.

No man had ever found the treasure. But it was said that the chart still existed throughout the centuries, hidden somewhere no less securely than the loot of the Moon-God's temple. Of late there were rumors that some sailor, inheriting it from his fathers, had brought the map to Mirouane. Mior Lumivix, through agents both human and preterhuman, had tried vainly to trace the sailor; knowing that Sarcand and the other wizards of the city were also seeking him.

This much was known to me; and the Master told me more while, at his bidding, I collected hastily such provisions as were needed for a voyage of several days.

"I have watched Sarcand like an osprey watching its nest," he said. "My familiars told me that he had found the chart's owner, and had hired some thief to steal it; but they could tell me little else. Even the eyes of my devil-cat, peering through his windows, were baffled by the cuttle-fish darkness with which his magic surrounds him at will.

"Tonight I did a dangerous thing, since there was no other way. Drinking the juice of the purple *dedaim*, which induces profound trance, I projected my ka into his elemental-guarded chamber. The elementals knew my presence, they gathered about me in shapes of fire and shadow, menacing me unspeakably. They opposed me, they drove me forth. . . but I had seen—enough."

The Master paused, bidding me gird myself with a consecrated magic sword, similar to his own but of less antiquity, which he had never before allowed me to wear. By this time I had gathered together the required provision of food and drink, storing it in a strong fish-net that I could carry easily over my shoulder by the handle. The net was one that we used mainly for catching certain sea-reptiles, from which Mior Lumivix extracted a venom possessing unique virtue.

It was not till we had locked all the portals, and had plunged into the dark seaward-winding streets, that the Master resumed his account:

"A man was leaving Sarcand's chamber at the moment of my entrance. I saw him briefly, ere the black arras parted and closed; but I shall know him again. He was young and plump, with powerful sinews under the plumpness, with slanted squinting eyes in a girlish face and the swart yellow skin of a man from the southern isles. He wore the short breeks and ankle-topping boots of a mariner, being otherwise naked.

"Sarcand was sitting with his back half-turned, holding an unrolled sheet of papyrus, yellow as the sailor's face, to that evil, four-horned lamp which he feeds with cobras' oil. The lamp glared like a ghoul's eye. But I looked over his shoulder. . . long enough. . . before his demons could hurry me from the room. The papyrus was indeed the chart of Omvor. It was stiff with age, and stained with blood and seawater. But its title and purpose and appellations were still legible, though inscribed in an archaic script that few can read nowadays.

"It showed the western shore of the continent Zothique, and the seas beyond. An isle lying due westward from Mirouane was indicated as the burial-place of the treasure. It was named the Island of Crabs on the chart: but plainly it is none other than the one now called Iribos which, though seldom visited, lies at a distance of only two days' voyaging. There are no other islands within a hundred leagues, either north or south, excepting a few desolate rocks and small atolls."

Urging me to greater haste, Mior Lumivix continued:

"I woke too tardily from the swoon induced by the *dedaim*. A lesser adept would never have awakened at all.

"My familiars warned me that Sarcand had left his house a full hour ago. He was prepared for a journey, and went wharfward. But we will overtake him. I think that he will go without companions to Iribos, desiring to keep the treasure wholly secret. He is indeed strong and terrible, but his demons are of a kind that cannot cross water, being entirely earthbound. He has left them behind with the moiety of his magic. Have no fear for the outcome."

The wharves were still and almost deserted, except for a few sleeping sailors who had succumbed to the rank wine and arrack of the taverns. Under the late moon, that had curved and sharpened to a slim scimitar, we unmoored our boat and pushed away, the Master holding the tiller, while I bent my shoulders to the broad-bladed oars. Thus we threaded the huddled maze of far-gathered ships, of xebecs and galleys, of river-barges and scows and feluccas, that thronged that immemorial harbor. The sluggish air, hardly stirring our tall lateen sail, was pregnant with sea-smells, with the reek of laden fishing-boats and the spices of exotic cargoes. None hailed us; and we heard only the calling of watchmen on shadowy decks, proclaiming the hour in outlandish tongues.

Our boat, though small and open, was stoutly built of orient beef-wood. Sharply prowed and deeply keeled, with high bulwarks, it had proven itself seaworthy even in tempests such as were not to be ap-prehended at this season.

Blowing over Mirouane, from fields and orchards and desert king-doms, a wind freshened behind us as we cleared the harbor. It stiff-ened, till the sail bellied like a dragon's wing. The furrows of foam curved high beside our sharp prow, as we followed Capricornus down the west.

Far out on the waters before us, in the dim moonlight, something seemed to move, to dance and waver like a phantom. Perhaps it was Sarcand's boat. . . or another's. Doubtless the Master also saw it; but he said only:

"You may sleep now."

So I, Manthar the apprentice, composed myself to slumber, while Mior Lumivix steered on, and the starry hooves and horns of the Goat sank seaward.

The sun was high above our stern when I awakened. The wind still blew, strong and favorable, driving us into the west with unabated speed. We had passed beyond sight of the shore-line of Zothique. The sky was void of clouds, the sea vacant of any sail, unrolling before us like a vast scroll of somber azure, lined only with the shifting and fad-ing foam-crests.

The day went by, ebbing beyond the still-empty horizon; and night overtook us like the heaven-blotting purple sail of a god, sewn with the Signs and planets. The night too went over, and a second dawn.

All this time, without sleeping, the Master had steered the boat, with eyes peering implacably westward like those of an ocean-hawk; and I wondered greatly at his endurance. Now for awhile he slept, sitting upright at the helm. But it seemed that his eyes were still vigilant behind their lids; and his hand still held the rudder straight, without slackening.

In a few hours the Master opened his eyes; but hardly stirred from the posture he maintained throughout.

He had spoken little during our voyage. I did not question him, knowing that he would tell me whatever was needful at the due time. But I was full of curiosities; and was not without fear and doubt regarding Sarcand, whose rumored necromancies might well have dismayed others than a mere novice. I could surmise nothing of the Master's thoughts, except that they concerned dark and esoteric matters.

Having slept for the third time since our embarkment, I was roused by the Master crying loudly. In the dimness of the third dawn, an island towered before us, impending with jagged cliffs and jutting crags, and barring the sea for several leagues to northward and southward. It was shaped somewhat like a monster, facing north. Its head was a high-horned promontory, dipping a great griffin-like beak in the ocean.

"This is Iribos," the Master told me. "The sea is strong about it, with strange tides and perilous currents. There are no landing-places on this side, and we must not venture too close. We must round the northern headland. There is a small cove amid the western cliffs, entered only through a sea-cavern. It is there that the treasure lies."

We tacked northward slowly and deviously against the wind, at a distance of three or four bow-shots from the island. All our sea-craft was required to make progress: for the wind strengthened wildly, as if swollen by the breath of devils. Above its howling we heard the surf's clamor upon those monstrous rocks that rose bare and gaunt from cerements of foam.

"The isle is unpeopled," said Mior Lumivix. "It is shunned by sailors and even by the sea-fowl. Men say that the curse of the maritime gods was laid upon it long ago, forbidding it to any but the creatures of the submarine deep. Its coves and caverns are haunted by crabs and octopi. . . and perhaps by stranger things."

We sailed on in a tedious serpentine course, beaten back at times or borne perilously shoreward by the shifting gusts that opposed us like evil demons. The sun climbed in the orient, shining starkly down on the desolation of crags and scarps that was Iribos. Still we tacked and veered; and I seemed to sense the beginning of a strange unease in the Master. But of this, if such there was, his manner betrayed no sign.

It was almost noon when we rounded at last the long beak of the northern promontory. There, when we turned southerly, the wind fell in a weird stillness, and the sea was miraculously calmed as if by wizard oils. Our sail hung limp and useless above mirror-like waters, in which it seemed that the boat's reflected image and ours, unbroken, moveless, might float forever amid the unchanging reflection of the monster-shapen isle. We both began to ply the broad oars; but even thus the boat crawled with a singular slowness.

I observed the isle strictly as we passed along, noting several inlets where, to all appearance, a vessel could have landed readily.

"There is much danger here," said Mior Lumivix, without elucidating his statement.

Again, as we continued, the cliffs became a wall that was broken only by rifts and chasms. They were crowned in places by a sparse, funereal-colored vegetation that hardly served to soften their formidable aspect. High up in the clefted rocks, where it seemed that no natural tide or tempest could have flung them, I observed the scattered spars and timbers of antique vessels.

"Row closer," enjoined the Master. "We are nearing the cavern that leads to the hidden inlet."

Even as we veered landward through the crystalline calm, there was a sudden seething and riffling about us, as if some monster had risen beneath. The boat began to shoot with plummet-like speed toward the cliffs, the sea foaming and streaming all around as though some kraken were dragging us to its caverned lair. Borne like a leaf on a cataract, we toiled vainly with straining oars against the ineluctable current.

Heaving higher momentarily, the cliffs seemed to shear the heavens above us, unscalable, without ledge or foothold. Then, in the sheer wall, appeared the low, broad arch of a cavern-mouth that we had not discerned heretofore, toward which the boat was drawn with dreadful swiftness.

"It is the entrance!" cried the Master. "But some wizard tide has flooded it."

We shipped our useless oars and crouched down behind the thwarts as we neared the opening: for it seemed that the lowness of the arch would afford bare passage to our high-built prow. There was no time to unstep the mast, which broke instantly like a reed as we raced on without slackening into blind torrential darkness.

Half-stunned, and striving to extricate myself from the fallen, spar-weighted sail, I felt the chillness of water splashing about me and knew that the boat was filling and sinking. A moment more, and the water was in my ears and eyes and nostrils: but even as I sank and drowned there was still the sense of swift onward motion. Then it seemed dimly that arms were around me in the strangling darkness; and I rose suddenly, choking and gasping and spewing, into sunlight.

When I had rid my lungs of the brine and regained my senses more fully, I found that Mior Lumivix and I were floating in a small haven, shaped like a half-moon, and surrounded by crags and pinnacles of sullen-colored rock. Close by, in a sheer, straight wall, was the inner mouth of the cavern through which the mysterious current had carried us, with faint ripples spreading around it and fading away into water smooth and green as a platter of jade. Opposite, on the haven's farther side, was the long curve of a shelving beach strewn with boulders and driftwood. A boat resembling ours, with an unshipped mast and a furled sail the color of fresh blood, was moored to the beach. Near it, from the shoaling water, protruded the broken-off mast of another boat, whose sunken outlines we discerned obscurely. Two objects which we took for human figures were lying half in and half out of the shallows a little farther along the strand. At that distance we could hardly know whether they were living men or cadavers. Their contours were half-hidden by what seemed a curious sort of brownish-yellow drapery that trailed away amid the rocks, appearing to move and shift and waver incessantly.

"There is mystery here," said Mior Lumivix in a low voice. "We must proceed with care and circumspection."

We swam ashore at the near end of the beach, where it narrowed like the tip of a crescent moon to meet the sea-wall. Taking his arthame from its sheath the Master wiped it dry with the hem of his cloak, bidding me do likewise with my own weapon lest the brine corrode it. Then, hiding the wizard blades beneath our raiment, we followed the broadening beach toward the moored boat and the two reclining figures.

"This is indeed the place of Omvor's chart," observed the Master. "The boat with the blood-red sail belongs to Sarcand. No doubt he has found the cave, which lies hidden somewhere among the rocks. But who are these others? I do not think that they came with Sarcand."

As we neared the figures, the appearance of a yellowish-brown drapery that covered them resolved itself in its true nature. It consisted of a great number of crabs who were crawling over their half-submerged bodies and running to and fro behind a heap of immense boulders.

We went forward and stooped over the bodies, from which the

crabs were busily detaching morsels of bloody flesh. One of the bodies lay on its face; the other stared with half-eaten features at the sun. Their skin, or what remained of it, was a swarthy yellow. Both were clad in short purple breeks and sailor's boots, being otherwise naked.

"What hellishness is this?" inquired the Master. "These men are but newly dead—and already the crabs rend them. Such creatures are wont to wait for the softening of decomposition. And look—they do not even devour the morsels they have torn, but bear them away."

This indeed was true, for I saw now that a constant procession of crabs departed from the bodies, each carrying a shred of flesh, to vanish beyond the rocks; while another procession came, or perhaps returned, with empty pincers.

"I think," said Mior Lumivix, "that the man with the upturned face is the sailor that I saw leaving Sarcand's room; the thief who had stolen the chart for Sarcand from its owner."

In my horror and disgust I had picked up a fragment of rock and was about to crush some of the hideously laden crabs as they crawled away from the corpses.

"Nay," the Master stayed me, "let us follow them."

Rounding the great heap of boulders, we saw that the twofold procession entered, and emerged from, the mouth of a cavern that had heretofore been hidden from view.

With hands tightening on the hilts of our arthames, we went cautiously and circumspectly toward the cavern and paused a little short of its entrance. From this vantage, however, nothing was visible within except the lines of crawling crabs.

"Enter!" cried a sonorous voice that seemed to prolong and repeat the word in far-receding reverberations, like the voice of a ghoul echoing in some profound sepulchral vault.

The voice was that of the sorcerer Sarcand. The Master looked at me, with whole volumes of warning in his narrowed eyes and we entered the cavern.

The place was high-domed and of indeterminable extent. Light was afforded by a great rift in the vault above, through which, at this hour, the direct rays of the sun slanted in, falling goldenly on the cavern's foreground and tipping with light the great fangs of stalactites and stalagmites in the gloom beyond. At one side was a pool of water, fed by a thin rill from a spring that dripped somewhere in the darkness.

With the shafted splendor shining full upon him, Sarcand reposed half-sitting, half-recumbent, with his back against an open chest of age-darkened bronze. His huge ebon-black body, powerfully muscled though inclining toward corpulence, was nude except for a necklace of rubies, each the size of a plover's egg, that depended about his throat. His crimson sarong, strangely tattered, bared his legs as they lay outstretched amid the cavern's rubble. The right leg had manifestly been broken somewhere below the knee, for it was rudely bound with splints of driftwood and strips torn from the sarong.

Sarcand's cloak of lazuli-colored silk was outspread beside him. It was strewn with graven gems and amulets, with gold coins and jewel-crusted altar-vessels, that flashed and glittered amid volumens of parchments and papyrus. A book with black metal covers lay open as if newly put aside, showing illuminations drawn in fiery ancient inks.

Beside the book, within reach of Sarcand's fingers, was a mound of raw and bloody shreds. Over the cloak, over the coins and scrolls and jewels, crawled the incoming lines of crabs, each of which added its torn-off morsel to the mound and then crept on to join the outgoing column.

I could well believe the tales regarding Sarcand's ancestry. Indeed, it seemed that he favored his mother entirely: for his hair and features as well as his skin were those of the negro cannibals of Naat as I had seen them depicted in travellers' drawings. He fronted us inscrutably, his arms crossed on his bosom. I noticed a great emerald shining darkly on the index finger of his right hand.

"I knew that you would follow me," he said, "even as I knew that the thief and his companion would follow. All of you have thought to slay me and take the treasure. It is true that I have suffered an injury: a fragment of loosened rock fell from the cavern-roof, breaking my leg as I bent over to inspect the treasures in the opened chest. I must lie here till the bone has knit. In the meanwhile I am well armed. . . and well served and guarded."

"We came to take the treasure," replied Mior Lumivix directly. "I had thought to slay you, but only in fair combat, man to man and wizard to wizard, with none but my neophyte Manthar and the rocks of Iribos for witness."

"Aye, and your neophyte is also armed with an arthame. However, it matters little. I shall feast on your liver, Mior Lumivix, and wax stronger by such power of sorcery as was yours."

This the Master appeared to disregard.

"What foulness have you conjured now?" he inquired sharply, pointing to the crabs who were still depositing their morsels on the grisly mound.

Sarcand held aloft the hand on whose index finger gleamed the immense emerald, set, as we now perceived, in a ring that was wrought with the tentacles of a kraken clasping the orb-like gem.

"I found this ring amid the treasure," he boasted. "It was closed in a cylinder of unknown metal, together with a scroll that informed me of the ring's uses and its mighty magic. It is the signet-ring of Basatan, the sea-god. He who looks long and deeply into the emerald may behold distant scenes and happenings at will. He who wears the ring can exert control over the winds and currents of the sea and over the sea's creatures, by describing certain signs in air with his finger."

While Sarcand spoke it seemed that the green jewel brightened and darkened and deepened strangely, like a tiny window with all the sea's mystery and immensity lying beyond. Enthralled and entranced, I forgot the circumstances of our situation: for the jewel swelled upon my vision, blotting from view the black fingers of Sarcand, with a swirling as of tides and of shadowy fins and tentacles far down in its glimmering greenness.

"Beware, Manthar," the Master murmured in my ear. "We face a dreadful magic, and must retain the command of all our faculties. Avert your eyes from the emerald."

I obeyed the dimly heard whisper. The vision dwindled away, vanishing swiftly, and the form and features of Sarcand returned. His lubber lips were curved in a broad sardonic grin, showing his strong white teeth that were pointed like those of a shark. He dropped the huge hand that wore the signet of Basatan, plunging it into the chest behind him and bringing it forth filled with many-tinted gems, with pearls, opals, sapphires, bloodstones, diamonds, chatoyants. These he let dribble in a flashing rill from his fingers, as he resumed his peroration:

"I preceded you to Iribos by many hours. It was known to me that the outer cavern could be entered safely only at low tide, with an unstepped mast.

"Perhaps you have already inferred whatever else I might tell you. At any rate the knowledge will perish with you very shortly.

"After learning the uses of the ring I was able to watch the seas around Iribos in the jewel. Lying here with my shattered leg, I saw the approach of the thief and his fellow. I called up the sea-current by which their boat was drawn into the flooded cavern, sinking swiftly. They would have swum ashore: but at my command the crabs in the haven drew them under and drowned them; letting the tide beach their corpses later. . . . That cursed thief! I had paid him well for the stolen chart, which he was too ignorant to read, suspecting only that it concerned a treasure-trove. . . .

"Still later I trapped you in the same fashion, after delaying you awhile with contrary winds and an adverse calm. I have preserved you, however, for another doom than drowning."

The voice of the necromancer sank away in profound echoes, leaving a silence fraught with insufferable suspense. It seemed that we stood amid the gaping of undiscovered gulfs, in a place of awful darkness, lit only by the eyes of Sarcand and the ring's talismanic jewel.

The spell that had fallen upon me was broken by the cold ironic tones of the Master:

"Sarcand, there is another sorcery that you have not mentioned."

Sarcand's laughter was like the sound of a mounting surf. "I follow the custom of my mother's people; and the crabs serve me with that which I require, summoned and constrained by the sea-god's ring."

So saying, he raised his hand and described a peculiar sign with the index finger, on which the ring flashed like a circling orb. The double column of crabs suspended their crawling for a moment. Then, moved as if by a single impulse, they began to scuttle toward us, while others appeared from the cavern's entrance and from its inner recesses to swell their rapidly growing numbers. They surged upon us with a speed beyond belief, assailing our ankles and shins with their knife-sharp pincers as if animated by demons. I stooped over, striking and thrusting with my arthame; but the few that I crushed in this manner were replaced by scores; while others, catching the hem of my cloak, began to climb it from behind and weigh it down. Thus encumbered, I lost my footing on the slippery ground and fell backward amid the scuttling multitude.

Lying there while the crabs poured over me like a seething wave, I saw the Master shed his burdened cloak and cast it aside. Then, while the spell-drawn army still besieged him, climbing upon each other's backs and scaling his very knees and thighs, he hurled his arthame with a strange circular motion at the upraised arm of Sarcand. Straightly the blade flew, revolving like a disk of brightness; and the hand of the black necromancer was sundered cleanly at the wrist, and the ring flashed on its index finger like a falling star as it fell groundward.

Blood spouted in a fountain from the handless wrist, while Sarcand sat as in a stupor, maintaining for a brief instant the gesture of his conjuration. Then the arm dropped to his side and the blood rilled out upon the littered cloak, spreading swiftly amid the gems and coins and volumens, and staining the mound of crab-deposited morsels. As if the arm's movement had been another signal, the crabs fell away from the Master and myself and swarmed in a long, innumerable tide toward Sarcand. They covered his legs, they climbed his great torso, they scrambled for place on his escaladed shoulders. He tore them away with his one hand, roaring terrible curses and imprecations that rolled in countless echoes throughout the cavern. But the crabs still assailed him as if driven by some demoniac frenzy; and blood trickled forth more and more copiously from the small wounds they had made, to suffuse their pincers and streak their shells with broadening rillets of crimson.

It seemed that long hours went by while the Master and I stood watching. At last the prostrate thing that was Sarcand had ceased to heave and toss under the living shroud that enswathed it. Only the splint-bound leg and the lopped-off hand with the ring of Basatan remained untouched by the loathsomely busied crabs.

"Faugh!" the Master exclaimed. "He left his devils behind when he came here; but he found others. . . . It is time that we went out for a walk in the sun. Manthar, my good lubberly apprentice, I would have you build a fire of driftwood on the beach. Pile on the fuel without sparing, to make a bed of coals deep and hot and red as the hearth of hell, in which to roast us a dozen crabs. But be careful to choose the ones that have come freshly from the sea."

THE DEATH OF ILALOTHA

Black Lord of bale and fear, master of all confusion!
By thee, thy prophet saith,
New power is given to wizards after death,
And witches in corruption draw forbidden breath
And weave such wild enchantment and illusion
As none but lamiæ may use;
And through thy grace the charneled corpses lose
Their horror, and nefandous loves are lighted
In noisome vaults long nighted;
And vampires make their sacrifice to thee—
Disgorging blood as if great urns had poured
Their bright vermilion hoard
About the washed and weltering sarcophagi.
                          —*Ludar's Litany to Thasaidon.*

According to the custom in old Tasuun, the obsequies of Ilalotha,
lady-in-waiting to the self-widowed Queen Xantlicha, had formed
an occasion of much merrymaking and prolonged festivity. For three
days, on a bier of diverse-colored silks from the Orient, under a rose-
hued canopy that might well have domed some nuptial couch, she had
lain clad with gala garments amid the great feasting-hall of the royal
palace in Miraab. About her, from morning dusk to sunset, from cool
even to torridly glaring dawn, the feverish tide of the funeral orgies
had surged and eddied without slackening. Nobles, court officials,
guardsmen, scullions, astrologers, eunuchs, and all the high ladies,
waiting women and female slaves of Xantlicha, had taken part in that

97

prodigal debauchery which was believed to honor most fitly the deceased. Mad songs and obscene ditties were sung, and dancers whirled in vertiginous frenzy to the lascivious pleading of untirable lutes. Wines and liquors were poured torrentially from monstrous amphoras; the tables fumed with spicy meats piled in huge hummocks and forever replenished. The drinkers offered libation to Ilalotha, till the fabrics of her bier were stained to darker hues by the spilt vintages. On all sides around her, in attitudes of disorder or prone abandonment, lay those who had yielded to amorous license or the fullness of their potations. With half-shut eyes and lips slightly parted, in the rosy shadow cast by the catafalque, she wore no aspect of death but seemed a sleeping empress who ruled impartially over the living and the dead. This appearance, together with a strange heightening of her natural beauty, was remarked by many: and some said that she seemed to await a lover's kiss rather than the kisses of the worm.

On the third evening, when the many-tongued brazen lamps were lit and the rites drew to their end, there returned to court the Lord Thulos, acknowledged lover of Queen Xantlicha, who had gone a week previous to visit his domain on the western border and had heard nothing of Ilalotha's death. Still unaware, he came into the hall at that hour when the saturnalia began to flag and the fallen revelers to outnumber those who still moved and drank and made riot.

He viewed the disordered hall with little surprise, for such scenes were familiar to him from childhood. Then, approaching the bier, he recognized its occupant with a certain startlement. Among the numerous ladies of Miraab who had drawn his libertine affections, Ilalotha had held sway longer than most; and, it was said, she had grieved more passionately over his defection than any other. She had been superseded a month before by Xantlicha, who had shown favor to Thulos in no ambiguous manner; and Thulos, perhaps, had abandoned her not without regret: for the role of lover to the queen, though advantageous and not wholly disagreeable, was somewhat precarious. Xantlicha, it was universally believed, had rid herself of the late King Archain by means of a tomb-discovered vial of poison that owed its peculiar subtlety and virulence to the art of ancient sorcerers. Following this act of disposal, she had taken many lovers, and those who failed to please her came invariably to ends no less violent than that of Archain. She was exigent, exorbitant, demanding a strict fidelity somewhat irksome to Thulos; who, pleading urgent affairs on his remote estate, had been glad enough of a week away from court.

Now, as he stood beside the dead woman, Thulos forgot the queen and bethought him of certain summer nights that had been honeyed by the fragrance of jasmine and the jasmine-white beauty of Ilalotha. Even less than the others could he believe her dead: for her present aspect differed in no wise from that which she had often assumed during their old intercourse. To please his whim, she had feigned the inertness and complaisance of slumber or death; and at such times he had loved her with an ardor undismayed by the pantherine vehemence with which, at other whiles, she was wont to reciprocate or invite his caresses.

Moment by moment, as if through the working of some powerful necromancy, there grew upon him a curious hallucination, and it seemed that he was again the lover of those lost nights, and had entered that bower in the palace gardens where Ilalotha waited him on a couch strewn with overblown petals, lying with bosom quiet as her face and hands. No longer was he aware of the crowded hall: the high-flaring lights, the wine-flushed faces had become a moon-bright parterre of drowsily nodding blossoms, and the voices of the courtiers were no more than a faint suspiration of wind amid cypress and jasmine. The warm, aphrodisiac perfumes of the June night welled about him; and again, as of old, it seemed that they arose from the person of Ilalotha no less than from the flowers. Prompted by intense desire, he stooped over and felt her cool arm stir involuntarily beneath his kiss.

Then, with the bewilderment of a sleep-walker awakened rudely, he heard a voice that hissed in his ear with soft venom: "Hast forgotten thyself, my Lord Thulos? Indeed, I wonder little, for many of my bawcocks deem that she is fairer in death than in life." And, turning from Ilalotha, while the weird spell dissolved from his senses, he found Xantlicha at his side. Her garments were disarrayed, her hair was unbound and dishevelled, and she reeled slightly, clutching him by the shoulder with sharp-nailed fingers. Her full, poppy-crimson lips were curled by a vixenish fury, and in her long-lidded yellow eyes there blazed the jealousy of an amorous cat.

Thulos, overwhelmed by a strange confusion, remembered but partially the enchantment to which he had succumbed; and he was unsure whether or not he had actually kissed Ilalotha and had felt her flesh quiver to his mouth. Verily, he thought, this thing could not have been, and a waking dream had momentarily seized him. But he was troubled by the words of Xantlicha and her anger, and by the half-furtive drunken laughters and ribald whispers that he heard passing among the people about the hall.

"Beware, my Thulos," the queen murmured, her strange anger seeming to subside; "for men say that she was a witch. . . ."

"How did she die?" queried Thulos.

"From no other fever than that of love, it is rumored."

"Then, surely, she was no witch," Thulos argued with a lightness that was far from his thoughts and feelings; "for true sorcery should have found the cure."

"It was from love of thee," said Xantlicha darkly; "and, as all women know, thy heart is blacker and harder than black adamant. No witchcraft, however potent, could prevail thereon." Her mood, as she spoke, appeared to soften suddenly. "Thy absence has been long, my lord. Come to me at midnight: I will wait for thee in the south pavil-ion." Then, eyeing him sultrily for an instant from under drooped lids, and pinching his arm in such manner that her nails pierced through cloth and skin like a cat's talons, she turned from Thulos to hail certain of the harem-eunuchs.

Thulos, when the queen's attention was disengaged from him, ventured to look again at Ilalotha; pondering, meanwhile, the curious remarks of Xantlicha. He knew that Ilalotha, like many of the court-ladies, had dabbled in spells and philtres; but her witchcraft had never concerned him, since he felt no interest in other charms or enchantments than those with which nature had endowed the bodies of women. And it was quite impossible for him to believe that Ilalotha had died from a fatal passion: since, in his experience, passion was never fatal.

Indeed, as he regarded her with confused emotions, he was again beset by the impression that she had not died at all. There was no repetition of the weird, half-remembered hallucination of other time and place; but it seemed to him that she had stirred from her former position on the wine-stained bier, turning her face toward him a little, as a woman turns to an expected lover; that the arm he had kissed (either in dream or reality) was outstretched a little farther from her side.

Thulos bent nearer, fascinated by the mystery and drawn by a stranger attraction that he could not have named. Again, surely, he had dreamt or had been mistaken. But even as the doubt grew, it seemed that the bosom of Ilalotha stirred in faint respiration and he heard an almost inaudible but thrilling whisper: "Come to me at midnight. I will wait for thee . . . in the tomb."

At this instant there appeared beside the catafalque certain people in the sober and rusty raiment of sextons, who had entered the hall silently, unperceived by Thulos or by any of the company. They carried among them a thin-walled sarcophagus of newly welded and burnished bronze. It was their office to remove the dead woman and bear her to the sepulchral vaults of her family, which were situated in the old necropolis lying somewhat to northward of the palace-gardens.

Thulos would have cried out to restrain them from their purpose; but his tongue clove tightly; nor could he move any of his members. Not knowing whether he slept or woke, he watched the people of the cemetery as they placed Ilalotha in the sarcophagus and bore her quickly from the hall, unfollowed and still unheeded by the drowsy bacchanalians. Only when the somber cortège had departed was he able to stir from his position by the empty bier. His thoughts were sluggish, and full of darkness and indecision. Smitten by an immense fatigue that was not unnatural after his daylong journey, he withdrew to his apartments and fell instantly into death-deep slumber.

Freeing itself gradually from the cypress-boughs, as if from the long, stretched fingers of witches, a waning and misshapen moon glared horizontally through the eastern window when Thulos awoke. By this token, he knew that the hour drew toward midnight, and recalled the assignation which Queen Xantlicha had made with him: an assignation which he could hardly break without incurring the queen's deadly displeasure. Also, with singular clearness, he recalled another rendezvous. . . at the same time but in a different place. Those incidents and impressions of Ilalotha's funeral, which, at the time, had seemed so dubitable and dreamlike, returned to him with a profound conviction of reality, as if etched on his mind by some mordant chemistry of sleep. . . or the strengthening of some sorcerous charm. He felt that Ilalotha had indeed stirred on her bier and spoken to him; that the sextons had borne her still living to the tomb. Perhaps her supposed demise had been merely a sort of catalepsy; or else she had deliberately feigned death in a last effort to revive his passion. These thoughts awoke within him a raging fever of curiosity and desire; and he saw before him her pale, inert, luxurious beauty, presented as if by enchantment.

Direly distraught, he went down by the lampless stairs and hallways to the moonlit labyrinth of the gardens. He cursed the untimely exigence of Xantlicha. However, as he told himself, it was more than likely that the queen, continuing to imbibe the liquors of Tasuun, had long since reached a condition in which she would neither keep nor recall her appointment. This thought reassured him: in his queerly bemused mind, it soon became a certainty; and he did not hasten toward the south pavilion but strolled vaguely amid the wan and somber boscage.

More and more it seemed unlikely that any but himself was abroad: for the long, unlit wings of the palace sprawled as in vacant stupor; and in the gardens there were only dead shadows, and pools of still fragrance in which the winds had drowned. And over all, like a pale, monstrous poppy, the moon distilled her death-white slumber.

Thulos, no longer mindful of his rendezvous with Xantlicha, yielded without further reluctation to the urgence that drove him toward another goal. . . . Truly, it was no less than obligatory that he should visit the vaults and learn whether or not he had been deceived in his belief concerning Ilalotha. Perhaps, if he did not go, she would stifle in the shut sarcophagus, and her pretended death would quickly become an actuality. Again, as if spoken in the moonlight before him, he heard the words she had whispered, or seemed to whisper, from the bier: "Come to me at midnight. . . I will wait for thee. . . in the tomb."

With the quickening steps and pulses of one who fares to the warm, petal-sweet couch of an adored mistress, he left the palace-grounds by an unguarded northern postern and crossed the weedy common between the royal gardens and the old cemetery. Unchilled and undismayed, he entered those always-open portals of death, where ghoul-headed monsters of black marble, glaring with hideously pitted eyes, maintained their charnel postures before the crumbling pylons.

The very stillness of the low-bosomed graves, the rigor and pallor of the tall shafts, the deepness of bedded cypress shadows, the inviolacy of death by which all things were invested, served to heighten the singular excitement that had fired Thulos' blood. It was as if he had drunk a philtre spiced with mummia. All around him the mortuary silence seemed to burn and quiver with a thousand memories of Ilalotha, together with those expectations to which he had given as yet no formal image. . . .

Once, with Ilalotha, he had visited the subterranean tomb of her ancestors; and, recalling its situation clearly, he came without indirec-

tion to the low-arched and cedar-darkened entrance. Rank nettles and
fetid fumitories, growing thickly about the seldom-used adit, were
crushed down by the tread of those who had entered there before
Thulos; and the rusty, iron-wrought door sagged heavily inward on its
loose hinges. At his feet there lay an extinguished flambeau, dropped,
no doubt, by one of the departing sextons. Seeing it, he realized that he
had brought with him neither candle nor lanthorn for the exploration
of the vaults, and found in that providential torch an auspicious omen.

Bearing the lit flambeau, he began his investigation. He gave no
heed to the piled and dusty sarcophagi in the first reaches of the subterrane: for, during their past visit, Ilalotha had shown to him a niche
at the innermost extreme, where, in due time, she herself would find
sepulture among the members of that decaying line. Strangely, insidi-
ously, like the breath of some vernal garden, the languid and luscious
odor of jasmine swam to meet him through the musty air, amid the
tiered presence of the dead; and it drew him to the sarcophagus that
stood open between others tightly lidded. There he beheld Ilalotha, lying in the gay garments of her funeral, with half-shut eyes and half-
parted lips; and upon her was the same weird and radiant beauty, the
same voluptuous pallor and stillness, that had drawn Thulos with a
necromantic charm.

"I knew that thou wouldst come, O Thulos," she murmured, stirring a little, as if involuntarily, beneath the deepening ardor of his kisses that passed quickly from throat to bosom. . . .

The torch that had fallen from Thulos' hand expired in the thick
dust. . . .

Xantlicha, retiring to her chamber betimes, had slept illy. Perhaps she
had drunk too much or too little of the dark, ardent vintages; perhaps
her blood was fevered by the return of Thulos, and her jealousy still
troubled by the hot kiss which he had laid on Ilalotha's arm during the
obsequies. A restlessness was upon her; and she rose well before the

hour of her meeting with Thulos, and stood at her chamber window seeking such coolness as the night air might afford.

The air, however, seemed heated as by the burning of hidden furnaces; her heart appeared to swell in her bosom and stifle her; and her unrest and agitation were increased rather than diminished by the spectacle of the moon-lulled gardens. She would have hurried forth to the tryst in the pavilion; but, despite her impatience, she thought it well to keep Thulos waiting. Leaning thus from her sill, she beheld Thulos when he passed amid the parterres and arbors below. She was struck by the unusual haste and intentness of his steps; and she wondered at their direction, which could bring him only to places remote from the rendezvous she had named. He disappeared from her sight in the cypress-lined alley that led to the north garden-gate; and her wonderment was soon mingled with alarm and anger when he did not return.

It was incomprehensible to Xantlicha that Thulos, or any man, would dare to forget the tryst in his normal senses; and seeking an explanation, she surmised that a baleful and potent sorcery was probably involved. Nor, in the light of certain incidents that she had observed, and much else that had been rumored, was it hard for her to identify the possible sorceress. Ilalotha, the queen knew, had loved Thulos to the point of frenzy, and had grieved inconsolably after his desertion of her. People said that she had wrought various ineffectual spells to bring him back; that she had vainly invoked demons and sacrificed to them, and had made futile invultuations and death-charms against Xantlicha. In the end, she had died of sheer chagrin and despair, or perhaps had slain herself with some undetected poison. . . . But, as was commonly believed in Tasuun, a witch dying thus, with unslaked desires and frustrate cantraips, could turn herself into a lamia or vampire and procure thereby the consummation of all her sorceries. . . .

The queen shuddered, remembering these things; and all too well she surmised the destination of Thulos, and the danger to which he had gone forth if her suspicions were true. And, with the knowledge that she must face an equal danger, Xantlicha determined to follow him.

She made little preparation, for there was no time to waste; but took from beneath the silken cushions of her bed a small, straight-bladed dagger that she kept always within reach. The dagger had been anointed from point to hilt with such venom as was believed effica-cious against either the living or the dead. Bearing it in her right hand, and carrying in the other a slot-eyed lanthorn that she might require later, Xantlicha stole swiftly from the palace.

The last lees of the evening's wine ebbed wholly from her brain, and dim, ghastly fears awoke, warning her like the voices of ancestral phantoms. But, firm in her determination, she followed the path taken by Thulos; the path taken earlier by those sextons who had borne Ila-lotha to her place of sepulture. Hovering from tree to tree, the moon ac-companied her like a worm-hollowed visage; and the gaunt cypresses, rearing stilly in their cerements of light, had assumed a rigid and funereal watch over that fatal way. The soft, quick patter of Xantlicha's cothurns, breaking the white silence, seemed to tear the filmy cobweb pall that withheld from her a world of spectral abominations. And more and more she recalled, of those legendries that concerned such beings as Ilalotha; and her heart was shaken within her: for she knew that she would meet no mortal woman but a thing raised up and inspirited by the seventh hell. But amid the chill of these horrors, the thought of Thulos in the lamia's arms was like a red brand that seared her bosom.

Now the necropolis yawned before Xantlicha, and her path en-tered the cavernous gloom of far-vaulted trees, as if passing into mon-strous and shadowy mouths that were tusked with white monuments. The air grew dank and noisome, as if filled with the breathings of open crypts. Here the queen faltered, for it seemed that black, unseen caco-demons rose all about her from the graveyard ground, towering higher than the shafts and boles, and standing in readiness to assail her if she went farther. Nevertheless, she came anon to the dark adit that she sought. Tremulously she lit the wick of the slot-eyed lanthorn; and, piercing the gross underground darkness before her with its bladed beam, she paused with ill-subdued terror and repugnance into that abode of the dead. . . and perhaps to that of the Undead.

However, as she followed the first turnings of the catacomb, it seemed that she was to encounter nothing more abhorrent than charnel mould and century-sifted dust; nothing more formidable than the serried sarcophagi that lined the deeply hewn shelves of stone: sarcophagi that had stood silent and undisturbed ever since the time of their deposition. . . . Here, surely the slumber of all the dead was unbroken, and the nullity of death was inviolate. . . .

Almost the queen doubted that Thulos had preceded her there; till, turning her light on the ground, she discerned the print of his poulaines, long-tipped and slender in the deep dust amid those footmarks left by the rudely shod sextons. And she saw that the footprints of Thulos pointed only in one direction, while those of the others plainly went and returned.

Then, at an undetermined distance in the shadows ahead, Xantlicha heard a sound in which the sick moaning of some amorous woman was blent with a snarling as of jackals over their meat. Her blood returned frozen upon her heart as she went onward step by slow step, clutching her dagger in a hand drawn sharply back, and holding the light high in advance. The sound grew louder and more distinct; and there came to her now a perfume as of flowers in some warm June night; but, as she still advanced, the perfume was blended with more and more of a smothering foulness such as she had never heretofore known, and was touched with the hot reeking of blood.

A few paces more, and Xantlicha stood as if a demon's arm had arrested her: for her lanthorn's light had found the inverted face and upper body of Thulos, hanging from the end of a burnished, newly wrought sarcophagus that occupied a scant interval between others green with rust. One of Thulos' hands clutched rigidly the rim of the sarcophagus, while the other hand, moving feebly, seemed to caress a shadowy shape that leaned above him with arms showing jasmine-white in the narrow beam, and dark fingers plunging into his bosom. His head and body seemed but an empty hull, and his hand hung skeleton-thin on the bronze rim, and his whole aspect was vein-drawn, as if he had lost more blood than was evident on his torn throat and face, and in his sodden raiment and dripping hair.

From the thing stooping above Thulos, there came ceaselessly that sound which was half moan and half snarl. And as Xantlicha stood in petrific fear and loathing, she seemed to hear from Thulos' lips an indistinct murmur, more of ecstasy than pain. The murmur ceased, and his head hung slacklier than before, so that the queen deemed him verily dead. At this she found such wrathful courage as enabled her to step nearer and raise the lanthorn higher: for, even amid her extreme panic, it came to her that by means of the wizard-poisoned dagger she might still haply slay the thing that had slain Thulos.

Waveringly the light crept aloft, disclosing inch by inch that infamy which Thulos had caressed in the darkness. . . . It crept even to the crimson-smeared wattles, and the fanged and ruddled orifice that was half mouth and half beak. . . till Xantlicha knew why the body of Thulos was a mere shrunken hull. . . . In what the queen saw, there remained nothing of Ilalotha except the white, voluptuous arms, and a vague outline of human breasts melting momently into breasts that were not human, like clay moulded by a demon sculptor. The arms too began to change and darken; and, as they changed, the dying hand of Thulos stirred again and fumbled with a caressing movement toward the horror. And the thing seemed to heed him not but withdrew its fingers from his bosom, and reached across him with members stretching enormously, as if to claw the queen or fondle her with its dribbling talons.

It was then that Xantlicha let fall the lanthorn and the dagger, and ran with shrill, endless shriekings and laughters of immitigable madness from the vault.

NADA

This wakeful death affords not any rift
        where root of weed or blossom cleaves the tomb.
Ungrown as yet, no yewen bowers lift,
bringing serene misericordal gloom
upon this sepulture adust and bare,
writ with a legend plain to one alone
whose voice could quicken the unvital air,
recalling Lazarus from his room of stone.

Oblivion's river flows I other lands
than this where memory feeds a mordant spring:
the walking dead beseech with parching hands
the cool, far shadow of the raven's wing;
and, leaning from the mouldered bed of lust,
love's skeleton writes *Nada* in the dust.

THE WEAVER IN THE VAULT

The instructions of Famorgh, fifty-ninth king of Tasuun, were minutely circumstantial and explicit, and, moreover, were not to be disobeyed without the incurring of penalties that would make mere death a pleasant thing. Yanur, Grotara, and Thirlain Ludoch, three of the king's hardiest henchmen, riding forth at morn from the palace in Miraab, debated with a thin semblance of jocosity whether, in their case, obedience or disobedience would prove the direr evil.

The commission they had just received from Famorgh was no less singular than distasteful. They were to visit Chaon Gacca, the long-forsaken seat of the kings of Tasuun, lying more than ninety miles to the north of Miraab amid the desert hills; and, descending into the burial-vaults beneath the ruined palace, were to find and bring back to Miraab whatever remained of the mummy of King Tnepreez, founder of the dynasty to which Famorgh belonged. No one had entered Chaon Gacca for centuries, and the preservation of its dead in the catacombs was uncertain; but even if only the skull of Tnepreez was left, or the bone of his little finger, or the dust of mummia into which he had crumbled, the men-at-arms were to fetch it carefully, guarding it like a holy relic.

"'Tis an errand for hyenas rather than warriors," grumbled Yanur in his black and spade-shaped beard. "By the god Yululun, Keeper of the Tombs, I deem it an ill thing to disturb the peaceful dead. And truly it is not well for men to enter Chaon Gacca, where Death has made his capital, and has gathered all the ghouls to do him homage."

"The king should have sent his embalmers," opined Grotara. He was the youngest and hugest of the three, being taller by a full head than Yanur or Thirlain Ludoch; and like them, he was a veteran of savage wars and desperate perils.

"Yea, I said it was an errand for hyenas," rejoined Yanur. "But the king knew well that there were no mortal beings in all Miraab, saving ourselves, who would dare to enter the accursed vaults of Chaon Gacca. Two centuries ago, King Mandis, wishing to retrieve the golden mirror of Queen Avaina for his favorite leman, commanded two of his bravos to descend within the vaults, where the mummy of Avaina sits enthroned in her separate tomb, holding the mirror in her withered hand . . . . And the bravos went to Chaon Gacca . . . but they did not return; and King Mandis, being warned by a soothsayer, made no second attempt to procure the mirror, but contented his leman with another gift."

"Yanur, thy tales would gladden those who await the scything of the executioner," said Thirlain Ludoch, the oldest of the trio, whose brown beard was faded to a hempen hue by desert suns. "But I chide thee not. It is common knowledge that the catacombs are ridden with worse hauntings than those of liches or phantoms. Strange devils came there long ago from the mad, unholy desert of Dloth; and I have heard it told that the kings forsook Chaon Gacca because of certain Shadows, that appeared at full noon in the palace-halls, with no visible form to cast them, and would not depart thereafter, being changeless amid all the changings of the light, and wholly undimmed by the exorcisms of priests and sorcerers. Men say that the flesh of any who dared to touch the Shadows, or to tread upon them, became black and putrid like the flesh of month-old corpses, all in a mere instant. Because of such testing, when one of the Shadows came and sat upon his throne, the right hand of King Agmeni rotted to the wrist, and fell away like the sloughing of a leper . . . . And after that, no man would dwell in Chaon Gacca."

"Verily, I have heard other stories," said Yanur. "The town's abandonment was due mainly to the failure of the wells and cisterns, from which the water vanished following an earthquake that left the land riven with hell-deep chasms. The palace of the kings was sundered to its nethermost vault by one of the chasms; and King Agmeni was seized by a violent madness when he inhaled the infernal vapors issuing from the rent; nor was he ever wholly sane in his latter lifetime, after the quitting of Chaon Gacca and the rearing of Miraab."

"Now that is a tale that I can believe," said Grotara. "And surely I must deem that Famorgh has inherited the madness of his forefather, Agmeni. Methinks that the royal house of Tasuun rots and totters to its fall. Harlots and sorcerers swarm in the palace of Famorgh like charnel-worms; and now, in this princess Lunalia of Xylac whom he has taken to wife, he has found a harlot and a witch in one. He has sent us on this errand at the prompting of Lunalia, who desires the mummy of Tnepreez for her own unhallowed purpose. Tnepreez, I have heard, was a great wizard in his time; and Lunalia would avail herself of the potent virtue of his bones and dust in the brewing of her philtres. Pah! I like not the task of such purveyance. There are mummies enow in Miraab for the making of potions to madden the Queen's lovers. Famorgh is utterly besotted and befooled."

"Beware," admonished Thirlain Ludoch, "for Lunalia is a vampire who lusts ever for the young and strong . . . and thy turn may come next, O Grotara, if fortune brings us back alive from this enterprise. I have seen her watching thee."

"I would sooner mate with the wild lamia," protested Grotara in virtuous indignation.

"Thy aversion would help thee not," said Thirlain Ludoch . . . "for I know others who have drunk the potions. . . . But we are now nearing the last wineshop in Miraab; and my throat is dusty beforehand with the very thought of this journey. I shall need a whole stoup of wine from Yoros to wash the dust away."

"Thou sayest sooth," agreed Yanur. "Already, I have become dry as the mummy of Tnepreez. And thou, Grotara?"

"I will quaff any drink, if it be not the philtre-brew of Queen Lunalia."

Mounted on swift, untiring dromedaries, and followed by a fourth camel bearing on its back a light wooden sarcophagus for the accommodation of King Tnepreez, the three henchmen had soon left behind them the bright and noisy streets of Miraab, and the fields of sesame, the crofts of apricot and pomegranate, lying for miles about the city. Before noon, they had parted from the route of caravans, and had taken a road that was seldom used by any but lions and jackals. However, the way to Chaon Gacca was plain, for the ruts of olden chariots were still deeply marked in the desert soil, where rain no longer fell at any season.

On the first night, they slept beneath the cold and crowding stars, and kept watch by turn lest a lion should come upon them unaware, or a viper should crawl among them for warmth. During the second day, they passed amid steepening hills and deep ravines that retarded their progress. Here there was no rustling of serpent or lizard, and naught but their own voices and the shuffling of the camels to break the silence that lay upon all things like a mute malediction. Sometimes, on the desiccating tors above them, against the darkly litten sky, they saw the boughs of century-withered cacti, or the boles of trees that immemorial fires had blasted.

The second sunset found them in sight of Chaon Gacca, rearing its dilapidated walls at a distance of less than four leagues in a broad open valley. Coming then to a wayside shrine of Yuckla, the small and grotesque god of laughter, whose influence was believed to be mainly benignant, they were glad to go no farther on that day, but took shelter in the crumbling shrine for fear of the ghouls and devils, who might dwell in such vicinage to those accursed ruins. They had brought with them from Miraab a wineskin filled with the fervent ruby wine of Yoros; and though the skin was now three-fourths empty, they poured a libation in the twilight on the broken altar, and prayed to Yuckla for such protection as he might give them against the demons of the night.

They slept on the worn and chilly flags about the altar, watching by turn, as before. Grotara, who kept the third watch, beheld at last the paling of the close-hung stars, and aroused his companions in a dawn that was like a sifting of ashes through the cinder-black darkness.

After a scanty meal of figs and dried goat-flesh, they resumed their journey, guiding their camels down the valley, and weaving back and forth on the bouldered slopes when they came to abysmal rents in the earth and rock. Their approach to the ruins was rendered slow and tortuous by such divagations. The way was lined by the stocks of orchard trees that had perished long ago, and by cotes and granges where even the hyena no longer made his lair.

Because of their many detours, it was hard upon noon when they rode through the hollow-ringing streets of the city. Like ragged purple cloaks, the shadows of the ruining houses were drawn close to their walls and portals. Everywhere the havoc of earthquake was manifest, and the fissured avenues and mounded mansions served to verify the tales that Yanur had heard concerning the reason of the city's abandonment.

The palace of the kings, however, was still pre-eminent above the other buildings. A tumbled pile, it frowned in dark porphyry on a low acropolis amid the northern quarter. For the making of this acropolis, a hill of red syenite had been stripped of its covering soil in elder days, and had been hewn to sheer and rounding walls, circled by a road that wound slowly about it to the summit. Following this road, and nearing the portals of the courtyard, the henchmen of Famorgh came to a fissure that clove their path from wall to precipice, yawning far in the cliff. The chasm was less than a yard in width; but the dromedaries balked before it. The three dismounted; and, leaving the camels to await their return, they leapt lightly across the fissure. Grotara and Thirlain Ludoch carrying the sarcophagus, and Yanur bearing the wineskin, they passed beneath the shattered barbican.

The great courtyard was heavily strewn with the wreckage of once-lofty towers and balconies, over which the warriors climbed with much wariness, eyeing the shadows closely, and loosening their swords in the sheath, as if they were surmounting the barricades of a hidden foe. All three were startled by the pale and naked form of a colossean female, which they saw reclining on the blocks and rubble in a portico beyond the court. But, drawing nearer, they found that the shape was not that of a she-demon, as they had apprehended, but was merely a marble statue that had once stood like a caryatid among the mighty pillars.

Following the directions given them by Famorgh, they entered the main hall. Here, beneath the chasmed and collapsing roof, they moved with the utmost caution, fearing that a light jar, a whisper, would bring the suspended ruin upon their heads like an avalanche. Overturned tripods of greening copper, tables and trivets of splintered ebony, and the shards of gayly painted porcelains, were mingled with the huge fragments of pedestals and fusts and entablatures; and upon a shivered dais of green, blood-spotted heliotrope, the tarnished silver throne of the kings careened amid the mutilated sphinxes, carved from jasper, that kept eternal guard beside it.

At the further end of the hall, they found an alcove, still unblocked by fallen debris, in which were the stairs that led downward to the catacombs. They paused briefly ere beginning their descent. Yanur applied himself without ceremony to the skin which he carried, and lightened it considerably before giving it into the hands of Thirlain Ludoch, who had marked his potations with solicitude. Thirlain Ludoch and Grotara drank the remainder of the vintage between them; and the latter did not grumble at the thick lees which fell to his lot. Thus replenished, they lit three torches of pitchy terebinth, which they had brought along in the sarcophagus. Yanur led the way, daring the tenebrous depths with drawn sword, and a torch flaming smokily in his left hand. His companions followed, bearing the sarcophagus, in which, by raising the hinged lid slightly, they had socketed the other torches. The

potent wine of Yoros mounted within them, driving away their shadowy fears and apprehensions; but all three were seasoned drinkers, and
they moved with great care and circumspection, and did not stumble
on the dim, uncertain steps.

Passing through a series of wine-cellars, full of cracked and sharded jars, they came at last, after many zig-zag plungings of the stairs, to
a vast corridor hewn in the nether syenite, below the level of the city
streets. It stretched before them through illimitable gloom, its walls
unshattered, and its roof admitting no crevice-filtered ray. It seemed
that they had entered some impregnable citadel of the dead. On the
right hand were the tombs of the elder kings; on the left, were the sepulchers of the queens; and lateral passages led to a world of subsidiary
vaults, reserved for other members of the royal family. At the further
end of the main hall, they would find the burial-chamber of Tnepreez.

Yanur, following the right-hand wall, soon came to the first tomb.
According to custom, its portals were open, and were lower than a
man's stature, so that all who entered must bow in humbleness to
death. Yanur held his torch to the lintel, and read stumblingly the legend graven in the stone, which told that the vault was that of King
Acharnil, father of Agmeni.

"Verily," he said, "we shall find nothing here, other than the harm-
less dead." Then, the wine he had drunk impelling him to a sort of
bravado, he stooped before the portals and thrust his flickering flambeau into the tomb of Acharnil.

Surprised, he swore a loud and soldierly oath, that made the others
drop their burden and crowd behind him. Peering into the square,
concamerated chamber, which had a kingly spaciousness, they saw that
it was unoccupied by any visible tenant. The tall chair of mystically
graven gold and ebony, in which the mummy should have sat crowned
and robed as in life, was addorsed against the farther wall on a low dais. In it, there lay an empty robe of sable and carmine, and a miter-
shaped crown of silver set with black sapphires, as if the dead king had

doffed them and had gone away!

Startled, with the wine dying swiftly in their brains, the warriors felt the crawling chill of an unknown mystery. Yanur, however, steeled himself to enter the vault. He examined the shadowy corners, he lifted and shook the raiment of Achanil, but found no clue to the riddle of the mummy's disappearance. The tomb was clean of dust, and there was no visible sign nor faintest odor of mortal decay.

Yanur rejoined his comrades, and the three eyed each other in eerie consternation. They resumed their exploring of the hall; and Yanur, as he came to the doorway of each tomb, paused before it and thrust his flambeau into the wavering murk, only to discover a vacant throne, and the cast-off regalia of royalty.

There was, it seemed, no reasonable explanation for the vanishing of the mummies, in whose preservation the powerful spices of the Orient had been employed, together with natron, rendering them virtually incorruptible. From the circumstances, it did not appear that they had been removed by human robbers, who would hardly have left behind the precious jewels, fabrics and metals; and it was even more unlikely that they had been devoured by animals: for in that case the bones would have remained, and the vestments would have been torn and disordered. The mythic terrors of Chaon Gacca began to assume a darker imminence; and the seekers peered and listened fearfully as they went on in the hushed sepulchral hall.

Presently, after they had verified the vacancy of more than a dozen tombs, they saw the glimmering of several steely objects before them on the floor of the corridor. These, on investigation, proved to be two swords, two helmets and cuirasses of a slightly antiquated type, such as had formerly been worn by the warriors of Tasuun. They might well have belonged to the unreturning braves sent by King Mandis to retrieve the mirror of Avaina.

Yanur, Grotara and Thirlain Ludoch, viewing these sinister relics, were seized by an almost frantic desire to accomplish their errand and regain the sunlight. They hurried on, no longer pausing to inspect the separate tombs, and debating, as they went, the curious problem that would be presented if the mummy sought by Famorgh and Lunalia should have vanished like the others. The king had commanded them to fetch the remains of Tnepreez; and they knew that no excuse or explanation of their failure to do this would be accepted. Under such circumstances, their return to Miraab would be inadvisable; and the only safety would lie in flight beyond the northern desert, along the route of caravans to Zul-Bha-Sair or Xylac.

It seemed that they traversed an enormous distance, among the more ancient vaults. Here the formation of the stone was softer and more friable, and the earthquake had wrought considerable damage. The floor was littered with detritus, the sides and roof were full of fractures, and some of the chambers had partially fallen in, so that their vacancy was revealed to the casual peering of Yanur and his companions.

Nearing the hall's end, they were confronted by a chasm, dividing both floor and roof, and splitting the sill and lintel of the last chamber. The gulf was about four feet wide, and the torch of Yanur could not disclose its bottom. He found the name of Tnepreez on the lintel, whose antique inscription, telling the deeds and titles of the king, had been sundered in twain by the cataclysm. Then, walking on a narrow ledge, he entered the vault. Grotara and Thirlain Ludoch crowded behind him, leaving the sarcophagus in the hall.

The sepulchral throne of Tnepreez, overturned and broken, was lying across the fissure that had rifted the whole tomb from side to side. There was no trace of the mummy, which, from the chair's inverted position, had doubtless fallen into those yawning depths in the hour of its overthrow.

Before the seekers could voice their disappointment and their dismay, the silence about them was broken by a dull rumbling as of distant thunder. The stone trembled beneath their feet, the walls shook and wavered, and the rumbling noise, in long, shuddering undulations, grew louder and more ominous. The solid floor appeared to rise and flow with a continuous, sickening motion; and then, as they turned to flee, it seemed that the universe came down upon them in a roaring deluge of night and ruin.

Grotara, wakening in darkness, was aware of an agonizing burden, as if some monumental shaft were builded on his crushed feet and lower legs. His head throbbed and ached as if from the stroke of a stunning mace. He found that his arms and body were free; but the pain in his extremities became insufferable, causing him to swoon anew, when he tried to drag them from beneath their incumbrance.

Terror closed upon him like the clutch of ghoulish fingers, as he realized his situation. An earthquake, such as had caused the abandonment of Chaon Gacca, had occurred; and he and his fellows were entombed in the catacombs. He called aloud, repeating the names of Yanur and Thirlain Ludoch many times; but there was no groan nor rustle to assure him that they still lived.

Reaching out with his right hand, he encountered numerous pieces of rubble. Slewing himself toward them, he found several boulder-sized fragments of stone, and among them a smooth and roundish thing, with a sharp ridge in the center, which he knew for the crested helmet worn by one of his companions. Even with the most painful striving, he could reach no further, and was unable to identify the owner. The metal was heavily dented, and the comb was bent as if by the impact of some ponderous mass.

In spite of his predicament, the fierce nature of Grotara refused to yield itself to despair. He drew himself to a sitting position, and, doubling forward, he contrived to reach the enormous block that had fallen across his nether limbs. He pushed against it with herculean effort, raging like a trapped lion, but the mass was immovable. For hours, it seemed, he strove as if with some monstrous cacodemon. His frenzy was calmed only by exhaustion. He lay back at length; and the darkness weighed upon him like a live thing, and seemed to gnaw him with fangs of pain and horror.

Delirium hovered near, and he thought that he heard a dim and hideous humming, far below in the stony bowels of the earth. The noise grew louder, as if ascending from a riven hell. He became aware of a wan, unreal light that wavered above him, disclosing in doubtful glimpses the shattered roof. The light strengthened; and lifting himself a little, he saw that it poured from the earthquake chasm in the floor.

It was a light such as he had never seen: a livid luster, that was not the reflection of lamp or torch or firebrand. Somehow, as if the senses of hearing and sight were confused, he identified it with the hideous humming.

Like a sourceless dawn, the luminosity crept upon the ruin wrought by the temblor. Grotara saw that the whole entrance of the tomb, and much of its concameration, had caved in. A fragment, striking him on the head, had knocked him senseless; and a huge section of the roof had fallen across his extremities.

The bodies of Thirlain Ludoch and Yanur were lying close to the broadened chasm. Both, he felt sure, were dead. The grizzled beard of Thirlain Ludoch was dark and stiff with blood that had run down from the crushed cranium; and Yanur was half-buried in a pile of blocks and detritus, from which his torso and left arm were emergent. His torch had burned itself out in his stiffly clutching fingers, as if in a blackened socket.

All this Grotara noted in a vague dream-like manner. Then he perceived the real source of the strange illumination. A coldly shining, hueless globe, round as a puffball and large as a human head, had risen from the fissure and was hovering above it like a mimic moon. The thing oscillated with a slight but ceaseless vibratory motion. From it, as if caused by this vibration, the heavy humming poured, and the light fell in ever-trembling waves.

A dim awe was upon Grotara; but he felt no terror. It seemed that the light and sound were woven upon his senses like some Lethean spell. Rigid he sat, forgetful of his pain and despair, while the globe hovered for a few instants above the chasm, and then floated slowly and horizontally, till it hung directly over the upturned features of Yanur.

With the same deliberate slowness, the same ceaseless oscillation, it descended upon the face and neck of the dead man, which appeared to melt away like tallow as the globe settled lower and lower. The humming deepened, the globe flamed with an eerier luster, and its deathlike pallor was mottled with impure iris. It swelled and bloated obscenely, while the whole head of the warrior shrank within the helmet, and the plates of his cuirass fell in as if the very torso were shrivelling beneath them.

Grotara's eyes beheld the horrific vision clearly; but his brain was numbed as if by a merciful hemlock. It was hard to remember, hard to think . . . but somehow he recalled the empty tombs, the ownerless crowns and vestments. The enigma of the missing mummies, over which he and his companions had puzzled vainly, was now resolved. But the thing that battened upon Yanur was beyond all mortal knowledge or surmise. It was some ghoulish denizen of a nether world, set free by the demons of earthquake.

Now, in the catalepsy that thralled him, he saw the gradual settling of the piled débris in which the legs and hips of Yanur were inhumed. The helmet and body-mail were like empty shards, the outflung arm had withered, had shortened, and the very bones were dwindling away, appearing to melt and liquefy. The globe had grown enormous. It was flushed with unclean ruby, like a vampire moon. From it, there issued palpable ropes and filaments, pearly, shuddering into strange colors, that appeared to fasten themselves to the ruined floor and walls and roof, like the weaving of a spider. Thickly and more thickly they multiplied, forming a curtain between Grotara and the chasm, and falling upon Thirlain Ludoch and himself, till he saw the sanguine burning of the globe as through arabesques of baleful opal.

Now the web had filled the entire tomb. It ran and glistened with a hundred changing hues, it dripped with glories drawn from the spectrum of dissolution. It bloomed with ghostly blossoms, and foliages that grew and faded as if by necromancy. The eyes of Grotara were blinded; more and more he was meshed in the weird web. Unearthly, chill as the fingers of death, its gossamers clung and quivered upon his face and hands.

He could not tell the duration of the weaving, the term of his enthrallment. Dimly, at last, he beheld the thinning of the luminous threads, the retraction of the trembling arabesques. The globe, a thing of evil beauty, alive and aware in some holocryptic fashion, had risen now from the empty armor of Yanur. Diminishing to its former size, and putting off its colors of blood and opal, it hung for a little above the chasm. Grotara felt that it was watching him . . . was watching Thirlain Ludoch. Then, like a satellite of the nether caverns, it fell slowly into the fissure, and the light faded from the tomb and left Grotara in deepening darkness.

After that, there were ages of fever, thirst and madness, of torment and slumber, and recurrent strugglings against the massive block that held him prisoner. He babbled insanely, he howled like a wolf; or, lying supine and silent, he heard the multitudinous, muttering voices of ghouls that conspired against him. Gangrening swiftly, his crushed extremities seemed to throb like those of a Titan. He drew his sword with the strength of delirium, and endeavored to saw himself free at the shins, only to swoon from loss of blood.

Awakening feebly, and scarce able to lift his head, he saw that the light had returned, and heard once more the incessant vibrant humming that filled the vault. His mind was clear, and a weak terror stirred within him: for he knew that the Weaver had risen again from the chasm . . . and knew the reason of its coming.

He turned his head laboriously, and watched the glowing ball as it hung and oscillated, and then came down in leisurely descent on the face of Thirlain Ludoch. Again he saw it bloat obscenely, like a blood-flushed moon, fed with the wasting of the old warrior's body. Again, with dazzled eyes, he beheld the weaving of the web of impure iris, patterned with deathly splendor, veiling the ruinous catacomb with its weird illusions. Again, like a dying beetle, he was meshed in its chill, unearthly strands; and its necromantic flowers, blooming and perishing, latticed the void air above him. But, ere the retracting of the web, his delirium came upon him and brought a demon-peopled darkness; and the Weaver finished its toil unseen, and returned unheeded to the chasm.

He tossed in the hells of fever, or lay at the black, undivined nadir of oblivion. But death tarried, still aloof; and he lived on by sheer virtue of his youth and giant strength. Once more, toward the end, his senses cleared, and he saw for the third time the unholy light and heard again the thrice-odious humming. The Weaver was poised above him, pale, shining and vibrant . . . and he knew that it was waiting for him to die.

Lifting his sword with weak fingers, he sought to drive it away. But the thing hovered, alert and vigilant, beyond his reach; and he thought that it watched him like a vulture. The sword dropped from his hand. The luminous horror did not depart. It drew nearer, like an eyeless, pertinacious face; and it seemed to follow him, swooping through the ultimate night as he fell deathward.

With none to behold the glory of its weaving, with darkness before and after, the Weaver spun its final web in the tomb of Tnepreez.

THE DEAD WILL CUCKOLD YOU

A DRAMA IN SIX SCENES

 PERSONAE
Smaragad, King of Yoros
Queen Somelis
Galeor, a wandering poet and lute-player, guest of Smaragad
Natanasna, a necromancer
Baltea, tiring-woman to Somelis
Kalguth, Natanasna's negro assistant
Sargo, the King's treasurer
Boranga, captain of the King's guards
Waiting-women, court-ladies, courtiers, guards and chamberlains.

THE SCENE: *Faraad, capital of Yoros, in Zothique*

SCENE I

A large chamber in the Queen's suite, in the palace of Smaragad. Somelis sits on a high throne-like chair. Galeor stands before her, holding a lute. Baltea and several other women are seated on divans, at a distance. Two black chamberlains stand in attendance at the open door.

Galeor (playing on his lute and singing):
Make haste, and tarry not, O ardent youth,
To find upon the night,
Outlined in fuming fire,
The footsteps of the goddess Ililot.

Her mouth and eyes make fair the bourns of sleep,
Between her brows a moon
Is seen. A magic lute
Foretells her with wild music everywhere.

Her opened arms, which are the ivory gates
Of some lost land of lote
Where from charmed attars flow,
Will close upon you 'neath the crimson star.

    Somelis: I like the song. Tell me, why do you sing
So much of Ililot?

    Galeor: She is the goddess
Whom all men worship in the myrrh-sweet land
Where I was born. Do men in Yoros not
Adore her also? She is soft and kind,
Caring alone for love and lovers' joy.

    Somelis: She is a darker goddess here, where blood
Mingles too often with delight's warm foam. . . .
But tell me more of that far land wherein
A gentler worship lingers.

    Galeor: By a sea
Of changing damaskeen it lies, and has
Bowers of cedar hollowed for love's bed
And plighted with a vine vermilion-flowered.
There are moss-grown paths where roam white-fleecèd goats;
And sard-thick beaches lead to caves in which
The ebbing surge has left encrimsoned shells
Like lips by passion parted. From small havens
The fishers slant their tall, dulse-brown lateens
To island-eyries of the shrill sea-hawk;

And when with beaks low-dipping they return
Out of the sunset, fires are lit from beams
And spars of broken galleys on the sand,
Around whose nacreous flames the women dance
A morris old as ocean.

Somelis: Would I had
Been born in such a land, and not in Yoros.

Galeor: I wish that I might walk with you at evening
Beside the waters veined with languid foam,
And see Canopus kindle on cypressed crags
Like a far pharos.

Somelis: Be you more tacit: there are ears
That listen, and mouths that babble amid these halls.
Smaragad is a jealous king—(*She breaks off, for at this moment
King Smaragad enters the room.*)

Smaragad: This is a pretty scene. Galeor, you seem at home
In ladies' chambers. I am told you entertain
Somelis more than could a dull sad king
Grown old too soon with onerous royalty.

Galeor: I would please, with my poor songs and sorry lute,
Both of your Majesties.

Smaragad: Indeed, you sing
Right sweetly, as does the simorgh when it mates.
You have a voice to melt a woman's vitals
And make them run to passion's turgid sluice.
How long have you been here?

Galeor: A month.

Smaragad: It has been
A summer moon full-digited. How many
Of my hot court-ladies have you already bedded?
Or should I ask how many have bedded you?

Galeor: None, and I swear it by the crescent horns
O Ililot herself, who fosters love
And swells the pulse of lovers.

Smaragad: By my troth,
I would confirm you in such continence,
It is rare in Yoros. Even I when young
Delved deep in whoring and adultery. (*Turning to the queen*)
Somelis, have you wine? I would we drank
To a chastity so rathe and admirable
In one whose years can hardly have chastened him.
(*The queen indicates a silver ewer standing on a taboret together with goblets of the same metal. Smaragad turns his back to the others and pours wine into three goblets, opening, as if casually the palm of his free hand over one of them. This he gives to Galeor. He serves another to the queen, and raises the third to his lips.*)
See, I have served you with my royal hand,
Doing you honor, and we all must drink
To Galeor that he persevere in virtue,
And he must drink with us. (*He drinks deeply. The queen raises her goblet to her lips but barely tastes it. Galeor lifts the wine, then pauses, looking in to it.*)

Galeor: How strangely it foams.

Smaragad: Indeed, such bubbles seem
To rise as if from lips of a drowning man
In some dark purple sea.

Somelis: Your humor is strange,
Nor are there bubbles in the cup you gave me.

Smaragad: Perhaps it was poured more slowly. (*To Galeor*)

Drink the wine,

It is old and cordial, made by men long dead.
(*The poet still hesitates, then empties his goblet at one draught.*)
How does it taste to you?

Galeor: It tastes as I have thought that love might taste,
Sweet on the lips, and bitter in the throat. (*He reels, then sinks to his knees, still clutching the empty goblet.*)
You have poisoned me, who never wronged you. Why
Have you done it?

Smaragad: That you may never wrong me. You have drunk
A vintage that will quench all mortal thirst.
You will not look on queens nor they on you
When the thick maggots gather in your eyes,
And issue in lieu of love-songs from your lips,
And geld you by slow inches.

Somelis: (*descending from her seat and coming forward*):

Smaragad,

This deed will reek through Yoros and be blazed
Beyond the murky marches of the damned. (*She sinks to her knees beside Galeor, now prostrate on the floor and dying slowly. Tears fall from her eyes as she lays her hand on Galeor's brow.*)

Smaragad: Was he so much to you? Almost I have a mind
That the bowstring should straiten your soft throat,
But no, you are too beautiful. Go quickly,
And keep to your bed-chamber till I come.

Somelis: I shall abhor you, and my burning heart
Consume with hate till only meatless cinders
Remain to guest the mausolean maggots. (*Exit Somelis, followed by Baltea*

and the other women. The two chamberlains remain.)

Smaragad: (*beckoning to one of the chamberlains*):
Go call the sextons. I would have them drag
This carcass out and bury it privily. (*Exit the chamberlain. The king turns to
Galeor, who still lives.*)
Think on your continence eternalized:
You had not fleshed as yet your rash desire,
And now you never will.

Galeor: (*in a faint but audible voice*): I would pity you,
But there is no time for pity. In your heart
You bear the hells that I have never known,
To which the few brief pangs I suffer
Are less than the wasp-stings of an afternoon
Sweet with the season's final fruit.

(*Curtain*)

SCENE II

The king's audience hall. Smaragad sits on a double-daised throne,
a guard bearing a trident standing at each hand. Guards are posted at
each of the four entrances. A few women and chamberlains pass
through the hall on errands. Sargo, the royal treasurer, stands in one
corner, Baltea, passing by, pauses to chat with him.

Baltea: Why sits the king in audience today?
Is it some matter touching on the state?
Still thunder loads his brow, and pard-like wrath
Waits leashed in his demeanor.

Sargo: 'Tis a wizard,
One Natanasna, whom he summons up
For practise of nefandous necromancy.

Baltea: I've heard of him. Do you know him? What's he like?

Sargo: I cannot wholly tell you. It's no theme
For a morning's tattle.

Baltea: You make me curious.

Sargo: Well,
I'll tell you this much. Some believe he is
A cambion, devil-sired though woman-whelped.
He is bold in every turpitude, as those
Hell-born are prone to be. His lineage
Leads him to paths forbanned and pits abhorred,
And traffic in stark nadir infamies
Not plumbed by common mages.

Baltea: Is that all?

Sargo: Such beings have a smell by which to know them,
As olden tomes attest. This Natanasna
Stinks like a witch's after-birth, and evil
Exhales from him, lethal as that contagion
Which mounts from corpses mottled by the plague.

Baltea: Well, that's enough to tell me, for I never
Have liked ill-smelling men.
(*Enter Natanasna through the front portals. He strides forward, bearing a staff on which he does not lean, and stands before Smaragad.*)

Sargo: I must go now.

Baltea: And I'll not linger, for the wind comes up
From an ill quarter. (*Exeunt Sargo and Baltea, in different directions.*)

Natanasna (*without knelling or even bowing*): You have summoned me?

Smaragad: Yes. I am told you practise arts forbid
And hold an interdicted commerce, calling
Ill demons and the dead to do you service.
Are these things true?

Natanasna:　　　　It is true that I can call
Both lich and ka, though not the soul, which roams
In regions past my scope, and can constrain
The genii of the several elements
To toil my mandate.

Smaragad:　　　　What! you dare avow it
The thing both men and sods abominate?
Do you not know the ancient penalties
Decreed in Yoros for these crimes abhorred?
The cauldron of asphaltum boiling-hot
To bathe men's feet, and the nail-studded rack
On which to stretch their scalded stumps?

Natanasna:　　　　　　　　Indeed
I know your laws, and also know that you
Have a law forbidding murder.

Smaragad: What do you mean?

Natanasna: I mean but this, that you the king have filled
More tombs than I the outlawed necromancer
Have ever emptied, and detest not idly
The raising of dead men. Would you have me summon
For witness here against you the grey shade
Of Famostan your father, in his bath
Slain by the toothed envenomed fish from Taur
Brought privily and installed by you? Or rather
Would you behold your brother Aladad,

Whose huntsmen left him with a splintered spear
At your instruction, to confront the fen-cat
That he had merely pricked? Yet these would be
Only the heralds of that long dark file
Which you have hurried into death.

    Smaragad (half-rising from his seat): By all
The sooted hells, you dare such insolence?
Though you be man or devil, or be both,
I'll flay you, and leave your hide to hang in strips
Like a kilt about you, and will have your guts
Drawn out and wound on a windlass.

    Natanasna: These be words
Like froth upon a shallow pool. No finger
Of man may touch me. I can wave this staff
And ring myself with circles of tall fires
Spawned by the ambient space arcane. You fear me,
And you have reason. I know all the secrets
Of noisome deed and thought that make your soul
A cavern where close-knotted serpent's nest.
Tell me, was there not yestereve a youth
Named Galeor, who played the lute and sans,
Making sweet music for an evil court?
Why have you slain him? Was it not through your fear
Of cuckoldom, thinking he pleased too much
The young Somelis? But this thing is known
To me, and I know moreover the dim grave
Where Galeor waits the worm.

    Smaragad (standing erect, his features madly contorted): Begone! begone!
Out of my presence! Out of Faraad!
And here's a word to speed you: when you entered

This hall, my sheriffs went to find your house
And seize Kalguth, your negro neophyte
For whom 'tis said you have the curious fondness
That I might keep for a comely ebon wench.
Ponder this well: Kalguth must lie by now
Embowelled in our dankest dungeon-crypt.
He will rejoin you if tomorrow's sun
Meet you outside the city. If you linger,
I'll give him to my sinewy torturers.

   Natanasna: King Smaragad, if young Kalguth be harmed,
Hell will arise and sweep your palace clean
With fiery besoms and with flails of flame. (*Exit Natanasna.*)

(*Curtain*)

SCENE III

   The necropolis of Faraad. Dying and half-decayed cypresses droop over creviced headstones and ruinous mausoleums. A gibbous moon shines through wispy clouds. Enter Natanasna, humming:

   A toothless vampire tugs and mumbles
   Some ancient trot's whitleather hide,
   But he'll fly soon to the abattoir
   And the pooling blood where the stuck pig died.

(*Kalguth emerges from behind the half-unhinged door of a tomb close at hand. He carries a dark bag, which he lays on the ground at Natanasna's feet.*)

   Kalguth: Greetings, O Master.

   Natanasna: It was well I sent you
To wait me here among the tacit dead—
Lugging you from your slumber at morning dusk

While none but blind-drunk bowsers were abroad.
As I prevised, the king took advantage
Of my commanded presence in his halls,
And sent his hounds to sniff for you. He'll not
Venture to harry me, who have climbed too high
In magedom's hierarchy, but would fang
His baffled spleen on one not fully armed
And bucklered with arts magical. We must
Depart from Yoros promptly, leaving it
To all its many devils, amid which
This king is not the least. (*He pauses, looking about him at the tombs and
    graves.*) It is a land
Where murder has made much work for necromancy,
And there's a task to do before we go
That we be not forgotten. I perceive,
My good Kalguth, that you have found the spot
Which my strix-eyed familiar did describe:
Those yonder are the yellowing cypresses
That death has pollarded, and this the tomb
Of the lord Thamamar, which sheltered you
Daylong from eyes still mortal. . . . See, where it bears
The lichen-canceled legend of his titles
And the name itself, half-blotted out. (*He paces about, peering closely at the
ground, and holding his staff extended horizontally. Over a certain spot the staff
seems to twist violently in his hand, like a dowser's wand, until it points downward
with the tip almost touching the earth.*)   This is
The grave that covers Galeor. The turf
Was lately broken here, and spaded back
With the grass turned upward. (*He faces in the direction of Faraad, whose
towers loom indistinctly beyond the necropolis. Raising both arms, he intertwines his
fingers with the thumbs pointing skyward in the Sign of the horns.*)
                   By this potent Sign,

O jealous king who dreaded cuckoldom,

Murder shall not avert from your proud head

The horns of that opprobrium: for I know

A spell whereby the dead will cuckold you. (*Turning to Kalguth*)

Now to our ceremonies. While you set

The mantic censers forth, I'll make the circles. (*Taking a short sword, the magic arthame, from under his cloak, he traces a large circle in the turf, and a smaller one within it, trenching them both deeply and broadly. Kalguth opens the dark bag and brings out four small perforated censers whose handles are wrought in the form of the double triangle, Sign of the Macrocosm. He places them between the circles, each censer facing one of the four quarters, and lights them. The necromancers then take their positions within the inner circle. Natanasna gives the arthame to Kalguth, and retains his magic staff, which he holds aloft. Both face toward the grave of Galeor.*)

Natanasna (chanting):

Muntbauut, maspratha butu, [Mumbavut, lewd and evil spirit,]
Varvas runu, vha rancutu. [Wheresoever thou roamest, hear me]
Incubus, my cousin, come,

Drawn from out the night you haunt,

From the hollow mist and murk

Where discarnate larvae lurk,

By the word of masterdom.

Hell will keep its covenant,

You shall have the long-lost thing

That you howl and hunger for.

Borne on sable, sightless wing,

Leave the void that you abhor,

Enter in this new-made grave,

You that would a body have:

Clothed with the dead man's flesh,

Rising through the riven earth

In a jubilant rebirth,
Wend your ancient ways a fresh,
By the mantra laid on you
Do the deed I bid you do.
Vora votha Thasaidona [By (or through) Thasaidon's power]
Sorgha nagrakronitlhona. [Arise from the death-time-dominion.]
(*After a pause*)
Vachat pantari vora nagraban [The spell (or mantra) is finished by the necromancer.]

Kalguth: *Za, mozadrim: vachama vongh razan.* [Yes, master: the vongh (corpse animated by a demon) will do the rest.
(These words are from Umlengha, an ancient language of Zothique, used by scholars and wizards.)]

(*The turf heaves and divides, and the incubus-driven Lich of Galeor rises from the grave. The grime of interment is on its face, hands, and clothing. It shambles forward and presses close to the outer circle, in a menacing attitude. Natanasna raises the staff, and Kalguth the arthame, used to control rebellious sprits. The Lich shrinks back.*)

The Lich (*in a thick, unhuman voice*): You have summoned me,
And I must minister
To your desire.

Natanasna: Heed closely these instructions:
By alleys palled and posterns long disused,
Well-hidden from the moon and from men's eyes,
You shall find ingress to the palace. There,
Through stairways only known to mummied kings
And halls forgotten save by ghosts, you must
Seek out the chamber of the queen Somelis,
And woo her lover-wise till that be done
Which incubi and lovers burn to do.

The Lich: You have commanded, and I must obey. (*Exit the Lich. When it has gone from sight, Natanasna steps from the circles, and Kalguth extinguishes the censers and repacks them in the bag.*)

Kalguth: Where go we now?

Natanasna: Whither the first road leads
Beyond the boundary of Yoros. We'll
Not wait the sprouting of the crop we've sowed
But leave it to lesson him, who would have crimped
My well-loved minion and my acolyte
For the toothed beds of his dark torture-chambers. (*Exeunt Natanasna and Kalguth, singing:*)

> The fresh fat traveller whom the ghouls
> Waylaid in the lonesome woodland gloom,
> He got away, and they'll so now
> For gamy meat in a mouldy tomb.

(*Curtain*)

SCENE IV

The queen's bed-chamber. Somelis half-sits, half-reclines on a cushioned couch. Enter Baltea, bearing a steaming cup.

Baltea: With wine that stores the warmth of suns departed,
And fable-breathing spices brought from isles
Far as the morn, I have made this hippocras
Slow-mulled and powerful. Please to drink it now
That you may sleep.

Somelis (waving the cup away): Ah, would that I might drink
The self-same draft that Galeor drank, and leave
This palace where my feet forever pace
From shades of evil to a baleful sun.

Too slow, too slow the poison that consumes me—
Compounded of a love for him that's dead
And loathing for the king.

  Baltea: I'll play for you
And sing, though not as gallant Galeor sang. (*She takes up a dulcimer, and sings*):
  Lone upon the roseate gloom
  Shone the golden star anew,
  Calling like a distant bell,
  Falling, dimming into death.

  Came my lover with the night,
  Flame and darkness in his eyes—
  Drawn by love from out the grave—
  Gone through all the loveless day—
(*She pauses, for steps are heard approaching along the hall.*)

  Somelis: Whose footsteps come? I fear it is the king.
(*The door is flung open violently, and the fiend-animated Lich of Galeor enters.*)

  Baltea: What thing is this, begot by hell on death?
Oh! How it leers and slobbers! It doth look
Like Galeor, and yet it cannot be.
(*The Lich sidles forward, grinning, mewing and gibbering.*)

  Somelis: If you be Galeor, speak and answer me
Who was your friend, wishing you only well
In a bitter world unfriendly to us both.
(*Baltea darts past the apparition, which does not seem to have perceived her presence, and runs from the room*).
But if you be some fiend in Galeor's form,
I now adjure you by the holy name
Of the goddess Ililot to go at once.

(The features, limbs, and body of the Lich are convulsed as if by some dreadful struggle with an unseen antagonist. Then, by degrees, the convulsions slacken, the lurid flame dies down in the dead man's eyes, and his face assumes a look of gentle and piteous bewilderment.)

Galeor. How came I here? Meseems that I was dead
And men had heaped the hard dry earth on me.

Somelis. There is much mystery here, and little time
In which to moot the wherefores. But I see
That you are Galeor and none other now,
The dear sweet Galeor that I thought had died
With all the love between us unavowed,
And this contents me.

Galeor. I must still be dead,
Though I behold and hear and answer you,
And love leaps up to course along my veins
Where death had set his sullen winter.

Somelis.   What
Can you recall?

Galeor.   Little but night-black silence
That seemed too vast for Time, wherein I was
Both bounded and diffused; and then a voice
Most arrogant and magisterial, bidding
Me, or another in my place, to do
A deed that I cannot remember now.
These things were doubtful; but I feel as one
Who in deep darkness struggled with a fiend
And cast him forth because another voice
Had bade the fiend begone.

Somelis: Truly, I think
There is both magic here and necromancy,
Though he that called you up and sent you forth
Did so with ill intent. It matters not,
For I am glad to have you, whether dead
Or living as men reckon bootless things.
'Tis a small problem now: Baltea has gone
For Smaragad, and he'll be here full soon,
Mammering for twofold murder. (*She goes to the door, closes it, and draws the ponderous metal bars in their massive sockets. Then, with a broidered kerchief and water from a pitcher, she washes the grave-mould from Galeor's face and hands, and tidies his garments. They embrace. He kisses her, and caresses her cheeks and hair.*)

                           Ah, your touch
Is tenderer than I have known before.
And yet, alas, your lips, your hands.
Poor Galeor, the grave has left you cold:
I'll warm you in my bed and in my arms
For those short moments ere the falling sword
Shatter the fragile bolts of mystery
And open what's beyond.

(*Heavy footsteps approach in the hall outside and there is a babbling of loud, confused voices, followed by a metallic clang like that of a sword-hilt hammering on the door.*)

(*Curtain*)

SCENE V

The king's pavilion in the palace-gardens. Smaragad sits at the head of a long table littered with goblets, wine-jars and liquor-flask, some empty or overturned, others still half-full. Sargo and Boranga are seated on a bench near the table's foot. A dozen fellow-revelers, laid low by their potations, lie sprawled about the floor or on benches and couches Sargo and Boranga are singing:

> A ghoul there was in the days of old,
> And he drank the wine-dark blood
> Without a goblet, with never a flagon,
> Fresh from the deep throat-veins of the dead.
> But we instead, but we instead,
> Will drink from goblets of beryl and gold
> A blood-dark wine that was made by the dead
> In the days of old.

(*A silence ensues, while the singers wet their husky throats. Smaragad fills and empties his flagon, then fills it again.*)

Boranga (*in a lowered voice*): Something has ired or vexed
The king: he drinks
Like one stung by the dipsas, whose dread bite
Induces lethal thirst.

Sargo: He's laid the most
Of our tun-gutted guzzlers 'neath the board,
And I'm not long above it. . . . This forenoon
He held much parley with the necromancer
Whose stygian torts outreek the ripened charnel.
Mayhap it has left him thirsty. 'Twas enough
For me when Natanasna passed to windward.
I'm told the king called for incensories
To fume the audience-hall, and fan-bearers
To waft the nard-born vapors round and round
And ventilate with moa-plumes his presence
When the foul mage was gone.

Boranga: They say that Natanasna

And his asphalt-colored ingle have both vanished,
Though none knows whither. Faraad will lose
One bone for gossip's gnawing. I would not give you
A fig-bird's tooth or an aspic's tail-end feather
For all your conjurers. Let's bawl a catch. (*They sing:*)

    —There's a thief in the house, there's a thief in the house,
    My master, what shall we do?
    The fuzzled bowser, he called for Towser,
    But Towser was barking the moon.

(*Enter Baltea, breathless and disheveled.*)

    Baltea: Your Majesty, there's madness loose from hell.

    Smaragad: What's wrong? Has someone raped you without?

    Baltea: No, 'tis about the queen, from whose bed-chamber
I have come post-haste.

    Smaragad: Well, what about her? Why
Have you left her? Is she alone?

    Baltea: She's not alone
But has for company a nameless thing
Vomited forth by death.

    Smaragad (*half-starting from his seat*): What's all this coil?
A nameless thing, you say? There's nothing nameless.
I'd have a word for what has sent you here,
Panting, with undone hair.

    Baltea: Well, then 'tis Galeor.

    Smaragad: Hell's privy-fumes!
He's cooling underground, if my grave-diggers

Shirked not their office.

Baltea: And yet he has returned
To visit Queen Somelis, with dark stains
Of earth upon his brow, and goblin torches
Lighting his torrid gaze.

Smaragad (*standing up*): Tell me about it,
Though I cannot believe you. Though he be
Quick or dead, by Thasaidon's dark horns
What does he in the chamber of the queen?

Baltea: I wot not how he came nor why. But she
Was parleying with him, speaking gentle words
When I ran forth to seek you.

Smaragad: Sargo, Boranga, hear you this? Attend me,
And we'll inquire into this nightmare's nest
And find what's at the bottom. (*He starts toward the door, followed by the
others.*)   By all the plagues
Afflicting the five senses, there's too much
That stinks amid these walls tonight. . . . Where were
The guards? I'll prune their ears with a blunt sickle
And douche their eyes with boiling camel-stale
For such delinquency as lets
Goblin or man or lich go by them.

(*Curtain*)

SCENE VI

The hall before Somelis' bed-chamber. Enter Smaragad, Sargo
Borga and Baltea, followed by two chamberlains. Smaragad tries the
queen's door. Finding that it will not open, he beats upon it with the
hilt of his drawn sword, but without response.

Smaragad: Who has barred this door? Was it the queen? I vow
That she shall never close another door
When this is broken down. I'll bolt the next one for her,
And it will be the tomb's. Boranga, Sargo,
Give here your shoulders, side by side with mine. (*All three apply their
weight to the door but cannot budge it. Sargo, more intoxicated that loses his bal-
ance and falls. Boranga helps him to his feet.*)
Truly, my stout forefathers built this palace
And all its portals to withstand a siege.

Boranga: There are siege-engines in the arsenal,
Great rams, that have thrown down broad-builded towers
And torn the gates of cities from their hinges.
With your permission, Sire, I'll call for one
Together with men to wield it.

Smaragad: I'll not have
A legion here to witness what lies couched
In the queen's chamber. Nor am I accustomed
To beat on closen doors that open not.
In all my kingdom, or in Thasaidon's
Deep tortuous maze of torments multi-circled,
There is no darker gulf than this shut room
Which reason cannot fathom, being shunted
From the blank walls to madness.

Sargo: Your Majesty,
If this indeed be Galeor, it smells
Of Natanasna, who has called up others
From tomb or trench, inspiriting with demons
Malign or lewd their corpses. There'll be need
Of exorcism. I would have the priests
Brought in, and rites performed.

Smaragad: I hardly doubt
That the curst necromancer is the getter
Of this graveyard fetus. But I will not have it
Either your way or Boranga's. (*Turning to the chamberlains*) Bring to me
Fagots of pitch-veined terebinth, and naphtha.

Boranga: Sire, what is your purpose?

Smaragad: You will see full soon.

Baltea: Your Majesty, bethink you, there are windows
To which armed men could climb by ladders, finding
Ingress to the queen's room. It may be she's
In peril from this intruder, who had about him
The air of an incubus.

Smaragad: Truly, I think
That he is no intruder to the queen
Who has barred these portals. Nor am I a thief
To enter in by a window.
(*The chamberlains return, bearing armfuls of fagots and jars of oil.*)
                    Pile the wood
Before the door, and drench it with the naphtha. (*The chamberlains obey.*
Smaragad seizes a cresset from one of the sconces along the hall, and applies it to
the fagots. Flames leap up immediately and lick the cedarn door.)
I'll warm the bed of this black lechery
That lairs within my walls.

Boranga: Have you gone mad?
You'll fire the palace!

Smaragad: Fire's the one pure thing
To cleanse it. And for fuel we lack only
The necromancer and his swart catamite.

(*The fire spreads quickly to the curtains of the hallway, from which flaming patches begin to fall. Baltea and the chamberlains flee. A section of the burning arras descends upon Sargo. He reels, and falls. Unable to rise, he crawls away, screaming, with his raiment ignited. A loosened splotch sets fire to the king's mantle. He flings the garment front him with an agile gesture. The flames eat steadily into the door, and assail its heavy wooden framework. The heat and smoke compel Boranga and Smaragad to stand back.*)

Boranga: Your Majesty, the palace burns about us.
There's little time for our escape.

Smaragad: You tell me
A thing that's patent. Ah! the goodly flames!
They will lay bare the secret of this chamber
Whose mystery maddens me. . . . And at the last
There will be only ashes
For the summoning of any sorcerer.

Boranga: Sire, we must go.

Smaragad: Be still. It is too late for any words,
And only deeds remain.

(*After some minutes the charred door collapses inward with its red-hot bars, Boranga seizes the king's arm and tries to drag him away. Smaragad wrenches himself loose and beats at Boranga with the flat of his sword.*)

Leave me, Boranga.
I'll go and carve the lechers while they roast
Into small collops for the ghouls to eat.

(*Brandishing his sword, he leaps over the fallen door into the flaming chamber beyond.*)

(*Curtain*)

THE WITCHCRAFT OF ULUA

Sabmon the anchorite was famed no less for his piety than for his prophetic wisdom and knowledge of the dark art of sorcery. He had dwelt alone for two generations in a curious house on the rim of the northern desert of Tasuun: a house whose floor and walls were built from the large bones of dromedaries, and whose roof was a wattling composed of the smaller bones of wild dogs and men and hyenas. These ossuary relics, chosen for their whiteness and symmetry, were bound securely together with well-tanned thongs, and were joined and fitted with marvellous closeness, leaving no space for the blown sand to penetrate. This house was the pride of Sabmon, who swept it daily with a besom of mummy's hair, till it shone immaculate as polished ivory both within and without.

Despite his remoteness and reclusion, and the hardships that attended a journey to his abode, Sabmon was much consulted by the people of Tasuun, and was even sought by pilgrims from the further shores of Zothique. However, though not ungracious or inhospitable, he often ignored the queries of his visitors, who, as a rule, wished merely to divine the future or to ask advice concerning the most advantageous government of their affairs. He became more and more taciturn with age, and spoke little with men in his last years. It was said, perhaps not untruly, that he preferred to talk with the ever-murmuring palms about his well, or the desert-wandering stars that went over his hermitage.

In the summer of Sabmon's ninety-third year, there came to him the youth Amalzain, his great-nephew, and the son of a niece that Sabmon had loved dearly in days before his retirement to a gymnosophic seclusion. Amalzain, who had spent all of his one-and-twenty years in the upland home of his parents, was on his way to Miraab, the capital of Tasuun, where he would serve as a cupbearer to Famorgh the king. This post, obtained for him by influential friends of his father, was much coveted among the youth of the land, and would lead to high advancement if he were fortunate enough to win the king's favor. In accord with his mother's wish, he had come to visit Sabmon and to ask the counsel of the sage regarding various problems of worldly conduct.

Sabmon, whose eyes were undimmed by age and astronomy and much poring over volumes of archaic ciphers, was pleased with Amalzain and found in the boy something of his mother's beauty. And for this reason he gave freely of his hoarded wisdom; and, after uttering many profound and pertinent maxims, he said to Amalzain:

"It is indeed well that you have come to me: for, innocent of the world's turpitude, you fare to a city of strange sins and strange witcheries and sorceries. There are numerous evils in Miraab. Its women are witches and harlots, and their beauty is a foulness wherein the young, the strong, the valiant, are limed and taken."

Then, ere Amalzain departed, Sabmon gave to him a small amulet of silver, graven curiously with the migniard skeleton of a girl. And Sabmon said:

"I counsel you to wear this amulet at all times henceforward. It contains a pinch of ashes from the pyre of Yos Ebni, sage and archimage, who won supremacy over men and demons in elder years by defying all mortal temptation and putting down the insubordination of the flesh. There is a virtue in these ashes, and they will protect you from such evils as were overcome by Yos Ebni. And yet, peradventure, there are ills and enchantments in Miraab from which the amulet cannot defend you. In such case you must return to me. I shall watch over you carefully, and shall know all that occurs to you in Miraab: for I have long since become the owner of certain rare faculties of sight and hearing whose exercise is not debarred or limited by mere distance."

Amalzain, being ignorant of the matters at which Sabmon hinted, was somewhat bewildered by this peroration. But he received the amulet gratefully. Then, bidding Sabmon a reverential farewell, he resumed his journey to Miraab, wondering much as to the fortune that would befall him in that sinful and many-legended city.

II

Famorgh, who had grown old and senile amid his debaucheries, was the ruler of an aging, semi-desert land; and his court was a place of far-sought luxury, of obliquitous refinement and corruption. The youth Amalzain, accustomed only to the simple manners, the rude virtues and vices of country-dwelling folk, was dazzled at first by the sybaritic life around him. But a certain innate strength of character, fortified by the moral teachings of his parents and the precepts of his great-uncle, Sabmon, preserved him from any grave errors or lapses.

Thus it was that he served as a cupbearer at bacchanalian revels, but remained abstemious throughout, pouring night after night in the ruby-crusted cup of Famorgh the maddening wines that were drugged with cannabis and the stupefying arrack with its infusion of poppy. With untainted heart and flesh he beheld the infamous mummeries whereby the courtiers, vying with each other in shamelessness, attempted to lighten the king's ennui. Feeling only wonder or disgust, he watched the nimble and lascivious contortions of black dancers from Dooza Thom in the north, or saffron-bodied girls from the southern isles. His parents, who believed implicitly in the superhuman goodness of monarchs, had not prepared him for this spectacle of royal vice; but the reverence they had instilled so thoroughly into Amalzain led him to regard it all as being the peculiar but mysterious prerogative of the kings of Tasuun.

During his first month in Miraab, Amalzain heard much of the Princess Ulua, sole daughter of Famorgh and Queen Lunalia; but since

the women of the royal family seldom attended the banquets or appeared in public, he did not see her. The huge and shadowy palace,
however, was filled with whispers concerning her amours. Ulua, he
was told, had inherited the sorceries of her mother Lunalia, whose
dark, luxurious beauty, so often sung by bewitched poets, was now
fallen to a haggish decrepitude. The lovers of Ulua were innumerable,
and she often procured their passion or insured their fidelity by other
charms than those of her person. Though little taller than a child, she
was exquisitely formed and endowed with the loveliness of some female demon that might haunt the slumbers of youth. She was feared
by many and her ill will was deemed a dangerous thing. Famorgh, no
less blind to her sins and witcheries than he had been to those of Lunalia, indulged her in all ways and denied her nothing.

Amalzain's duties left him much idle time, for Famorgh usually
slept the double sleep of age and intoxication after the evening revels.
Much of this time he gave to the study of algebra and the reading of
olden poems and romances. One morning, while he was engaged with
certain algebraic calculations, there came to Amalzain a huge negress
who had been pointed out to him as one of Ulua's waiting-women. She
told him peremptorily that he was to follow her to the apartments of
Ulua. Bewildered and amazed by this singular interruption of his studies, he was unable to reply for a moment. Thereupon, seeing his hesita-
tion, the great black woman lifted him in her naked arms and carried
him easily from the room and through the palace halls. Angry, and full
of discomfiture, he found himself deposited in a chamber hung with
shameless designs, where, amid the fuming of aphrodisiac vapors, the
princess regarded him with luxurious gravity from a couch of fire-
bright scarlet. She was small as a woman of the elf-folk, and voluptuous as a coiled lamia. The incense floated about her like sinuous veils.

"There are other things than the pouring of wine for a sottish
monarch, or the study of worm-eaten volumes," said Ulua in a voice
that was like the flowing of hot honey. "Sir cupbearer, your youth

should have a better employment than these."

"I ask no employment, other than my duties and studies," replied Amalzain ungraciously. "But tell me, O princess, what is your will? Why has your serving-woman brought me here in a fashion so unseemly?"

"For a youth so erudite and clever, the question should be needless," answered Ulua, smiling obliquely. "See you not that I am beautiful and desirable? Behold! my arms are the portals of strange felicities. The pleasures I give are keener than the pangs of a fiery death. The dead kings of Tasuun will whisper enviously of our love to their dead queens in the immemorial granite vaults below Chaon Gacca. Thasaidon, the black, shadowy lord of hell, grown jealous of our raptures, will wish to become incarnate in a mortal body."

The vapors, mounting thickly from golden thuribles before the couch, were parted with a motion as of drawn draperies; and Amalzain saw that Ulua was clad only in breast-cups of coral and mother-of-pearl, and bracelets and anklets of jet. . . .

"The matters whereof you speak are nothing to me," said the youth, untempted.

Ulua laughed lightly, and the vapors undulated as if in unison with her laughter, and were shaped dimly into obscene forms.

"Soon you will answer otherwise," she told the youth. "Few men have denied me long—and these few have regretted their refusal in the end. You may go now: but you will return to me presently—of your own accord."

For many days thereafter, Amalzain, going about his duties as usual, was aware of a strange haunting. It seemed now that Ulua was everywhere. Appearing at the revels, as if by some new caprice, she flaunted her evil beauty in the eyes of the young cupbearer; and often, by day, he met her in the palace gardens and corridors. All men spoke of her, as if conspiring tacitly to keep her in his thoughts; and it seemed that even the heavy arrases whispered her name as they rustled in the lost winds that wandered through the gloomy and interminable halls.

This, however, was not all: for her undesired image began to trouble his nightly dreams; and awakening, he heard the warm, dulcet languor of her voice, and felt the caress of light and subtle fingers in the darkness. Peering at the pale moon that waxed beyond the windows, above the black cypresses, he saw her dead, corroded face assume the living features of Ulua. The lithe and migniard form of the young witch appeared to move among the fabulous queens and goddesses that thronged the opulent hangings with their amours. Beheld as if through enchantment, her face leaned beside his in the mirrors; and she came and vanished, phantom-like, with seductive murmurs and wanton gestures, as he bent over his books. But though he was perturbed by these appearances, in which he could scarce distinguish the real from the illusory, Amalzain was still indifferent toward Ulua, being surely protected from her charms by the amulet containing the ashes of Yos Ebni, saint and sage and archimage. From certain curious flavors detected more than once in his food and drink, he suspected that the love-potions for which she had become infamous were being administered to him; but beyond a light and passing qualmishness, he experienced no ill effect whatever; and he was wholly ignorant of the spells woven against him in secret, and the thrice-lethal invultuations that were designed to wound his heart and senses.

Now (though he knew it not) his indifference was a matter of much gossip at the court. Men marvelled greatly at such exemption: for all whom the princess had chosen heretofore, whether captains, cupbearers or high dignitaries, or common soldiers and grooms, had yielded easily to her bewitchments. So it came to pass that Ulua was angered, since all men knew that her beauty was scorned by Amalzain, and her sorcery was impotent to ensnare him. Thereupon she ceased to appear at the revels of Famorgh; and Amalzain beheld her no longer in the halls and gardens; and neither his dreams nor his waking hours were haunted any more by the spell-wrought semblance of Ulua. So, in his innocence, he rejoiced as one who has encountered a grave peril and has come forth unharmed.

Then, later, on a certain night, as he lay sleeping tranquilly in the moonless hours before dawn, there came to him in his dream a figure muffled from crown to heel with the vestments of the tomb. Tall as a caryatid, awful and menacing, it leaned above him in silence more malignant than any curse; and the cerements fell open at the breast, and charnel-worms and death-scarabs and scorpions, together with shreds of rotting flesh, rained down upon Amalzain. Then, as he awoke from his nightmare, sick and stifled, he breathed a carrion fetor, and felt against him the pressure of a still, heavy body. Affrighted, he rose and lit the lamp; but the bed was empty. Yet the odor of putrefaction still lingered; and Amalzain could have sworn that the corpse of a woman, two weeks dead and teeming with maggots, had lain closely at his side in the darkness.

Thereafter, for many nights, his slumbers were broken by such foulnesses as this. Hardly could he sleep at all for the horror of that which came and went, invisible but palpable, in his chamber. Always he awoke from ill dreams, to find about him the stiffened arms of long-dead succubi, or to feel at his side the amorous trembling of fleshless skeletons. He was choked by the natron and bitumen of mummied breasts; he was crushed by the unremoving weight of gigantic liches; he was kissed nauseously by lips that were oozing tatters of corruption.

Nor was this all; for other abominations came to him by day, visible, and perceived through all his senses, and more loathsome even than the dead. Things that seemed as the leavings of leprosy crawled before him at high noon in the halls of Famorgh; and they rose up from the shadows and sidled toward him, leering whitely with faces that were no longer faces, and trying to caress him with their half-eaten fingers. About his ankles, as he went to and fro, there clung lascivious empusæ with breasts that were furred like the bat; and serpent-bodied lamiæ minced and pirouetted before his eyes, like the dancers before the king.

No longer could he read his books or solve his problems of algebra in peace: for the letters changed from moment to moment beneath his scrutiny and were twisted into runes of evil meaning; and the signs and ciphers he had written were turned into devils no bigger than large emmets, that writhed foully across the paper as if on a field, performing those rites which are acceptable only to Alila, queen of perdition and goddess of all iniquities.

Thus plagued and bedevilled, the youth Amalzain was near to madness; yet he dared not complain or speak to others of aught that he beheld; for he knew that these horrors, whether immaterial or substantial, were perceived only by himself. Nightly, for the full period of a moon, he lay with dead things in his chamber; and daily, in all his comings and goings, he was besought by abhorrent specters. And he doubted not that all these were the sendings of Ulua, angered by his refusal of her love; and he remembered that Sabmon had hinted darkly of certain enchantments from which the ashes of Yos Ebni, preserved in the silver amulet, might be powerless to defend him. And, knowing that such enchantments were upon him now, he recalled the final injunction of the old archimage.

So, feeling that there was no help for him save in the wizardry of Sabmon, he went before King Famorgh and begged a short leave of absence from the court. And Famorgh, who was well pleased with the cupbearer, and moreover had begun to note his thinness and pallor, granted the request readily.

Mounted on a palfrey chosen for speed and endurance, Amalzain rode northward from Miraab on a sultry morning in autumn. A strange heaviness had stilled all the air; and great coppery clouds were piled like towering, many-domed palaces of genii on the desert hills. The sun appeared to swim in molten brass. No vultures flew on the silent heavens; and the very jackals had retired to their lairs, as if in fear of some unknown doom. But Amalzain, riding swiftly toward Sabmon's hermitage, was haunted still by leprous larvæ that rose before him, posturing foully on the dun sands; and he heard the desirous moaning of succubi under the hooves of his horse.

The night waylaid him, airless and starless, as he came to a well amid dying palms. Here he lay sleepless, with the curse of Ulua still upon him: for it seemed that the dry, dusty liches of desert tombs reclined rigidly at his side; and bony fingers wooed him toward the unfathomable sand-pits from which they had risen.

Weary and devil-ridden, he reached the wattled house of Sabmon at noon of the next day. The sage greeted him affectionately, showing no surprise, and listened to his story with the air of one who harkens a twice-told tale.

"These things, and more, were known to me from the beginning," he said to Amalzain. "I could have saved you from the sendings of Ulua ere now; but it was my wish that you should come to me at this time, forsaking the court of the dotard Famorgh and the evil city of Miraab, whose iniquities are now at the full. The imminent doom of Miraab, though unread by her astrologers, has been declared in the heavens; and I would not that you should share the doom.

"It is needful," he went on, "that the spells of Ulua should be broken on this very day, and the sendings returned to her that sent them; since otherwise they would haunt you forever, remaining as a visible and tangible plague when the witch herself has gone to her black lord, Thasaidon, in the seventh hell."

Then, to the wonderment of Amalzain, the old magician brought forth from a cabinet of ivory an elliptic mirror of dark and burnished metal and placed it before him. The mirror was held aloft by the muffled hands of a veiled image; and peering within it, Amalzain saw neither his own face nor the face of Sabmon, nor aught of the room itself reflected. And Sabmon enjoined him to watch the mirror closely, and then repaired to a small oratory that was curtained off from the chamber with long and queerly painted rolls of camel-parchment.

Watching the mirror, Amalzain was aware that certain of the sendings of Ulua still came and went beside him, striving ever to gain his attention with unclean gestures such as harlots use. But resolutely he fixed his eyes on the void and unreflecting metal; and anon he heard the voice of Sabmon chanting without pause the powerful words of an antique formula of exorcism; and now from between the oratory curtains there issued the intolerable pungency of burning spices, such as are employed to drive away demons.

Then Amalzain perceived, without lifting his eyes from the mirror, that the sendings of Ulua had all vanished like vapors blown away by the desert wind. But in the mirror a scene limned itself darkly, and he seemed to look on the marble towers of the city of Miraab beneath overlooming bastions of ominous cloud. Then the scene shifted, and he saw the palace-hall where Famorgh nodded in wine-stained purple, senile and drunken, amid his ministers and sycophants. Again the mirror changed, and he beheld a room with tapestries of shameless design, where, on a couch of fire-bright crimson, the Princess Ulua sat with her latest lovers amid the fuming of golden thuribles.

Marvelling as he peered within the mirror, Amalzain witnessed a strange thing: for the vapors of the thuribles, mounting thickly and voluminously, took from instant to instant the form of those very apparitions by which he had been bedevilled so long. Ever they rose and multiplied, till the chamber teemed with the spawn of hell and the vomitings of the riven charnel. Betwixt Ulua and the lover at her right hand, who was a captain of the king's guard, there coiled a monstrous lamia, enfolding them both in its serpentine volumes and crushing them with its human bosom; and close at her left hand appeared a half-eaten corpse, leering with lipless teeth, from whose cerements worms were sifted upon Ulua and her second lover, who was a royal equerry. And, swelling like the fumes of some witches' vat, those other

abominations pressed about the couch of Ulua with obscene mouth-
ings and fingerings.

At this, like the mark of a hellish branding, horror was printed on
the features of the captain and the equerry; and a terror rose in the
eyes of Ulua like a pale flame ignited in sunless pits; and her breasts
shuddered beneath the breast-cups. And now, in a trice, the mirrored
room began to rock violently, and the censers were overturned on the
tilting flags, and the shameless hangings shook and bellied like the
blown sails of a vessel in storm. Great cracks appeared in the floor;
and beside the couch of Ulua a chasm deepened swiftly, and then widened from wall to wall. The whole chamber was riven asunder, and the
Princess and her two lovers, with all her loathly sendings about them,
were hurled tumultuously into the chasm.

After that, the mirror darkened, and Amalzain beheld for a moment the pale towers of Miraab, tossing and falling on heavens black as
adamant. The mirror itself trembled, and the veiled image of metal
supporting it began to totter and seemed about to fall; and the wattled
house of Sabmon shook in the passing earthquake, but, being stoutly
built, stood firm while the mansions and palaces of Miraab went down
in ruin.

When the earth had ceased its long trembling, Sabmon issued from
the oratory.

"It is needless to moralize on what has happened," he said. "You
have learned the true nature of carnal desire, and have likewise beheld
the history of mundane corruption. Now, being wise, you will turn early to those things which are incorruptible and beyond the world."

Thereafter, till the death of Sabmon, Amalzain dwelt with him, and
became his only pupil in the science of the stars and the hidden arts of
enchantment and sorcery.

THE CHARNEL GOD

M ordiggian is the god of Zul-Bha-Sair," said the innkeeper with unctuous solemnity. "He has been the god from years that are lost to man's memory in shadow deeper than the subterranes of his black temple. There is no other god in Zul-Bha-Sair. And all who die within the walls of the city are sacred to Mordiggian. Even the kings and the optimates, at death, are delivered into the hands of his muffled priests. It is the law and the custom. A little while, and the priests will come for your bride."

"But Elaith is not dead," protested the youth Phariom for the third or fourth time, in piteous desperation. "Her malady is one that assumes the lying likeness of death. Twice before has she lain insensible, with a pallor upon her cheeks, and a stillness in her very blood, that could hardly be distinguished from those of the tomb; and twice she has awakened after an interim of days."

The innkeeper peered with an air of ponderous unbelief at the girl who lay white and motionless as a mown lily on the bed in the poorly furnished attic chamber.

"In that case you should not have brought her into Zul-Bha-Sair," he averred in a tone of owlish irony. "The physician has pronounced her dead; and her death has been reported to the priests. She must go to the temple of Mordiggian."

"But we are outlanders, guests of a night. We have come from the land of Xylac, far in the north; and this morning we should have gone on through Tasuun, toward Faraad, the capital of Yoros, which lies near to the southern sea. Surely your god could have no claim upon Elaith, even if she were truly dead."

"All who die in Zul-Bha-Sair are the property of Mordiggian," insisted the taverner sententiously. "Outlanders are not exempt. The dark maw of his temple yawns eternally, and no man, no child, no woman, throughout the years, has evaded its yawning. All mortal flesh must become, in due time, the provender of the god."

Phariom shuddered at the oily and portentous declaration.

"Dimly have I heard of Mordiggian, as a legend that travellers tell in Xylac," he admitted. "But I had forgotten the name of his city; and Elaith and I came ignorantly into Zul-Bha-Sair .... Even had I known, I should have doubted the terrible custom of which you inform me .... What manner of deity is this, who imitates the hyena and the vulture? Surely he is no god, but a ghoul."

"Take heed, lest you utter blasphemy," admonished the innkeeper. "Mordiggian is old and omnipotent as death. He was worshipped in former continents, before the lifting of Zothique from out the sea. Through him, we are saved from corruption and the worm. Even as the people of other places devote their dead to the consuming flame, so we of Zul-Bha-Sair deliver ours to the god. Awful is the fane, a place of terror and obscure shadow untrod by the sun, into which the dead are borne by his priests and are laid on a vast table of stone to await his coming from the nether vault in which he dwells. No living men, other than the priests, have ever beheld him; and the faces of the priests are hidden behind masks of silver, and even their hands are shrouded, that men may not gaze on them that have seen Mordiggian."

"But there is a king in Zul-Bha-Sair, is there not? I shall appeal to him against this heinous and horrible injustice. Surely he will heed me."

"Phenquor is the king; but he could not help you even if he wished. Your appeal will not even be heard. Mordiggian is above all kings, and his law is sacred. Hark!—for already the priests come."

Phariom, sick at heart with the charnel terror and cruelty of the doom that impended for his girlish wife in this unknown city of nightmare, heard an evil, stealthy creaking on the stairs that led to the attic of the inn. The sound drew nearer with inhuman rapidity, and four strange figures came into the room, heavily garbed in funereal purple, and wearing huge masks of silver graven in the likeness of skulls. It was impossible to surmise their actual appearance, for, even as the taverner had hinted, their very hands were concealed by fingerless gloves; and the purple gowns came down in loose folds that trailed about their feet like unwinding cerecloths. There was a horror about them, of which the macabre masks were only a lesser element; a horror that lay partly in their unnatural, crouching attitudes, and the beast-like agility with which they moved, unhampered by their cumbrous habiliments.

Among them, they carried a curious bier, made from interwoven strips of leather, and with monstrous bones that served for frame and handles. The leather was greasy and blackened as if from long years of mortuary use. Without speaking to Phariom or the innkeeper, and with no delay or formality of any sort, they advanced toward the bed on which Elaith was lying.

Undeterred by their more than formidable aspect, and wholly distraught with grief and anger, Phariom drew from his girdle a short knife, the only weapon he possessed. Disregarding the minatory cry of the taverner, he rushed wildly upon the muffled figures. He was quick and muscular, and, moreover, was clad in light, close-fitting raiment, such as would seemingly have given him a brief advantage.

The priests had turned their backs upon him; but, as if they had foreseen his every action, two of them wheeled about with the swiftness of tigers, dropping the handles of bone that they carried. One of them struck the knife from Phariom's hand with a movement that the eye could barely follow in its snaky darting. Then both assailed him, beating him back with terrible flailing blows of their shrouded arms, and hurling him half across the room into an empty corner. Stunned by his fall, he lay senseless for a term of minutes.

Recovering dazedly, with eyes that blurred as he opened them, he beheld the face of the stout taverner stooping above him like a tallow-colored moon. The thought of Elaith, more sharp than the thrust of a dagger, brought him back to agonizing consciousness. Fearfully he scanned the shadowy room, and saw that the ceremented priests were gone, that the bed was vacant. He heard the orotund and sepulchral croaking of the taverner:

"The priests of Mordiggian are merciful, they make allowance for the frenzy and distraction of the newly bereaved. It is well for you that they are compassionate, and considerate of mortal weakness."

Phariom sprang erect, as if his bruised and aching body were scorched by a sudden fire. Pausing only to retrieve his knife, which still lay in the middle of the room, he started toward the door. He was stopped by the hand of the hosteler, clutching greasily at his shoulder.

"Beware, lest you exceed the bounds of the mercy of Mordiggian. It is an ill thing to follow his priests—and a worse thing to intrude upon the deathly and sacred gloom of his temple."

Phariom scarcely heard the admonition. He wrenched himself hastily away from the odious fingers, and turned to go; but again the hand clutched him.

"At least, pay me the money that you owe for food and lodging, ere you depart," demanded the innkeeper. "Also, there is the matter of the physician's fee, which I can settle for you, if you will entrust me with the proper sum. Pay now—for there is no surety that you will return."

Phariom drew out the purse that contained his entire worldly wealth, and filled the greedily cupped palm before him with coins that he did not pause to count. With no parting word or backward glance, he descended the mouldy and musty stairs of the worm-eaten hostelry, as if spurred by an incubus, and went out into the gloomy, serpentine streets of Zul-Bha-Sair.

II

Perhaps the city differed little from others, except in being older and darker; but to Phariom, in his extremity of anguish, the ways that he followed were like subterrene corridors that led only to some profound and monstrous charnel. The sun had risen above the overjutting houses, but it seemed to him that there was no light, other than a lost and doleful glimmering such as might descend into mortuary depths. The people, it may have been, were much like other people, but he saw them under a malefic aspect, as if they were ghouls and demons that went to and fro on the ghastly errands of a necropolis.

Bitterly, in his distraction, he recalled the previous evening, when he had entered Zul-Bha-Sair at twilight with Elaith, the girl riding on the one dromedary that had survived their passage of the northern desert, and he walking beside her, weary but content. With the rosy purple of afterglow upon its walls and cupolas, with the deepening golden eyes of its lit windows, the place had seemed a fair and nameless city of dreams, and they had planned to rest there for a day or two before resuming the long, arduous journey to Faraad, in Yoros.

This journey had been undertaken only through necessity. Phariom, an impoverished youth of noble blood, had been exiled because of the political and religious tenets of his family, which were not in accord with those of the reigning emperor, Caleppos. Taking his newly wedded wife, Phariom had set out for Yoros, where certain allied branches of the house to which he belonged had already established themselves, and would give him a fraternal welcome.

They had travelled with a large caravan of merchants, going directly southward to Tasuun. Beyond the borders of Xylac, amid the red sands of the Celotian waste, the caravan had been attacked by robbers, who had slain many of its members and dispersed the rest. Phariom and his bride, escaping with their dromedaries, had found themselves lost and alone in the desert, and, failing to regain the road toward

Tasuun, had taken inadvertently another track, leading to Zul-Bha-Sair, a walled metropolis on the south-western verge of the waste, which their itinerary had not included.

Entering Zul-Bha-Sair, the couple had repaired for reasons of economy to a tavern in the humbler quarter. There, during the night, Elaith had been overcome by the third seizure of the cataleptic malady to which she was liable. The earlier seizures, occurring before her marriage to Phariom, had been recognized in their true character by the physicians of Xylac, and had been palliated by skillful treatment. It was hoped that the malady would not recur. The third attack, no doubt, had been induced by the fatigues and hardships of the journey. Phariom had felt sure that Elaith would recover; but a doctor of Zul-Bha-Sair, hastily summoned by the innkeeper, had insisted that she was actually dead; and, in obedience to the strange law of the city, had reported her without delay to the priests of Mordiggian. The frantic protests of the husband had been utterly ignored.

There was, it seemed, a diabolic fatality about the whole train of circumstances through which Elaith, still living, though with that outward aspect of the tomb which her illness involved, had fallen into the grasp of the devotees of the charnel god. Phariom pondered this fatality almost to madness, as he strode with furious, aimless haste along the eternally winding and crowded streets.

To the cheerless information received from the taverner, he added, as he went on, more and more of the tardily remembered legends which he had heard in Xylac. Ill and dubious indeed was the renown of Zul-Bha-Sair, and he marvelled that he should have forgotten it, and cursed himself with black curses for the temporary but fatal forgetfulness. Better would it have been if he and Elaith had perished in the desert, rather than enter the wide gates that stood always open, gaping for their prey, as was the custom of Zul-Bha-Sair.

The city was a mart of trade, where outland travellers came, but did not care to linger, because of the repulsive cult of Mordiggian, the invisible eater of the dead, who was believed to share his provender with the shrouded priests. It was said that the bodies lay for days in the dark temple and were not devoured till corruption had begun. And people whispered of fouler things than necrophagism, of blasphemous rites that were solemnized in the ghoul-ridden vaults, and nameless uses to which the dead were put before Mordiggian claimed them. In all outlying places, the fate of those who died in Zul-Bha-Sair was a dreadful byword and a malediction. But to the people of that city, reared in the faith of the ghoulish god, it was merely the usual and expected mode of mortuary disposal. Tombs, graves, catacombs, funeral pyres, and other such nuisances, were rendered needless by this highly utilitarian deity.

Phariom was surprised to see the people of the city going about the common businesses of life. Porters were passing with bales of household goods upon their shoulders. Merchants were squatting in their shops like other merchants. Buyers and sellers chaffered loudly in the public bazaars. Women laughed and chattered in the door ways. Only by their voluminous robes of red, black and violet, and their strange, uncouth accents, was he able to distinguish the men of Zul-Bha-Sair from those who were outlanders like himself. The murk of nightmare began to lift from his impressions; and gradually, as he went on, the spectacle of everyday humanity all about him helped to calm a little his wild distraction and desperation. Nothing could dissipate the horror of his loss, and the abominable fate that threatened Elaith. But now, with a cool logic born of the cruel exigence, he began to consider the apparently hopeless problem of rescuing her from the ghoul-god's temple.

He composed his features, and constrained his febrile pacing to an idle saunter, so that none might guess the preoccupations that racked him inwardly. Pretending to be interested in the wares of a seller of men's apparel, he drew the dealer into converse regarding Zul-Bha-Sair and its customs, and made such inquiries as a traveller from far lands might make. The dealer was talkative, and Phariom soon learned from him the location of the temple of Mordiggian, which stood at the city's core. He also learned that the temple was open at all hours, and that people were free to come and go within its precincts. There were, however, no rituals of worship, other than certain private rites that were celebrated by the priesthood. Few cared to enter the fane, because of a superstition that any living person who intruded upon its gloom would return to it shortly as the provender of the god.

Mordiggian, it seemed, was indeed a benign deity in the eyes of the inhabitants of Zul-Bha-Sair. Curiously enough, no definite personal attributes were ascribed to him. He was, so to speak, an impersonal force akin to the elements—a consuming and cleansing power, like fire. His hierophants were equally mysterious; they lived in the temple and emerged from it only in the execution of their funeral duties. No one knew the manner of their recruiting, but many believed that they were both male and female, thus renewing their numbers from generation to generation with no ulterior commerce. Others thought that they were not human beings at all, but an order of subterranean earth-entities, who lived for ever, and who fed upon corpses like the god himself. Through this latter belief, of late years, a minor heresy had risen, some holding that Mordiggian was a mere hieratic figment, and the priests were the sole devourers of the dead. The dealer, quoting this heresy, made haste to disavow it with pious reprobation.

Phariom chatted for awhile on other topics, and then continued his progress through the city, going as forthrightly toward the temple as the obliquely running thoroughfares would permit. He had formed no conscious plan, but desired to reconnoiter the vicinage. In that which the garment-dealer had told him, the one reassuring detail was the openness of the fane and its accessibility to all who dared enter. The rarity of visitors, however, would make Phariom conspicuous, and he wished above all to avoid attention. On the other hand, any effort to remove bodies from the temple was seemingly unheard of—a thing audacious beyond the dreams of the people of Zul-Bha-Sair. Through the very boldness of his design, he might avoid suspicion, and succeed in rescuing Elaith.

The streets that he followed began to tend downward, and were narrower, dimmer and more tortuous than any he had yet traversed. He thought for awhile that he had lost his way, and he was about to ask the passers to redirect him, when four of the priests of Mordiggian, bearing one of the curious litter-like biers of bone and leather, emerged from an ancient alley just before him.

The bier was occupied by the body of a girl, and for one moment of convulsive shock and agitation that left him trembling, Phariom thought that the girl was Elaith. Looking again, he saw his mistake. The gown that the girl wore, though simple, was made of some rare exotic stuff. Her features, though pale as those of Elaith, were crowned with curls like the petals of heavy black poppies. Her beauty, warm and voluptuous even in death, differed from the blond pureness of Elaith as tropic lilies differ from narcissi.

Quietly, and maintaining a discreet interval, Phariom followed the sullenly shrouded figures and their lovely burden. He saw that people made way for the passage of the bier with awed, unquestioning alacrity; and the loud voices of hucksters and chafferers were hushed as the priests went by. Overhearing a murmured conversation between two of the townsfolk, he learned that the dead girl was Arctela, daughter of Quaos, a high noble and magistrate of Zul-Bha-Sair. She had died very quickly and mysteriously, from a cause unknown to the physicians, which had not marred or wasted her beauty in the least. There were those who held that an indetectable poison, rather than disease, had been the agency of death; and others deemed her the victim of malefic sorcery.

The priests went on, and Phariom kept them in sight as well as he could in the blind tangle of streets. The way steepened, without affording any clear prospect of the levels below, and the houses seemed to crowd more closely, as if huddling back from a precipice. Finally the youth emerged behind his macabre guides in a sort of circular hollow at the city's heart, where the temple of Mordiggian loomed alone and separate amid pavements of sad onyx, and funerary cedars whose green had blackened as if with the undeparting charnel shadows bequeathed by dead ages.

The edifice was built of a strange stone, hued as with the blackish purple of carnal decay: a stone that refused the ardent luster of noon, and the prodigality of dawn or sunset glory. It was low and windowless, having the form of a monstrous mausoleum. Its portals yawned sepulchrally in the gloom of the cedars.

Phariom watched the priests as they vanished within the portals, carrying the girl Arctela like phantoms who bear a phantom burden. The broad area of pavement between the recoiling houses and the temple was now deserted, but he did not venture to cross it in the blare of betraying daylight. Circling the area, he saw that there were several other entrances to the great fane, all open and unguarded. There was no sign of activity about the place; but he shuddered uncontrollably at the thought of that which was hidden within its walls, even as the feasting of worms is hidden in the marble tomb.

Like a vomiting of charnels, the abominations of which he had heard rose up before him in the sunlight; and again he drew close to madness, knowing that Elaith must lie among the dead, in the temple, with the foul umbrage of such things upon her, and that he, consumed with unremitting frenzy, must wait for the favorable shrouding of darkness before he could execute his nebulous, doubtful plan of rescue. In the meanwhile, she might awake, and perish from the mortal horror of her surroundings . . . or worse even than this might befall, if the whispered tales were true . . . .

III

Abnon-Tha, sorcerer and necromancer, was felicitating himself on the bargain he had made with the priests of Mordiggian. He felt, perhaps justly, that no one less clever than Abnon-Tha could have conceived and executed the various procedures that had made possible this bargain, through which Arctela, daughter of the proud Quaos, would became his unquestioning slave. No other lover, he told himself, could have been resourceful enough to obtain a desired woman in this way. Arctela, betrothed to Alos, a young noble of the city, was seemingly beyond the aspiration of a sorcerer. Abnon-Tha, however, was no common hedge-wizard, but an adept of long standing in the most awful and profound arcana of the black arts. He knew the spells that kill more quickly and surely than knife or poison, at a distance; and he knew also the darker spells by which the dead can be reanimated, even after years or ages of decay. He had slain Arctela in a manner that none could detect, with a rare and subtle invultuation that had left no mark; and her body lay now among the dead, in Mordiggian's temple. To-night, with the tacit connivance of the terrible, shrouded priests, he would bring her back to life.

Abnon-Tha was not native to Zul-Bha-Sair, but had come many years before from the infamous, half-mythic isle of Sotar, lying somewhere to the east of the huge continent of Zothique. Like a sleek young vulture, he had established himself in the very shadow of the charnel fane, and had prospered, taking to himself pupils and assistants.

His dealings with the priests were long and extensive, and the bargain he had just made was far from being the first of its kind. They had allowed him the temporary use of bodies claimed by Mordiggian, stipulating only that these bodies should not be removed from the temple during the course of any of his experiments in necromancy. Since the privilege was slightly irregular from their viewpoint, he had found it necessary to bribe them—not, however, with gold, but with the promise of a liberal purveyance of matters more sinister and corruptible than gold. The arrangement had been satisfactory enough to all concerned: cadavers had poured into the temple with more than their usual abundance ever since the coming of the sorcerer; the god had not lacked for provender; and Abnon-Tha had never lacked for subjects on which to employ his more baleful spells.

On the whole, Abnon-Tha was not ill-pleased with himself. He reflected moreover, that, aside from his mastery of magic and his sleightful ingenuity, he was about to manifest a well-nigh unexampled courage. He had planned a robbery that would amount to dire sacrilege: the removal of the reanimated body of Arctela from the temple. Such robberies (either of animate or exanimate corpses), and the penalty attached to them, were a matter of legend only; for none had occurred in recent ages. Thrice terrible, according to common belief, was the doom of those who had tried, and failed. The necromancer was not blind to the risks of his enterprise; nor, on the other hand, was he deterred or intimidated by them.

His two assistants, Narghai and Vemba-Tsith, apprised of his intention, had made with all due privity the necessary preparations for their flight from Zul-Bha-Sair. The strong passion that the sorcerer had conceived for Arctela was not his only motive, perhaps, in removing from that city. He was desirous of change, for he had grown a little weary of the odd laws that really served to restrict his necromantic practices, while facilitating them in a sense. He planned to travel southward, and establish himself in one of the cities of Tasuun, an empire famous for the number and antiquity of its mummies.

It was now sunset-time. Five dromedaries, bred for racing, waited in the inner courtyard of Abnon-Tha's house, a high and mouldering mansion that seemed to lean forward upon the open, circular area belonging to the temple. One of the dromedaries would carry a bale containing the sorcerer's most valuable books, manuscripts, and other

impedimenta of magic. Its fellows would bear Abnon-Tha, the two assistants—and Arctela.

Narghai and Vemba-Tsith appeared before their master to tell him
that all was made ready. Both were much younger than Abnon-Tha;
but, like himself, they were outlanders in Zul-Bha-Sair. They came of
the swart and narrow-eyed people of Naat, an isle that was little less
infamous than Sotar.

"It is well," said the necromancer, as they stood before him with
lowered eyes, after making their announcement. "We have only to
await the favorable hour. Midway between sunset and moonrise, when
the priests are at their supper in the nether adytum, we will enter the
temple and perform that which must be done for the rising of Arctela.
They feed well tonight, for I know that many of the dead grow ripe on
the great table in the upper sanctuary; and it may be that Mordiggian
feeds also. None will come to watch us at our doings."

"But, master," said Narghai, shivering a little beneath his robe of
nacarat red, "is it wise, after all, to do this thing? . . . Must you take the
girl from the temple? Always, ere this, you have contented yourself
with the brief loan that the priests allow, and have rendered back the
dead in the required state of exanimation. Truly, is it well to violate the
law of the god? Men say that the wrath of Mordiggian, though seldom
loosed, is more dreadful than the wrath of all other deities. For this
reason, none has dared to defraud him in latter years, or attempt the
removal of any of the corpses from his fane. Long ago, it is told, a high
noble of the city bore hence the cadaver of a woman he had loved, and
fled with it into the desert; but the priests pursued him, running more
swiftly than jackals . . . and the fate that overtook him is a thing
whereof the legends whisper but dimly."

"I fear neither Mordiggian nor his creatures," said Abnon-Tha,
with a sort of solemn vainglory in his voice. "My dromedaries can out-
run the priests—even granting that the priests are not men at all, but
ghouls, as some say. And there is small likelihood that they will follow

us: after their feasting tonight, they will sleep like gorged vultures. The morrow will find us far on the road to Tasuun, ere they awake."

"The master is right," interpolated Vemba-Tsith. "We have nothing to fear."

"But they say that Mordiggian does not sleep," insisted Narghai, "and that he watches all things eternally from his black vault beneath the temple."

"So I have heard," said Abnon-Tha, with a dry and learned air. "But I consider that such beliefs are mere superstition. There is nothing to confirm them in the real nature of corpse-eating entities. So far, I have never beheld Mordiggian, either sleeping or awake; but in all likelihood he is merely a common ghoul. I know these demons and their habits. They differ from hyenas only through their monstrous shape and size, and their immortality."

"Still, I must deem it an ill thing to cheat Mordiggian," muttered Narghai beneath his breath.

The words were caught by the quick ears of Abnon-Tha. "Nay, there is no question of cheating. Well have I served Mordiggian and his priesthood, and amply have I larded their black table. Also, I shall keep, in a sense, the bargain I have made concerning Arctela: the providing of a new cadaver in return for my necromantic privilege. Tomorrow, the youth Alos, the betrothed of Arctela, will lie in her place among the dead. Go now, and leave me, for I must devise the inward invultuation that will rot the heart of Alos, like a worm that awakens at the core of fruit."

IV

To Phariom, fevered and distraught, it seemed that the cloudless day went by with the sluggishness of a corpse-clogged river. Unable to calm his agitation, he wandered aimlessly through the thronged bazaars, till the western towers grew dark on a heaven of saffron flame, and the twilight rose like a grey and curdling sea among the houses. Then he returned to the inn where Elaith had been stricken, and claimed the dromedary which he had left in the tavern stables. Riding the animal through dim thoroughfares, lit only by the covert gleam of lamps or tapers from half-closed windows, he found his way once more to the city's center.

The dusk had thickened into darkness when he came to the open area surrounding Mordiggian's temple. The windows of mansions fronting the area were shut and lightless as dead eyes, and the fane itself, a colossal bulk of gloom, was rayless as any mausoleum beneath the gathering stars. No one, it seemed, was abroad, and though the quietude was favorable to his project, Phariom shivered with a chill of deathly menace and desolation. The hoofs of his camel rang on the pavement with a startling and preternatural clangor, and he thought that the ears of hidden ghouls, listening alertly behind the silence, must surely hear them.

However, there was no stirring of life in that sepulchral gloom. Reaching the shelter of one of the thick groups of ancient cedars, he dismounted and tied the dromedary to a low-growing branch. Keeping among the trees, like a shadow among shadows, he approached the temple with infinite wariness, and circled it slowly, finding that its four doorways, which corresponded to the four quarters of the Earth, were all wide-open, deserted, and equally dark. Returning at length to the eastern side, on which he had tethered his camel, he emboldened himself to enter the blackly gaping portal.

Crossing the threshold, he was engulfed instantly by a dead and clammy darkness, touched with the faint fetor of corruption, and a smell as of charred bone and flesh. He thought that he was in a huge corridor, and feeling his way forward along the right-hand wall, he soon came to a sudden turn, and saw a bluish glimmering far ahead, as if in some central adytum where the hall ended. Massy columns were silhouetted against the glimmering; and across it, as he drew nearer, several dark and muffled figures passed, presenting the profiles of enormous skulls. Two of them were sharing the burden of a human body which they carried in their arms. To Phariom, pausing in the shadowy hall, it appeared that the vague taint of putrescence upon the air grew stronger for a few instants after the figures had come and gone.

They were not succeeded by any others, and the fane resumed its mausolean stillness. But the youth waited for many minutes, doubtful and trepidant, before venturing to go on. An oppression of mortuary mystery thickened the air, and stifled him like the noisome effluvia of catacombs. His ears became intolerably acute, and he heard a dim humming, a sound of deep and viscid voices indistinguishably blent, that appeared to issue from crypts beneath the temple.

Stealing at length to the hall's end, he peered beyond into what was obviously the main sanctuary: a low and many-pillared room, whose vastness was but half-revealed by the bluish fires that glowed and flickered in numerous urnlike vessels borne aloft on slender stelae.

Phariom hesitated upon that awful threshold, for the mingled odors of burnt and decaying flesh were heavier on the air, as if he had drawn nearer to their sources; and the thick humming seemed to ascend from a dark stairway in the floor, beside the left-hand wall. But the room, to all appearance, was empty of life, and nothing stirred except the wavering lights and shadows. The watcher discerned the outlines of a vast table in the center, carved from the same black stone as the building itself. Upon the table, half-lit by the flaming urns, or shrouded by the umbrage of the heavy columns, a number of people lay side by side; and Phariom knew that he had found the black altar of Mordiggian, whereon were disposed the bodies claimed by the god.

A wild and stifling fear contended with a wilder hope in his bosom. Trembling, he went toward the table; and a cold clamminess, wrought by the presence of the dead, assailed him. The table was nearly thirty feet in length, and it rose waist-high on a dozen mighty legs. Beginning at the nearer end, he passed along the row of corpses, peer-

ing fearfully into each upturned face. Both sexes, and many ages and
differing ranks were represented. Nobles and rich merchants were
crowded by beggars in filthy rags. Some were newly dead, and others,
it seemed, had lain there for days, and were beginning to show the
marks of corruption. There were many gaps in the ordered row, suggesting that certain of the corpses had been recently removed. Phariom
went on in the dim light, searching for the loved features of Elaith. At
last, when he was nearing the further end, and had begun to fear that
she was not among them, he found her.

With the cryptic pallor and stillness of her strange malady upon
her, she lay unchanged on the chill stone. A great thankfulness was
born in the heart of Phariom, for he felt sure that she was not dead—
and that she had not awakened at any time to the horrors of the temple. If he could bear her away from the hateful purlieus of Zul-Bha-
Sair without detection, she would recover from her death-simulating
sickness.

Cursorily, he noted that another woman was lying beside Elaith,
and recognized her as the beautiful Arctela, whose bearers he had followed almost to the portals of the fane. He gave her no second glance,
but stooped to lift Elaith in his arms.

At that moment, he heard a murmur of low voices in the direction
of the door by which he had entered the sanctuary. Thinking that some
of the priests had returned, he dropped swiftly on hands and knees and
crawled beneath the ponderous table, which afforded the only accessible
hiding-place. Retreating into shadow beyond the glimmering shed from
the lofty urns, he waited and looked out between the pillar-thick legs.

The voices grew louder, and he saw the curiously sandaled feet and
shortish robes of three persons who approached the table of the dead
and paused in the very spot where he himself had stood a few instants
before. Who they were, he could not surmise; but their garments of
light and swarthy red were not the shroudings of Mordiggian's priests.
He was uncertain whether or not they had seen him; and crouching in

the low space beneath the table, he plucked his dagger from its sheath.

Now, he was able to distinguish three voices, one solemn and unctuously imperative, one somewhat guttural and growling, and the other shrill and nasal. The accents were alien, differing from those of the men of Zul-Bha-Sair, and the words were often strange to Phariom. Also, much of the converse was inaudible.

"... here ... at the end," said the solemn voice. "Be swift ... We have no time to loiter."

"Yes, Master," came the growling voice. "But who is this other? ... Truly, she is very fair."

A discussion seemed to take place, in discreetly lowered tones. Apparently the owner of the guttural voice was urging something that the other two opposed. The listener could distinguish only a word here and there; but he gathered that the name of the first person was Vemba-Tsith, and that the one who spoke in a nasal shrilling was called Narghai. At last, above the others, the grave accents of the man addressed only as the Master were clearly audible:

"I do not altogether approve ... It will delay our departure ... and the two must ride on one dromedary. But take her, Vemba-Tsith, if you can perform the necessary spells unaided. I have no time for a double incantation ... It will be a good test of your proficiency."

There was a mumbling as of thanks or acknowledgment from Vemba-Tsith. Then the voice of the Master: "Be quiet now, and make haste." To Phariom, wondering vaguely and uneasily as to the import of this colloquy, it seemed that two of the three men pressed closer to the table, as if stooping above the dead. He heard a rustling of cloth upon stone, and an instant later, he saw that all three were departing among the columns and stelae, in a direction opposite to that from which they had entered the sanctuary. Two of them carried burdens that glimmered palely and indistinctly in the shadows.

A black horror clutched at the heart of Phariom, for all too clearly he surmised the nature of those burdens—and the possible identity of one of them. Quickly he crawled forth from his hiding-place, and saw that Elaith was gone from the black table, together with the girl Arctela. He saw the vanishing of shadowy figures in the gloom that zoned the chamber's western wall. Whether the abductors were ghouls, or worse than ghouls, he could not know, but he followed swiftly, forgetful of all caution in his concern for Elaith.

Reaching the wall, he found the mouth of a corridor, and plunged into it headlong. Somewhere in the gloom ahead, he saw a ruddy glimmering of light. Then he heard a sullen, metallic grating; and the glimmer narrowed to a slit-like gleam, as if the door of the chamber from which it issued were being closed.

Following the blind wall, he came to that slit of crimson light. A door of darkly tarnished bronze had been left ajar, and Phariom peered in on a weird, unholy scene, illumined by the blood-like flames that flared and soared unsteadily from high urns upborne on sable pedestals.

The room was full of a sensuous luxury that accorded strangely with the dull, funereal stone of that temple of death. There were couches and carpets of superbly figured stuffs, vermilion, gold, azure, silver; and jewelled censers of unknown metals stood in the far corners. A low table at one side was littered with curious bottles, and occult appliances such as might be used in medicine or sorcery.

Elaith was lying on one of the couches, and near her, on a second couch, the body of the girl Arctela had been disposed. The abductors, whose faces Phariom now beheld for the first time, were busying themselves with singular preparations that mystified him prodigiously. His impulse to invade the room was repressed by a sort of wonder that held him enthralled and motionless.

One of the three, a tall, middle-aged man whom he identified as the Master, had assembled certain peculiar vessels, including a small brazier and a censer, and had set them on the floor beside Arctela. The second, a younger man with lecherously slitted eyes, had placed similar impedimenta before Elaith. The third, who was also young and evil of aspect, merely stood and looked on with an apprehensive, uneasy air.

Phariom divined that the men were sorcerers when, with a deftness born of long practice, they lit the censers and braziers, and began simultaneously the intonation of rhythmically measured words in a strange tongue accompanied by the sprinkling, at regular intervals, of black oils that fell with a great hissing on the coals in the braziers and sent up enormous clouds of pearly smoke. Dark threads of vapor serpentined from the censers, interweaving themselves like veins through the dim, misshapen figures as of ghostly giants that were formed by the lighter fumes. A reek of intolerably acrid balsams filled the chamber, assailing and troubling the senses of Phariom, till the scene wavered before him and took on a dreamlike vastness, a narcotic distortion.

The voices of the necromancers mounted and fell as if in some unholy paean. Imperious, exigent, they seemed to implore the consummation of forbidden blasphemy. Like thronging phantoms, writhing and swirling with malignant life, the vapors rose about the couches on which lay the dead girl and the girl who bore the outward likeness of death.

Then, as the fumes were riven apart in their baleful seething, Phariom saw that the pale figure of Elaith had stirred like a sleeper who awakens, that she had opened her eyes and was lifting a feeble hand from the gorgeous couch. The younger necromancer ceased his chanting on a sharply broken cadence; but the solemn tones of the other still went on, and still there was a spell on the limbs and senses of Phariom, making it impossible for him to stir.

Slowly, the vapors thinned like a rout of dissolving phantoms. The watcher saw that the dead girl, Arctela, was rising to her feet like a somnambulist. The chanting of Abnon-Tha, standing before her, came sonorously to an end. In the awful silence that followed, Phariom heard a weak cry from Elaith, and then the exultant, growling voice of Vemba-Tsith, who was stooping above her:

"Behold, O Abnon-Tha! My spells are swifter than yours, for she that I have chosen awakened before Arctela!"

Phariom was released from his thralldom, as if through the lifting of an evil enchantment. He flung back the ponderous door of darkened bronze, that ground with protesting clangors on its hinges. His dagger drawn, he rushed into the room.

Elaith, her eyes wide with piteous bewilderment, turned toward him and made an ineffectual effort to arise from the couch. Arctela, mute and submissive before Abnon-Tha, appeared to heed nothing but the will of the necromancer. She was like a fair and soulless automaton. The sorcerers, turning as Phariom entered, sprang back with instant agility before his onset, and drew the short, cruelly crooked swords which they all carried. Narghai struck the knife from Phariom's fingers with a darting blow that shattered its thin blade at the hilt, and Vemba-Tsith, his weapon swinging back in a vicious arc, would have killed the youth promptly if Abnon-Tha had not intervened and bade him stay.

Phariom, standing furious but irresolute before the lifted swords, was aware of the darkly searching eyes of Abnon-Tha, like those of some nyctalopic bird of prey.

"I would know the meaning of this intrusion," said the necromancer. "Truly, you are bold to enter the temple of Mordiggian."

"I came to find the girl who lies yonder," declared Phariom. "She is Elaith, my wife, who was claimed unjustly by the god. But tell me, why have you brought her to this room, from the table of Mordiggian, and what manner of men are you, that raise up the dead as you have raised this other woman?"

"I am Abnon-Tha, the necromancer, and these others are my pupils, Narghai and Vemba-Tsith. Give thanks to Vemba-Tsith, for verily he has brought back your wife from the purlieus of the dead with a skill excelling that of his master. She awoke ere the incantation was finished!"

Phariom glared with implacable suspicion at Abnon-Tha. "Elaith was not dead, but only as one in a trance," he averred. "It was not your pupil's sorcery that awakened her. And verily whether Elaith be dead or living is not a matter that should concern any but myself. Permit us to depart, for I wish to remove with her from Zul-Bha-Sair, in which we are only passing travellers."

So speaking, he turned his back on the necromancers, and went over to Elaith, who regarded him with dazed eyes but uttered his name feebly as he clasped her in his arms.

"Now this is a remarkable coincidence," purred Abnon-Tha. "I and my pupils are also planning to depart from Zul-Bha-Sair, and we start this very night. Perhaps you will honor us with your company."

"I thank you," said Phariom, curtly. "But I am not sure that our roads lie together. Elaith and I would go toward Tasuun."

"Now, by the black altar of Mordiggian, that is a still stranger co-incidence, for Tasuun is also our destination. We take with us the res-urrected girl Arctela, whom I have deemed too fair for the charnel god and his ghouls."

Phariom divined the dark evil that lay behind the oily, mocking speeches of the necromancer. Also, he saw the furtive and sinister sign that Abnon-Tha had made to his assistants. Weaponless, he could only give a formal assent to the sardonic proposal. He knew well that he would not be permitted to leave the temple alive, for the narrow eyes of Narghai and Vemba-Tsith, regarding him closely, were alight with the red lust of murder.

"Come," said Abnon-Tha, in a voice of imperious command, "it is time to go." He turned to the still figure of Arctela and spoke an un-known word. With vacant eyes and noctambulistic paces, she followed at his heels as he stepped toward the open door. Phariom had helped Elaith to her feet, and was whispering words of reassurance in an ef-fort to lull the growing horror and confused alarm that he saw in her eyes. She was able to walk, albeit slowly and uncertainly. Vemba-Tsith and Narghai drew back, motioning that she and Phariom should precede them; but Phariom, sensing their intent to slay him as soon as his back was turned, obeyed unwillingly and looked desperately about for something that he could seize as a weapon.

One of the metal braziers, full of smouldering coals, was at his very feet. He stooped quickly, lifted it in his hands, and turned upon the necromancers. Vemba-Tsith, as he had suspected, was prowling toward him with upraised sword, and was making ready to strike. Phariom hurled the brazier and its glowing contents full in the necromancer's face, and Vemba-Tsith went down with a terrible, smothered cry. Narghai, snarling ferociously, leapt forward to assail the defenseless youth. His scimitar gleamed with a wicked luster in the lurid glare of the urns as he swung it back for the blow. But the weapon did not fall; and Phariom, steeling himself against the impending death, became aware that Narghai was staring beyond him as if petrified by the vision of some Gorgonian specter.

As if compelled by another will than his own, the youth turned—and saw the thing that had arrested Narghai's blow. Arctela and Abnon-Tha, pausing before the open door, were outlined against a colossal shadow that was not wrought by anything in the room. It filled the portals from side to side, it towered above the lintel—and then, swiftly, it became more than a shadow: it was a bulk of darkness, black and opaque, that somehow blinded the eyes with a strange dazzlement. It seemed to suck the flame from the red urns and inform the chamber with a chill of utter death and voidness. Its form was that of a worm-shapen column, huge as a dragon, its further coils still issuing from the gloom of the corridor; but it changed from moment to moment, swirling and spinning as if with the vortical energies of dark eons. Briefly it took the semblance of some demoniac giant with eyeless head and limbless body; and then, leaping and spreading like smoky fire, it swept forward into the chamber.

Abnon-Tha fell back before it, with frantic mumblings of malediction or exorcism; but Arctela, pale and slight and motionless, remained full in its path, while the thing enfolded her and enveloped her with a hungry flaring until she was hidden wholly from view.

Phariom, supporting Elaith, who leaned weakly on his shoulder as if about to swoon, was powerless to move. He forgot the murderous Narghai, and it seemed that he and Elaith were but faint shadows in the presence of embodied death and dissolution. He saw the Blackness grow and wax with the towering of fed flame as it closed about Arctela; and he saw it gleam with eddying hues of somber iris, like the spectrum of a sable sun. For an instant, he heard a soft and flame-like murmuring. Then, quickly and terribly, the thing ebbed from the room. Arctela was gone, as if she had dissolved like a phantom on the air. Borne on a sudden gust of strangely mingled heat and cold, there came an acrid odor, such as would rise from a burnt-out funeral pyre.

"Mordiggian!" shrilled Narghai, in hysteric terror. "It was the god Mordiggian! He has taken Arctela!"

It seemed that his cry was answered by a score of sardonic echoes, unhuman as the howling of hyenas, and yet articulate, that repeated the name Mordiggian. Into the room, from the dark hall, there poured a horde of creatures whose violet robes alone identified them in Phariom's eyes as the priests of the ghoul-god. They had removed the skull-like masks, revealing heads and faces that were half-anthropomorphic, half-canine, and wholly diabolic. Also, they had taken off the fingerless gloves . . . . There were at least a dozen of them. Their curving talons gleamed in the bloody light like hooks of darkly tarnished metal; their spiky teeth, longer than coffin nails, protruded from snarling lips. They closed like a ring of jackals on Abnon-Tha and Narghai, driving them back into the farthest corner. Several others, entering tardily, fell with a bestial ferocity on Vemba-Tsith, who had begun to revive, and was moaning and writhing on the floor amid the scattered coals of the brazier.

They seemed to ignore Phariom and Elaith, who stood looking on as if in some baleful trance. But the hindmost, ere he joined the assailants of Vemba-Tsith, turned to the youthful pair and addressed them in a hoarse, hollow voice, like a tomb-reverberate barking:

"Go, for Mordiggian is a just god, who claims only the dead, and has no concern with the living. And we, the priests of Mordiggian, deal in our own fashion with those who would violate his law by removing the dead from the temple."

Phariom, with Elaith still leaning on his shoulder, went out into the dark hall, hearing a hideous clamor in which the screams of men were mingled with a growling as of jackals, a laughter as of hyenas. The clamor ceased as, they entered the blue-lit sanctuary and passed toward the outer corridor, and the silence that filled Mordiggian's fane behind them was deep as the silence of the dead on the black altar-table.

THE DARK EIDOLON

Thasaidon, lord of seven hells
Wherein the single Serpent dwells,
With volumes drawn from pit to pit
Through fire and darkness infinite—
Thasaidon, sun of nether skies,
Thine ancient evil never dies,
For aye thy somber fulgor flame
On sunken worlds that have no name,
Man's heart enthrones thee, still supreme,
Though the false sorcerers blaspheme.

—The Song of Xeethra.

On Zothique, the last continent of Earth, the sun no longer shone with the whiteness of its prime, but was dim and tarnished as if with a vapor of blood. New stars without number had declared themselves in the heavens, and the shadows of the infinite had fallen closer. And out of the shadows, the older gods had returned to man: the gods forgotten since Hyperborea, since Mu and Poseidonis, bearing other names but the same attributes. And the elder demons had also returned, battening mightily on the fumes of evil sacrifice, and fostering again the primordial sorceries.

Many were the necromancers and magicians of Zothique, and the infamy and marvel of their doings was legended everywhere in the latter days. But among them all there was none greater than Namirrha, who imposed his black yoke on the cities of Xylac, and later, in a proud delirium, deemed himself the veritable peer of Thasaidon, lord of Evil.

Namirrha had built his abode in Ummaos, the chief town of Xylac, to which he came from the desert realm of Tasuun with the dark renown of his thaumaturgies like a cloud of desert storm behind him. And no man knew that in coming to Ummaos he returned to the city of his birth, for all deemed him a native of Tasuun. Indeed, none could have dreamt that the great sorcerer was one with the beggar-boy, Narthos, an orphan of questionable parentage, who had begged his daily bread in the streets and bazaars of Ummaos. Wretchedly had he lived, alone and despised; and a hatred of the cruel, opulent city grew in his heart like a smothered flame that feeds in secret, biding the time when it shall become a conflagration consuming all things.

Bitterer always, through his boyhood and early youth, was the spleen and rancor of Narthos toward men. And one day the prince Zotulla, a boy but little older than he, riding a restive palfrey, came upon him in the square before the imperial palace; and Narthos implored an alms. But Zotulla, scorning his plea, rode arrogantly forward, spurring the palfrey; and Narthos was ridden down and trampled under its hooves. And afterwards, nigh to death from the trampling, he lay senseless for many hours, while the people passed him by unheeding. And at last, regaining his senses, he dragged himself to his hovel; but he limped a little thereafter all his days, and the mark of one hoof remained like a brand on his body, fading never. Later, he left Ummaos and was forgotten quickly by its people. Going southward into Tasuun, he lost his way in the great desert, and was near to perishing. But finally he came to a small oasis, where dwelt the wizard Ouphaloc, a hermit who preferred the company of honest hyenas and jackals to that of men. And Ouphaloc, seeing the great craft and evil in the starveling boy, gave succor to Narthos and sheltered him. He dwelt for years with Ouphaloc, becoming the wizard's pupil and the heir of his demon-wrested lore. Strange things he learned in that hermitage, being fed on fruits and grain that had sprung not from the watered earth, and wine that was not the juice of terrene grapes. And like Ouphaloc, he became a master in devildom and drove his own bond with the archfiend Thasaidon. When Ouphaloc died, he took the name of Namirrha, and went forth as a mighty sorcerer among the wandering peoples and the deep-buried mummies of Tasuun. But never could he forget the miseries of his boyhood in Ummaos and the wrong he had endured from Zotulla; and year by year he spun over in his thoughts the black web of revenge. And his fame grew ever darker and vaster, and men feared him in remote lands beyond Tasuun. With bated whispers they spoke of his deeds in the cities of Yoros, and in Zul-Bha-Sair, the abode of the ghoulish deity Mordiggian. And long before the coming of Namirrha himself, the people of Ummaos knew him as a fabled scourge that was direr than simoom or pestilence.

Now, in the years that followed the going-forth of the boy Narthos from Ummaos, Pithaim, the father of Prince Zotulla, was slain by the sting of a small adder that had crept into his bed for warmth on an autumn night. Some said that the adder had been purveyed by Zotulla, but this was a thing that no man could verily affirm. After the death of Pithaim, Zotulla, being his only son, was emperor of Xylac, and ruled evilly from his throne in Ummaos. Indolent he was, and tyrannic, and full of strange luxuries and cruelties; but the people, who were also evil, acclaimed him in his turpitude. So he prospered, and the lords of hell and heaven smote him not. And the red suns and ashen moons went westward over Xylac, falling into that seldom-voyaged sea, which, if the mariners' tales were true, poured evermore like a swiftening river past the infamous isle of Naat, and fell in a worldwide cataract upon nether space from the far, sheer edge of Earth.

Still grosser he grew, and his sins were as overswollen fruits that ripen above a deep abyss. But the winds of time blew softly; and the fruits fell not. And Zotulla laughed amid his fools and eunuchs and lemans; and the tale of his luxuries was borne afar, and was told by dim outland peoples, as a twin marvel with the bruited necromancies of Namirrha.

It came to pass, in the year of the Hyena, and the month of the star Canicule, that a great feast was given by Zotulla to the inhabitants of Ummaos. Meats that had been cooked in exotic spices from Sotar, isle of the east, were spread everywhere; and the ardent wines of Yoros and Xylac, filled as with subterranean fires, were poured inexhaustibly from huge urns for all. The wines awoke a furious mirth and a royal madness; and afterwards they brought a slumber no less profound than the Lethe of the tomb. And one by one, as they drank, the revellers fell down in the streets, the houses and gardens, as if a plague had struck them; and Zotulla slept in his banquet-hall of gold and ebony, with his odalisques and his chamberlains about him. So, in all Ummaos, there was no man or woman wakeful at the hour when Sirius began to fall toward the west.

Thus it was that none saw or heard the coming of Namirrha. But awakening heavily in the latter forenoon, the emperor Zotulla heard a confused babble, a troublous clamor of voices from such of his eunuchs and women as had awakened before him. Inquiring the cause, he was told that a strange prodigy had occurred during the night; but, being still bemused with wine and slumber, he comprehended little enough of its nature, till his favorite concubine, Obexah, led him to the eastern portico of the palace, from which he could behold the marvel with his own eyes.

Now the palace stood alone at the center of Ummaos, and to north, west and south, for wide intervals of distance, there stretched the imperial gardens, full of superbly arching palms and loftily spiring fountains. But to eastward was a broad open area, used as a sort of common, between the palace and the mansions of high optimates. And in this space, which had lain wholly vacant at eve, a building towered colossal and lordly beneath the full-risen sun, with domes like monstrous fungi of stone that had come up in the night. And the domes, rearing level with those of Zotulla, were builded of death-white marble; and the huge facade, with multi-columned porticoes and deep balconies, was wrought in alternate zones of night-black onyx and porphyry hued as with dragons'-blood. And Zotulla swore lewdly, calling with hoarse blasphemies on the gods and devils of Xylac; and great was his dumbfoundment, deeming the marvel a work of wizardry. The women gathered about him, crying out with shrill cries of awe and terror; and more and more of his courtiers, awakening, came to swell the fearful hub-bub; and the fat castradoes diddered in their cloth-of-gold like immense black jellies in golden basins. But Zotulla, mindful of his dominion as emperor of all Xylac, strove to conceal his own trepidation, saying:

"Now who is this that has presumed to enter Ummaos like a jackal in the dark, and has made his impious den in proximity and counterview of my palace? Go forth, and inquire the miscreant's name; but ere you go, instruct the imperial headsman to make sharp his double-handed sword."

Then, fearing the emperor's wrath if they tarried, certain of the chamberlains went forth unwillingly and approached the portals of the strange edifice. It seemed that the portals were deserted till they drew near, and then, on the threshold, there appeared a titanic skeleton, taller than any man of earth; and it strode forward to meet them with ell-long strides. The skeleton was swathed in a loin cloth of scarlet silk with a buckle of jet, and it wore a black turban, starred with diamonds, whose topmost foldings nearly touched the lofty lintel. Eyes like flickering marsh-fires burned in its deep eye-sockets; and a blackened tongue like that of a long-dead man protruded between its teeth; but otherwise it was clean of flesh, and the bones glittered whitely in the sun as it came onward.

The chamberlains were mute before it, and there was no sound except the golden creaking of their girdles, the shrill rustling of their silks, as they shook and trembled. And the foot-bones of the skeleton clicked sharply on the pavement of sable onyx as it paused; and the putrefying tongue began to quiver between its teeth; and it uttered these words in an unctuous, nauseous voice:

"Return, and tell the emperor Zotulla that Namirrha, seer and magician, has come to dwell beside him."

Hearing the skeleton speak as if it had been a living man, and hearing the dread name of Namirrha as men hear the tocsin of doom in some fallen city, the chamberlains could stand before it no longer, and they fled with ungainly swiftness and bore the message to Zotulla.

Now, learning who it was that had come to neighbor with him in Ummaos, the emperor's wrath died out like a feeble and blustering flame on which the wind of darkness has blown; and the vinous purple of his cheeks was mottled with a strange pallor; and he said nothing, but his lips mumbled loosely as if in prayer or malediction. And the news of Namirrha's coming passed like the flight of evil night-birds through all the palace and throughout the city, leaving a noisome terror that abode in Ummaos thereafter till the end. For Namirrha, through the black renown of his thaumaturgies and the frightful entities who served him, had become a power that no secular sovereign dared dispute; and men feared him everywhere, even as they feared the gigantic, shadowy lords of hell and of infinite space. And in Ummaos, people said that he had come on the desert wind from Tasuun with his underlings, even as the pestilence comes, and had reared his house in an hour with the aid of devils beside Zotulla's palace. And they said that the foundations of the house were laid on the adamantine cope of hell; and in its floors were pits at whose bottom burned the nether fires, or stars could be seen as they passed under in lowermost night. And the followers of Namirrha were the dead of strange kingdoms, the demons of sky and earth and the abyss, and mad, impious, hybrid things that the sorcerer himself had created from forbidden unions.

Men shunned the neighborhood of his lordly house; and in the palace of Zotulla, few cared to approach the windows and balconies that gave thereon; and the emperor himself spoke not of Namirrha, pretending to ignore the intruder; and the women of the harem babbled evermore with a baleful gossip concerning Namirrha and his supposed concubines. But the sorcerer himself was not beheld by the city's people, though some believed that he walked forth at will, clad with invisibility. His servitors were likewise not seen; but a howling as of the damned was sometimes heard to issue from his portals; and sometimes there came a stony cachinnation, as if some adamantine image had laughed aloud; and sometimes there was a chuckling like the sound of shattered ice in a frozen hell. Dim shadows moved in the porticoes when there was neither sunlight nor lamp to cast them; and red, eerie lights appeared and vanished in the windows at eve, like a blinking of demoniac eyes. And slowly the ember-colored suns went over Xylac, and were quenched in far seas; and the ashy moons were blackened as they fell nightly toward the hidden gulf. Then, seeing that the wizard had wrought no open evil, and that none had endured palpable harm from his presence, the people took heart; and Zotulla drank deeply, and feasted in oblivious luxury as before; and dark Thasaidon, prince of all turpitudes, was the true but never-acknowledged lord of Xylac. And in time the men of Ummaos bragged a little of Namirrha and his dread thaumaturgies, even as they had boasted of the purple sins of Zotulla.

But Namirrha, still unbeheld by living men and living women, sat in the inner walls of that house which his devils had reared for him, and spun over and over in his thoughts the black web of revenge. And in all Ummaos there was none, not even among his fellow-beggars, who recalled the beggar-boy Narthos. And the wrong done by Zotulla to Narthos in old times was the least of those cruelties which the emperor had forgotten.

Now, when the fears of Zotulla were somewhat lulled, and his women gossiped less often of the neighboring wizard, there occurred a new wonder and a fresh terror. For, sitting one eve at his banquet-table with his courtiers about him, the emperor heard a noise as of myriad iron-shod hooves that came trampling through the palace-gardens. And the courtiers also heard the sound, and were startled amid their mounting drunkenness; and the emperor was angered, and he sent certain of his guards to examine into the cause of the trampling. But, peering forth upon the moon-bright lawns and parterres, the guards beheld no visible shape, though the loud sounds of trampling still went to and fro. It seemed as if a rout of wild stallions passed and re-passed before the facade of the palace with tumultuous gallopings and capricoles. And a fear came upon the guards as they looked and listened; and they dared not venture forth, but returned to Zotulla. And the emperor himself grew sober when he heard their tale; and he went forth with high blusterings to inspect the prodigy. And all night the unseen hooves rang out sonorously on the pavements of onyx, and ran with deep thuddings over the grasses and flowers. The palm-fronds waved on the windless air, as if parted by racing steeds; and visibly the tall-stemmed lilies and broad-petalled exotic blossoms were trodden under. And rage and terror nested together in Zotulla's heart as he stood in a balcony above the garden, hearing the spectral tumult, and beholding the harm done to his rarest flower-beds. The women, the courtiers and eunuchs cowered behind him, and there was no slumber for any occupant of the palace; but toward dawn the clamor of hooves departed, going toward Namirrha's house.

When the dawn was full-grown above Ummaos, the emperor walked forth with his guards about him, and saw that the crushed grasses and broken-down stems were blackened as if by fire where the hooves had fallen. Plainly were the countless marks imprinted, like the tracks of a great company of horses, in all the lawns and parterres; but they ceased at the verge of the gardens. And though everyone believed that the visitation had come from Namirrha, there was no proof of this in the grounds that fronted the sorcerer's abode; for here the turf was untrodden.

"A pox upon Namirrha, if he has done this!" cried Zotulla. "For what harm have I ever done him? Verily, I shall set my heel on the dog's neck; and the torture-wheel shall serve him even as these horses from hell have served my blood-red lilies of Sotar and my vein-colored irises of Naat and my orchids from Uccastrog which were purple as the bruises of love. Yea, though he stand the viceroy of Thasaidon above earth, and overlord of ten thousand devils, my wheel shall break him, and fires shall heat the wheel white-hot in its turning, till he withers black as the seared blossoms." Thus did Zotulla make his brag; but he issued no orders for the execution of the threat; and no man stirred from the palace toward Namirrha's house. And from the portals of the wizard none came forth; or if any came, there was no visible sign or sound.

So the day went over, and the night rose, bringing later a moon that was slightly darkened at the rim. And the night was silent; and Zotulla, sitting long at the banquet-table, drained his wine-cup often and wrathfully, muttering new threats against Namirrha. And the night wore on, and it seemed that the visitation would not be repeated. But at midnight, lying in his chamber with Obexah, and fathom-deep in his slumber from his wine, Zotulla was awakened by a monstrous clangor of hooves that raced and capered in the palace-porticoes and in the long balconies. All night the hooves thundered back and forth, echoing awfully in the vaulted stone, while Zotulla and Obexah, listening, huddled close amid their cushions and coverlets; and all the occupants of the palace, wakeful and fearful, heard the noise but stirred not from their chambers. A little before dawn the hooves departed suddenly; and afterwards, by day, their marks were found on the marble flags of the porches and balconies; and the marks were countless, deep-graven, and black as if branded there by flame.

Like mottled marble were the emperor's cheeks when he saw the hoof-printed floors; and terror stayed with him henceforward, following him to the depths of his inebriety, since he knew not where the haunting would cease. His women murmured and some wished to flee from Ummaos, and it seemed that the revels of the day and evening

were shadowed by ill wings that left their umbrage in the yellow wine
and bedimmed the aureate lamps. And again, toward midnight, the
slumber of Zotulla was broken by the hooves, which came galloping
and pacing on the palace-roof and through all the corridors and the
halls. Thereafter, till dawn, the hooves filled the palace with their iron
clatterings, and they rung hollowly on the topmost domes, as if the
coursers of gods had trodden there, passing from heaven to heaven in
tumultuous cavalcade.

Zotulla and Obexah, lying together while the terrible hooves went
to and fro in the hall outside their chamber, had no heart or thought
for sin, nor could they find any comfort in their nearness. In the grey
hour before dawn, they heard a great thundering high on the barred
brazen door of the room, as if some mighty stallion, rearing, had
drummed there with his forefeet. And soon after this, the hooves went
away, leaving a silence like an interlude in some gathering storm of
doom. Later, the marks of the hooves were found everywhere in the
halls, marring the bright mosaics. Black holes were burnt in the gold-
en-threaded rugs and the rugs of silver and scarlet; and the high white
domes were pitted pox-wise with the marks; and far up on the brazen
door of Zotulla's chamber, the prints of a horse's forefeet were incised
deeply.

Now, in Ummaos, and throughout Xylac, the tale of this haunting
became known, and the thing was deemed an ominous prodigy,
though people differed in their interpretations. Some held that the
sending came from Namirrha, and was meant as a token of his supremacy above all kings and emperors; and some thought that it came
from a new wizard who had risen in Tinarath, far to the east, and who
wished to supplant Namirrha. And the priests of the gods of Xylac
held that their various deities had dispatched the haunting, as a sign
that more sacrifices were required in the temples.

Then, in his hall of audience, whose floor of sard and jasper had
been grievously pocked by the unseen hooves, Zotulla called together

many priests and magicians and soothsayers, and asked them to declare
the cause of the sending and devise a mode of exorcism. But, seeing
that there was no agreement among them, Zotulla provided the several
priestly sects with the wherewithal of sacrifice to their sundry gods,
and sent them away; and the wizards and prophets, under threat of decapitation if they refused, were enjoined to visit Namirrha in his mansion of sorcery and learn his will, if haply the sending were his and not
the work of another.

Loath were the wizards and the soothsayers, fearing Namirrha, and
caring not to intrude upon the frightful, obscure mysteries of his obscure mansion. But the swordsmen of the emperor drave them forth,
lifting great crescent blades against them when they tarried; so one, by
one, in a straggling order, the delegation went toward Namirrha's portals and vanished into the devil-built house.

Pale, muttering and distraught, like men who have looked upon
hell and have seen their doom, they returned before sunset to the emperor. And they said that Namirrha had received them courteously and
had sent them back with this message:

"Be it known to Zotulla that the haunting is a sign of that which
he has long forgotten; and the reason of the haunting will be revealed
to him at the hour prepared and set apart by destiny. And the hour
draws near: for Namirrha bids the emperor and all his court to a great
feast on the afternoon of the morrow."

Having delivered this message, to the wonder and consternation of
Zotulla, the delegation begged his leave to depart. And though the
emperor questioned them minutely, they seemed unwilling to relate the
circumstances of their visit to Namirrha; nor would they describe the
sorcerer's fabled house, except in a vague manner, each contradicting
the other as to what he had seen. So, after a little, Zotulla bade them
go, and when they had gone he sat musing for a long while on the invitation of Namirrha, which was a thing he cared not to accept but
feared to decline. That evening he drank even more liberally than was

his wont; and he slept a Lethean slumber, nor was there any noise of
loud, trampling hooves about the palace to awaken him. And silently,
during the night, the prophets and the magicians passed like furtive
shadows from Ummaos; and no man saw them depart; and at morning
they were gone from Xylac into other lands, never to return.

Now, on that same evening, in the great hall of his house, Namirrha sat alone, having dismissed the mummies, the monsters, the skeletons, and familiars who attended him ordinarily. Before him, on an
altar of jet, was the dark, gigantic statue of Thasaidon which a devil-
begotten sculptor had wrought in ancient days for an evil king of
Tasuun, called Pharnoc. The archdemon was depicted in the guise of a
full-armored warrior, lifting a spiky mace as if in heroic battle. Long
had the statue lain in the desert-sunken palace of Pharnoc, whose very
site was disputed by the nomads; and Namirrha, by his divination, had
found it and had reared up the infernal image to abide with him always
thereafter. And often, through the mouth of the statue, Thasaidon
would utter oracles to Namirrha, or would answer interrogations.

Before the black-armored image, there hung seven silver lamps,
wrought in the form of horses' skulls, with flames issuing changeably
in blue and purple and crimson from their eye-sockets. Wild and lurid
was their light, and the face of the demon, peering from under his
crested helmet, was filled with malign, equivocal shadows that shifted
and changed eternally. And sitting in his serpent-carven chair, Namirrha regarded the statue grimly, with a deep-furrowed frown between
his eyes: for he had asked a certain thing of Thasaidon, and the fiend,
replying through the statue, had refused him. And rebellion was in the
heart of Namirrha, grown mad with pride, and deeming himself the
lord of all sorcerers and a ruler by his own right among the princes of
devildom. So, after long pondering, he repeated his request in a bold
and haughty voice, like one who addresses an equal rather than the all-
formidable suzerain to whom he had sworn a fatal fealty.

"I have helped you heretofore in all things," said the image, with stony and sonorous accents that were echoed metallically in the seven silver lamps. "Yea, the undying worms of fire and darkness have come forth like an army at your summons, and the wings of nether genii have risen to occlude the sun when you called them. But, verily, I will not aid you in this revenge you have planned: for the emperor Zotulla has done me no wrong and has served me well though unwittingly; and the people of Xylac, by reason of their turpitudes, are not the least of my terrestrial worshippers. Therefore, Namirrha, it were well for you to live in peace with Zotulla, and well to forget this olden wrong that was done to the beggar-boy Narthos. For the ways of destiny are strange, and the workings of its laws sometimes hidden; and truly, if the hooves of Zotulla's palfrey had not spurned you and trodden you under, your life had been otherwise, and the name and renown of Namirrha had still slept in oblivion as a dream undreamed. Yea, you would tarry still as a beggar in Ummaos, content with a beggar's guerdon, and would never have fared forth to become the pupil of the wise and learned Ouphaloc, and I, Thasaidon, would have lost the lordliest of all necromancers who have accepted my service and my bond. Think well, Namirrha, and ponder these matters: for both of us, it would seem, are indebted to Zotulla in all gratitude for the trampling he gave you."

"Yea, there is a debt," Namirrha growled implacably. "And truly, I will pay the debt tomorrow, even as I have planned . . . . There are Those who will aid me, Those who will answer my summoning in your despite."

"It is an ill thing to affront me," said the image, after an interval. "And also, it is not wise to call upon Those that you designate. However, I perceive clearly that such is your intent. You are proud and stubborn and revengeful. Do, then, as you will, but blame me not for the outcome."

So, after this, there was silence in the hall where Namirrha sat before the eidolon; and the flames burned darkly, with changeable colors,

in the skull-shapen lamps; and the shadows fled and returned, unresting, on the face of the statue and the face of Namirrha. Then, toward
midnight, the necromancer arose and went upward by many spiral
stairs to a high dome of his house in which there was a single small
round window that looked forth on the constellations. The window
was set in the top of the dome; but Namirrha had contrived, by means
of his magic, that one entering by the last spiral of the stairs would
suddenly seem to descend rather than climb, and, reaching the final
step, would peer *downward* through the window while stars passed under him in a giddying gulf. There, kneeling, Namirrha touched a secret
spring in the marble, and the circular pane slid back without sound.
Then, lying prone on the curved interior of the dome, with his face
over the abyss, and his long beard trailing stiffly into space, he whispered a prehuman rune, and held speech with certain entities who belonged neither to hell nor the mundane elements, and were more
fearsome to invoke than the infernal genii or the devils of earth, air,
water, and flame. With them he made his compact, defying
Thasaidon's will, while the air curdled about him with their voices, and
rime gathered palely on his sable beard from the cold that was wrought
by their breathing as they leaned earthward.

Laggard and loth was the awakening of Zotulla from his wine; and
quickly, ere he opened his eyes, the daylight was poisoned for him by
the thought of that invitation which he feared to accept or decline. But
he spoke to Obexah, saying:

"Who, after all, is this wizardly dog, that I should obey his summons like a beggar called in from the street by some haughty lord?"

Obexah, a golden-skinned and oblique-eyed girl from Uccastrog,
Isle of the Torturers, eyed the emperor subtly, and said:

"O Zotulla, it is yours to accept or refuse, as you deem fitting. And
truly, it is a small matter for the lord of Ummaos and all Xylac, whether to go or to stay, since naught can impugn his sovereignty. There-

fore, were it not as well to go?" For Obexah, though fearful of the wizard, was curious regarding that devil-builded house of which so little was known; and likewise, in the manner of women, she wished to behold the famed Namirrha, whose mien and appearance were still but a far-brought legend in Ummaos.

"There is something in what you say," admitted Zotulla. "But an emperor, in his conduct, must always consider the public good; and there are matters of state involved, which a woman can scarcely be expected to understand."

So, later in the forenoon, after an ample and well-irrigated breakfast, he called his chamberlains and courtiers about him and took counsel with them. And some advised him to ignore the invitation of Namirrha; and others held that the invitation should be accepted, lest a graver evil than the trampling of ghostly hooves be sent later upon the palace and the city.

Then Zotulla called the many priesthoods before him in a body, and sought to resummon those wizards and soothsayers who had fled privily in the night. Among all the latter, there was none who answered the crying of his name through Ummaos; and this aroused a certain wonder. But the priests came in greater number than before, and thronged the hall of audience so that the paunches of the foremost were straightened against the imperial dais and the buttocks of the hindmost were flattened on the rear walls and pillars. And Zotulla debated with them the matter of acceptance or refusal. And the priests argued, as before, that Namirrha was nowise concerned with the sending; and his invitation, they said, portended no harm nor bale to the emperor; and it was plain, from the terms of the message, that an oracle would be imparted to Zotulla by the wizard; and this oracle, if Namirrha were a true archimage, would confirm their own holy wisdom and reestablish the divine source of the sending; and the gods of Xylac would again be glorified.

Then, having heard the pronouncement of the priests, the emperor instructed his treasurers to load them down with new offerings; and calling unctuously upon Zotulla and all his household the vicarious blessings of the several gods, the priests departed. And the day wore on, and the sun passed its meridian, falling slowly beyond Ummaos through the spaces of the afternoon that were floored with sea-ending deserts. And still Zotulla was irresolute; and he called his wine-bearers, bidding them pour for him the strongest and most magistral of their vintages; but in the wine he found neither certitude nor decision.

Sitting still on his throne in the hall of audience, he heard, toward middle afternoon, a mighty and clamorous outcry that arose at the palace portals. There were deep wailings of men and the shrillings of eunuchs and women, as if terror passed from tongue to tongue, invading the halls and apartments. And the fearful clamor spread throughout all the palace, and Zotulla, rousing from the lethargy of wine, was about to send his attendants to inquire the cause.

Then, into the hall, there filed an array of tall mummies, clad in royal cerements of purple and scarlet, and wearing gold crowns on their withered craniums. And after them, like servitors, came gigantic skeletons who wore loincloths of nacarat orange and about whose upper skulls, from brow to crown, live serpents of banded saffron and ebon had wrapped themselves for head-dresses. And the mummies bowed before Zotulla, saying with thin, sere voices:

"We, who were kings of the wide realm of Tasuun aforetime, have been sent as a guard of honor for the emperor Zotulla, to attend him as is befitting when he goes forth to the feast prepared by Namirrha."

Then, with dry clickings of their teeth, and whistlings as of air through screens of fretted ivory, the skeletons spoke:

"We, who were giant warriors of a race forgotten, have also been sent by Namirrha, so that the emperor's household, following him to the feast, should be guarded from all peril and should fare forth in such pageantry as is meet and proper."

Witnessing these prodigies, the wine-bearers and other attendants

cowered about the imperial dais or hid behind the pillars, while Zotulla, with pupils swimming starkly in a bloodshot white, with face
bloated and ghastly-pale, sat frozen on his throne and could utter no
word in reply to the ministers of Namirrha.

Then, coming forward, the mummies said in dusty accents: "All is
made ready, and the feast awaits the arrival of Zotulla." And the cerements of the mummies stirred and fell open at the bosom, and small
rodent monsters, brown as bitumen, eyed as with accursed rubies,
reared forth from the eaten hearts of the mummies like rats from their
holes and chittered shrilly in human speech, repeating the words. The
skeletons in their turn took up the solemn sentence; and the black and
saffron serpents hissed it from their skulls; and the words were repeated lastly in baleful rumblings by certain furry creatures of dubious
form, hitherto unseen by Zotulla, who sat behind the ribs of the skeletons as if in cages of white wicker.

Like a dreamer who obeys the doom of dreams, the emperor rose
from his throne and went forward, and the mummies surrounded him
like an escort. And each of the skeletons drew from the reddish-yellow
folds of his loincloth a curiously pierced archaic flute of silver; and all
began a sweet and evil and deathly fluting as the emperor went out
through the halls of the palace. A fatal spell was in the music: for the
chamberlains, the women, the guards, the eunuchs, and all members of
Zotulla's household even to the cooks and scullions, were drawn like a
procession of night-walkers from the rooms and alcoves in which they
had vainly hidden themselves; and, marshalled by the flutists, they followed after Zotulla. A strange thing it was to behold this mighty company of people, going forth in the slanted sunlight toward Namirrha's
house, with a cortège of dead kings about them, and the blown breath
of skeletons thrilling eldritchly in the silver flutes. And little was Zotulla comforted when he found the girl Obexah at his side, moving, as
he, in a thralldom of involitient horror, with the rest of his women
close behind.

Coming to the open portals of Namirrha's house, the emperor saw that they were guarded by great crimson-wattled things, half-dragon, half-man, who bowed before him, sweeping their wattles like bloody besoms on the flags of dark onyx. And the emperor passed with Obexah between the louting monsters, with the mummies, the skeletons and his own people behind him in strange pageant, and entered a vast and multi-columned hall, where the daylight, following timidly, was drowned by the baleful arrogant blaze of a thousand lamps.

Even amid his horror, Zotulla marvelled at the vastness of the chamber, which he could hardly reconcile with the mansion's outer length and height and breadth, though these indeed were of most palatial amplitude. For it seemed that he gazed adown great avenues of topless pillars, and vistas of tables laden with piled-up viands and thronged urns of wine, that stretched away before him into luminous distance and gloom as of starless night.

In the wide intervals between the tables, the familiars of Namirrha and his other servants went to and fro incessantly, as if a phantasmagoria of ill dreams were embodied before the emperor. Kingly cadavers in robes of time-rotten brocade, with worms seething in their eyepits, poured a blood-like wine into cups of the opalescent horn of unicorns. Lamias, trident-tailed, and four-breasted chimeras, came in with fuming platters lifted high by their brazen claws. Dog-headed devils, tongued with lolling flames, ran forward to offer themselves as ushers for the company. And before Zotulla and Obexah, there appeared a curious being with the full-fleshed lower limbs and hips of a great black woman and the clean-picked bones of some titanic ape from there-upward. And this monster signified by certain indescribable becks of its finger-bones that Zotulla and his favorite odalisque were to follow it.

Verily, it seemed to Zotulla that they had gone a long way into some malignly litten cavern of hell, when they came to the end of that perspective of tables and columns down which the monster had led them. Here, at the room's end, apart from the rest, was a table at which Namirrha sat alone, with the flames of the seven horse-skull lamps burning restlessly behind him, and the mailed black image of Thasaidon towering from the altar of jet at his right hand. And a little aside from the altar, there stood a diamond mirror upborne by the claws of black iron basilisks.

Namirrha rose to greet them, observing a solemn and funereal courtesy. His eyes were bleak and cold as distant stars in the hollows wrought by strange fearful vigils. His lips were like a pale-red seal on a shut parchment of doom. His beard flowed stiffly in black anointed banded locks across the bosom of his vermilion robe, like a mass of straight black serpents. Before him, Zotulla felt the blood pause and thicken about his heart, as if congealing into ice. And Obexah, peering beneath lowered lids, was abashed and frightened by the visible horror that invested this man and hung upon him even as royalty upon a king. But amid her fear, she found room to wonder what manner of man he was in his intercourse with women.

"I bid you welcome, O Zotulla, to such hospitality as is mine to offer," said Namirrha, with the iron ringing of some hidden funereal bell deep down in his hollow voice. "Prithee, be seated at my table."

Zotulla saw that a chair of ebony had been placed for him opposite Namirrha; and another chair, less stately and imperial, had been placed at the left hand for Obexah. And the twain seated themselves; and Zotulla saw that his people were sitting likewise at other tables throughout the huge hall, with the frightful servitors of Namirrha waiting upon them busily, like devils attending the damned.

Then Zotulla perceived that a dark and corpse-like hand was pouring wine for him in a crystal cup; and upon the hand was the signet-ring of the emperors of Xylac, set with a monstrous fire-opal in the mouth of a golden bat: even such a ring as Zotulla himself wore perpetually on his index-finger. And, turning, he beheld at his right hand a figure that bore the likeness of his father, Pithaim, after the poison of the adder, spreading through all his limbs, had left behind it the purple bloating of death. And Zotulla, who had caused the adder to be placed in the bed of Pithaim, cowered in his seat and trembled with a guilty fear. And the thing that wore the similitude of Pithaim, whether corpse or ghost or an image wrought by Namirrha's enchantment, came and went at Zotulla's elbow, waiting upon him with stark, black, swollen fingers that never fumbled. Horribly he was aware of its bulging, unregarding eyes, and its livid purple mouth that was locked in a rigor of mortal silence, and the spotted adder that peered at intervals with chill orbs from its heavy-folded sleeve as it leaned beside him to replenish his cup or to serve him with meat. And dimly, through the icy mist of his terror, the emperor beheld the shadowy-armored shape, like a moving replica of the still, grim statue of Thasaidon, which Namirrha had reared up in his blasphemy to perform the same office for himself. And vaguely, without comprehension, he saw the dreadful ministrant that hovered beside Obexah: a flayed and eyeless corpse in the image of her first lover, a boy from Cyntrom who had been cast ashore in shipwreck on the Isle of the Torturers. There Obexah had found him, lying beyond the ebbing wave; and reviving the boy, she had hidden him awhile in a secret cave for her own pleasure, and had brought him food and drink. Later, wearying, she had betrayed him to the Torturers, and had taken a new delight in the various pangs and ordeals inflicted upon him before death by that cruel, pernicious people.

"Drink," said Namirrha, quaffing a strange wine that was red and dark as if with disastrous sunsets of lost years. And Zotulla and Obexah drank the wine, feeling no warmth in their veins thereafter, but a chill as of hemlock mounting slowly toward the heart.

"Verily, 'tis a good wine," said Namirrha, "and a proper one in which to toast the furthering of our acquaintance: for it was buried long ago with the royal dead, in amphorae of somber jasper shapen like funeral urns; and my ghouls found it, whenas they came to dig in Tasuun."

Now it seemed that the tongue of Zotulla froze in his mouth, as a mandrake freezes in the rime-bound soil of winter; and he could find no reply to Namirrha's courtesy.

"Prithee, make trial of this meat," quoth Namirrha, "for it is very choice, being the flesh of that boar which the Torturers of Uccastrog are wont to pasture on the well-minced leavings of their wheels and racks; and, moreover, my cooks have spiced it with the powerful balsams of the tomb, and have farced it with the hearts of adders and the tongues of black cobras."

Naught could the emperor say; and even Obexah was silent, being sorely troubled by the presence of that flayed and piteous thing which had the likeness of her lover from Cyntrom. And her dread of the necromancer grew prodigiously; for his knowledge of this old, forgotten crime, and the raising of the phantasm, appeared to her a more baleful magic than all else.

"Now, I fear," said Namirrha, "that you find the meat devoid of savor, and the wine without fire. So, to enliven our feasting, I shall call forth my singers and my musicians."

He spoke a word unknown to Zotulla or Obexah, which sounded throughout the mighty hall as if a thousand voices in turn had taken it up and prolonged it. Anon there appeared the singers, who were she-ghouls with shaven bodies and hairy shanks, and long yellow tushes full of shredded carrion curving across their chaps from mouths that fawned hyena-wise on the company. Behind them entered the musicians, some of whom were male devils pacing erect on the hindquarters of sable stallions and plucking with the fingers of white apes at lyres of the bone and sinew of cannibals from Naat; and others were pied satyrs puffing their goatish cheeks at hautboys made from the femurs of young witches, or bagpipes formed from the bosom-skin of negro queens and the horn of rhinoceri.

They bowed before Namirrha with grotesque ceremony. Then, without delay, the she-ghouls began a most dolorous and execrable

howling, as of jackals that have sniffed their carrion; and the satyrs and
devils played a lament that was like the moaning of desert-born winds
through forsaken palace-harems. And Zotulla shivered, for the singing
filled his marrow with ice, and the music left in his heart a desolation
as of empires fallen and trod under by the iron-shod hooves of time.
Ever, amid that evil music, he seemed to hear the sifting of sand across
withered gardens, and the windy rustling of rotted silks upon couches
of bygone luxury, and the hissing of coiled serpents from the low fusts
of shattered columns. And the glory that had been Ummaos seemed to
pass away like the blown pillars of the simoom.

"Now that was a brave tune," said Namirrha when the music
ceased and the she-ghouls no longer howled. "But, verily I fear that
you find my entertainment somewhat dull. Therefore, my dancers shall
dance for you." He turned toward the great hall, and described in the
air an enigmatic sign with the fingers of his right hand. In answer to
the sign, a hueless mist came down from the high roof and hid the
room like a fallen curtain for a brief interim. There was a babel of
sounds, confused and muffled, beyond the curtain, and a crying of
voices faint as if with distance.

Then, dreadfully, the vapor rolled away, and Zotulla saw that the
laden tables were gone. In the wide interspaces of the columns, his
palace-inmates, the chamberlains, the eunuchs, the courtiers and odalisques and all the others, lay trussed with thongs on the floor, like so
many fowls of glorious plumage. Above them, in time to a music made
by the lyrists and flutists of the necromancer, a troupe of skeletons
pirouetted with light clickings of their toe-bones; and a rout of mummies bowed stiffly; and others of Namirrha's creatures moved with
mysterious caperings. To and fro they leapt on the bodies of the emperor's people, in the paces of an evil saraband. At every step they
grew taller and heavier, till the saltant mummies were as the mummies
of Anakim, and the skeletons were boned like colossi; and louder and
more lugubrious the music rose, drowning the faint cries of Zotulla's

people. And huger still became the dancers, towering far into vaulted shadow among the vast columns, with thudding feet that wrought thunder in the room; and those whereon they danced were as grapes trampled for a vintage in autumn; and the floor ran deep with a sanguine must.

As a man drowning in a noisome, night-bound fen, the emperor heard the voice of Namirrha:

"It would seem that my dancers please you not. So now I shall present you a most royal spectacle. Arise and follow me, for the spectacle is one that requires a whole empire for its stage."

Zotulla and Obexah rose from their chairs in the fashion of nightwalkers. Giving no backward glance at their ministering phantoms, or the hall where the dancers still bounded, they followed Namirrha to an alcove beyond the altar of Thasaidon. Thence, by the upward-coiling stairways, they came at length to a broad high balcony that faced Zotulla's palace and looked forth above the city roofs toward the bourn of sunset.

It seemed that several hours had gone by in that hellish feasting and entertainment; for the day was near to its close, and the sun, which had fallen from sight behind the imperial palace, was barring the vast heavens with bloody rays.

"Behold," said Namirrha, adding a strange vocable to which the stone of the edifice resounded like a beaten gong. The balcony pitched a little, and Zotulla, looking over the balustrade, beheld the roofs of Ummaos lessen and sink beneath him. It seemed that the balcony flew skyward to a prodigious height, and he peered down across the domes of his own palace, upon the houses, the tilled fields and the desert beyond, and the huge sun brought low on the desert's verge. And Zotulla grew giddy; and the chill airs of the upper heavens blew upon him. But Namirrha spoke another word, and the balcony ceased to ascend.

"Look well, O Zotulla," said the necromancer, "on the empire that was yours, but shall be yours no longer." Then, with arms outstretched toward the sunset, and the gulfs beyond the sunset, he called aloud the twelve names that were perdition to utter, and after them the tremendous invocation: *Gna padambis devompra thungis furidor avoragomon.*

Instantly, it seemed that great ebon clouds of thunder beetled against the sun. Lining the horizon, the clouds took the form of colossal monsters with heads and members somewhat resembling those of stallions. Rearing terribly, they trod down the sun like an extinguished ember; and racing as in some hippodrome of Titans, they rose higher and vaster, coming toward Ummaos. Deep, calamitous rumblings preceded them, and the earth shook visibly, till Zotulla saw that these were not immaterial clouds, but actual living forms that had come forth to tread the world in macrocosmic vastness. Throwing their shadows for many leagues before them, the coursers charged as if devil-ridden into Xylac, and their feet descended like falling mountain crags upon far oases and towns of the outer wastes.

Like a many-turreted storm they came, and it seemed that the world sank gulfward, tilting beneath the weight. Still as a man enchanted into marble, Zotulla stood and beheld the ruining that was wrought on his empire. And closer drew the gigantic stallions, racing with inconceivable speed, and louder was the thundering of their footfalls, that now began to blot the green fields and fruited orchards lying for many miles to the west of Ummaos. And the shadow of the stallions climbed like an evil gloom of eclipse, till it covered Ummaos; and looking up, the emperor saw their eyes half-way between earth and zenith, like baleful suns that glare down from soaring cumuli.

Then, in the thickening gloom, above that insupportable thunder, he heard the voice of Namirrha, crying in mad triumph:

"Know, Zotulla, that I have called up the coursers of Thamogorgos, lord of the abyss. And the coursers will tread your empire down, even as your palfrey trod and trampled in former time a beggar-boy named Narthos. And learn also that I, Namirrha, was that boy." And the eyes of Namirrha, filled with a vainglory of madness and bale, burned like malign, disastrous stars at the hour of their culmination.

To Zotulla, wholly mazed with the horror and tumult, the necromancer's words were no more than shrill, shrieked overtones of the tempest of doom; and he understood them not. Tremendously, with a rending of staunch-built roofs, and an instant cleavage and crumbling down of mighty masonries, the hooves descended upon Ummaos. Fair temple-domes were pashed like shells of the haliotis, and haughty mansions were broken and stamped into the ground even as gourds; and house by house the city was trampled flat with a sound as of hammers clanging on the anvils of cyclops and a crashing as of worlds beaten into chaos. Far below, in the darkened streets, men and camels fled like scurrying emmets but could not escape. And implacably the hooves rose and fell, till ruin was upon half the city, and night was over all. The palace of Zotulla was trodden under, and now the forelegs of the coursers loomed level with Namirrha's balcony, and their heads towered awfully above. It seemed that they would rear and trample down the necromancer's house; but at that moment they parted to left and right, and a dolorous glimmering came from the low sunset; and the coursers went on, treading under them that portion of Ummaos which lay to the eastward. And Zotulla and Obexah and Namirrha looked down on the city's fragments as on a shard-strewn midden, and heard the cataclysmic clamor of the hooves departing toward eastern Xylac.

"Now that was a goodly spectacle," quoth Namirrha. Then, turning to the emperor, he added malignly: "Think not that I have done with thee, however, or that doom is yet consummate."

It seemed that the balcony had fallen to its former elevation, which was still a lofty vantage above the sharded ruins. And Namirrha plucked the emperor by the arm and led him from the balcony to an inner chamber, while Obexah followed mutely. The emperor's heart was crushed within him by the trampling of such calamities, and despair weighed upon him like a foul incubus on the shoulders of a man lost in some land of accursed night. And he knew not that he had been parted from Obexah on the threshold of the chamber, and that certain of Namirrha's creatures, appearing like shadows, had compelled the girl to go downward with them by the stairs, and had stifled her outcries with their rotten cerements as they went.

The chamber was one that Namirrha used for his most unhallowed rites and alchemies. The rays of the lamps that illumed it were saffron-red like the spilt ichor of devils, and they flowed on aludels and crucibles and black athanors and alembics whereof the purpose was hardly to be named by mortal man. The sorcerer heated in one of the alembics a dark liquid full of star-cold lights, while Zotulla looked on unheeding. And when the liquid bubbled and sent forth a spiral vapor, Namirrha distilled it into goblets of gold-rimmed iron, and gave one of the goblets to Zotulla and retained the other himself. And he said to Zotulla with a stern imperative voice: "I bid thee quaff this liquor."

Zotulla, fearing that the draught was poison, hesitated. And the necromancer regarded him with a lethal gaze, and cried loudly: "Fearest thou to do as I?" and therewith he set the goblet to his lips.

So the emperor drank the draught, constrained as if by the bidding of some angel of death, and a darkness fell upon his senses. But, ere the darkness grew complete, he saw that Namirrha had drained his own goblet. Then, with unspeakable agonies, it seemed that the emperor died; and his soul floated free; and again he saw the chamber, though with bodiless eyes. And discarnate he stood in the saffron-crimson light, with his body lying as if dead on the floor beside him, and near it the prone body of Namirrha and the two fallen goblets.

Standing thus, he beheld a strange thing: for anon his own body stirred and arose, while that of the necromancer remained still as death. And Zotulla looked at his own lineaments and his figure in its short cloak of azure samite sewn with black pearls and balas-rubies; and the body lived before him, though with eyes that held a darker fire and a deeper evil than was their wont. Then, without corporeal ears,

Zotulla heard the figure speak, and the voice was the strong, arrogant voice of Namirrha, saying:

"Follow me, O houseless phantom, and do in all things as I enjoin thee."

Like an unseen shadow, Zotulla followed the wizard, and the twain went downward by the stairs to the great banquet hall. They came to the altar of Thasaidon and the mailed image, with the seven horse-skull lamps burning before it as formerly. Upon the altar, Zotulla's beloved leman Obexah, who alone of all women had power to stir his sated heart, was lying bound with thongs at Thasaidon's feet. But the hall beyond was deserted, and nothing remained of that Saturnalia of doom, except the fruit of the treading, which had flowed together in dark pools among the columns.

Namirrha, using the emperor's body in all ways for his own, paused before the dark eidolon; and he said to the spirit of Zotulla: "Be imprisoned in this image, without power to free thyself or to stir in any wise."

Being wholly obedient to the will of the necromancer, the soul of Zotulla was embodied in the statue, and he felt its cold, gigantic armor about him like a strait sarcophagus, and he peered forth immovably from the bleak eyes that were overhung by its carven helmet.

Gazing thus, he beheld the change that had now come on his own body through the sorcerous possession of Namirrha: for below the short azure cloak, the legs had turned suddenly to the hind legs of a black stallion, with hooves that glowed redly as if heated by infernal fires. And even as Zotulla watched this prodigy, the hooves glowed white and incandescent, and fumes mounted from the floor beneath them.

Then, on the black altar, the hybrid abomination came pacing haughtily toward Obexah, and smoking footprints appeared behind it as it came. Pausing beside the girl, who lay supine and helpless regarding it with eyes that were pools of bright-frozen horror, it raised one glowing hoof and set the hoof on her naked bosom between the small breast-cups of golden filigree begemmed with rubies. And the girl screamed beneath that atrocious treading as the soul of one newly damned might scream in hell; and the hoof glared with intolerable brilliance, as if freshly plucked from a furnace wherein the weapons of demons were forged.

At that moment, in the cowed and crushed and sodden shade of the emperor Zotulla, close-locked within the adamantine image, there awoke the manhood that had slumbered still-unaroused before the ruining of his empire and the trampling under of his retinue. Immediately a great abhorrence and a high wrath were alive in his soul, and mightily he longed for his own right arm to serve him, and a sword in his right hand.

Then it seemed that a voice spoke within him, chill and bleak and awful, and as if uttered inwardly by the statue itself. And the voice said: "I am Thasaidon, lord of the seven hells beneath the earth, and the hells of man's heart above the earth, which are seven times seven. For the moment, O Zotulla, my power is become thine for the sake of a mutual vengeance. Be one in all ways with the statue that has my likeness, even as the soul is one with the flesh. Behold! there is a mace of adamant in thy right hand. Lift up the mace, and smite."

Zotulla was aware of a great power within him, and giant thews about him that thrilled with the power and responded agilely to his will. He felt in his mailed right hand the haft of the huge spiky-headed mace; and though the mace was beyond the lifting of any man in mortal flesh, it seemed no more than a goodly weight to Zotulla. Then, rearing the mace like a warrior in battle, he struck down with one crashing blow the impious thing that wore his own rightful flesh united with the legs and hooves of a demon courser. And the thing crumpled swiftly down and lay with the brain spreading pulpily from its shattered skull on the shining jet. And the legs twitched a little and then grew still; and the hooves glowed from a fiery, blinding white to the redness of red-hot iron, cooling slowly.

For a space there was no sound, other than the shrill screaming of the girl Obexah, mad with pain and the terror of those prodigies which she had beheld. Then, in the soul of Zotulla, grown sick with that screaming, the chill, awful voice of Thasaidon spoke again, and said to him:

"Go free, for there is nothing more for thee to do." So the spirit of Zotulla passed from the image of Thasaidon, and found in the wide air the freedom of utter nothingness and oblivion.

But the end was not yet for Namirrha, whose mad, arrogant soul had been loosened from Zotulla's body by the blow, and had returned darkly, not in the manner planned by the magician, to its own body lying in the room of accursed rites and forbidden transmigrations. There Namirrha woke anon, with a dire confusion in his mind, and a partial forgetfulness: for the curse of Thasaidon was upon him now because of his blasphemies.

Nothing was clear in his thought except a malign, exorbitant longing for revenge; but the reason thereof, and the object, were as doubtful shadows. And still prompted by that obscure animus, he arose; and girding to his side an enchanted sword with runic sapphires and opals in the hilt, he descended the stairs and came again to the altar of Thasaidon, where the mailed statue stood as impassive as before, with the poised mace in its immovable right hand, and below it, on the altar, the double sacrifice.

A veil of weird darkness was upon the senses of Namirrha, and he saw not the stallion-legged horror that lay dead with slowly blackening hooves; and he heard not the moaning of the girl Obexah, who still lived beside it. But his eyes were drawn by the diamond mirror that was upheld in the claws of black iron basilisks beyond the altar; and going to the mirror, he saw therein a face that he knew no longer for his own. And because his eyes were shadowed, and his brain filled with the shifting webs of delusion, he took the face for that of the emperor Zotulla. Insatiable as hell's own flame, his old hatred rose within him;

and he drew the enchanted sword and began to hew therewith at the reflection. Sometimes, because of the curse laid upon him, and the impious transmigration which he had performed, he thought himself Zotulla warring with the necromancer; and again, in the shiftings of his madness, he was Namirrha smiting at the emperor; and then, without name, he fought a nameless foe. And soon the sorcerous blade, though tempered with formidable spells, was broken close to the hilt, and Namirrha beheld the image still unharmed. Then, howling aloud the half-forgotten runes of a most tremendous curse, made invalid through his own forgettings, he hammered still with the heavy sword-hilt on the mirror, till the runic sapphires and opals cracked in the hilt and fell away at his feet in little fragments.

Obexah, dying on the altar, saw Namirrha battling with his own image, and the spectacle moved her to mad laughter like the pealing of bells of ruined crystal. And above her laughter, and above the cursings of Namirrha, there came anon like the rumbling of swift-driven storm the thunder made by the macrocosmic stallions of Thamogorgos, returning gulfward through Xylac over Ummaos, to trample down the one house that they had spared aforetime.

MORTHYLLA

In Umbri, City of the Delta, the lights blazed with a garish brilliance after the setting of that sun which was now a coal-red decadent star, grown old beyond chronicle, beyond legend. Most brilliant, most garish of all were the lights that illumed the house of the ageing poet Famurza, whose Anacreontic songs had brought him the riches that he disbursed in orgies for his friends and sycophants. Here, in porticoes, halls and chambers the cressets were thick as stars in a cloudless vault. It seemed that Famurza wished to dissipate all shadows, except those in arrased alcoves set apart for the fitful amours of his guests.

For the kindling of such amours there were wines, cordials, aphrodisiacs. There were meats and fruits that swelled the flaccid pulses. There were strange exotic drugs that aroused and prolonged pleasure. There were curious statuettes in half-veiled niches; and wall-panels painted with bestial loves, or loves human or superhuman. There were hired singers of all sexes, who sang ditties diversely erotic; and dancers whose contortions were calculated to restore the outworn sense when all else had failed.

But to all such incitants Valzain, pupil of Famurza, and renowned both as poet and voluptuary, was insensible.

With indifference turning toward disgust, a half-emptied cup in his hand, he watched from a corner the gala throng that eddied past him, and averted his eyes involuntarily from certain couples who were too shameless or drunken to seek the shadows of privacy for their dalliance. A sudden satiety had claimed him. He felt himself strangely withdrawn from the morass of wine and flesh into which, not long before, he had still plunged with delight. He seemed as one who stands on an alien shore, beyond waters of deepening separation.

"What ails you, Valzain? Has a vampire sucked your blood?" It was Famurza, flushed, grey-haired, slightly corpulent, who stood at his elbow. Laying an affectionate hand on Valzain's shoulder, he hoisted aloft with the other that fescenninely graven quart goblet from which he was wont to drink only wine, eschewing the drugged and violent liquors often preferred by the sybarites of Umbri.

"Is it biliousness? Or unrequited love? We have cures here for both. You have only to name your medicine."

"There is no medicine for what ails me," countered Valzain. "As for love, I have ceased to care whether it be requited or unrequited. I can taste only the dregs in every cup. And tedium lurks at the middle of all kisses"

"Truly, yours is a melancholy case." There was concern in Famurza's voice. "I have been reading some of your late verses. You write only of tombs and yew trees, of maggots and phantoms and disembodied love. Such stuff gives me the colic. I need at least a half-gallon of honest vine-juice after each poem."

"Though I did not know it till lately," admitted Valzain, "there is in me a curiosity toward the unseen, a longing for things beyond the material world."

Famurza shook his head commiserately. "Though I have attained to more than twice your years, I am still content with what I see and hear and touch. Good juicy meat, women, wine, the songs of full-throated singers, are enough for me."

"In the dreams of slumber," mused Valzain, "I have clasped succubi who were more than flesh, have known delights too keen for the waking body to sustain. Do such dreams have any source, outside the earth-born brain itself? I would give much to find that source, if it exists. In the meanwhile there is nothing for me but despair."

"So young—and yet so exhausted! Well, if you're tired of women, and want phantoms instead, I might venture a suggestion. Do you know the old necropolis, lying midway between Umbri and Psiom—a matter of perhaps three miles from here? The goatherds say that a lamia haunts it—the spirit of the princess Morthylla, who died several centuries ago and was interred in a mausoleum that still stands, overtowering the lesser tombs. Why not go forth tonight and visit the necropolis? It should suit your mood better than my house. And perhaps Morthylla will appear to you. But don't blame me if you return with a nibbled throat—or fail to return at all. After all those years the lamia is still avid for human lovers; and she might well take a fancy to you."

"Of course, I know the place," said Valzain. . . . "But I think you are jesting."

Famurza shrugged his shoulders and moved on amid the revelers. A laughing dancer, blonde-limbed and lissom, came up to Valzain and threw a noose of plaited flowers about his neck, claiming him as her captive. He broke the noose gently, and gave the girl a tepid kiss that caused her to make wry faces. Unobtrusively but quickly, before others of the merry-makers could try to entice him, he left the house of Famurza.

Without impulses, other than that of an urgent desire for solitude, he turned his steps toward the suburbs, avoiding the neighborhood of taverns and lupanars, where the populace thronged. Music, laughter, snatches of songs, followed him from lighted mansions where symposia were held nightly by the city's richer denizens. But he met few roisterers on the streets: it was too late for the gathering, too early for the dispersal, of guests at such symposia.

Now the lights thinned out, with ever-widening intervals between, and the streets grew shadowy with that ancient night which pressed about Umbri, and would wholly quench its defiant galaxies of lamp-bright windows with the darkening of Zothique's senescent sun. Of such things, and of death's encircling mystery, were the musings of Valzain as he plunged into the outer darkness that he found grateful to his glare-wearied eyes.

Grateful too was the silence of the field-bordered road that he pursued for awhile without realizing its direction. Then, at some land-mark familiar despite the gloom, it came to him that the road was the one which ran from Umbri to Psiom, that sister city of the Delta; the road beside whose middle meanderings was situated the long-disused necropolis to which Famurza had ironically directed him.

Truly, he thought, the earthy-minded Famurza had somehow plumbed the need that lay at the bottom of his disenchantment with all sensory pleasures. It would be good to visit, to sojourn for an hour or so, in that city whose people had long passed beyond the lusts of mor-tality, beyond satiety and disillusion.

A moon, swelling from the crescent toward the half, arose behind him as he reached the foot of the low-mounded hill on which the cemetery lay. He left the paved road, and began to ascend the slope, half-covered with stunted gorse, at whose summit the glimmering marbles were discernible. It was without path, other than the broken trails made by goats and their herders. Dim, lengthened and attenuate, his shadow went before him like a ghostly guide. In his fantasy it seemed to him that he climbed the gently sloping bosom of a giantess, studded afar with pale gems that were tombstones and mausoleums. He caught himself wondering, amid this poetic whimsy, whether the giantess was dead, or merely slept.

Gaining the flat expansive ground of the summit, where dwarfish dying yews disputed with leafless briars the intervals of slabs blotched with lichen, he recalled the tale that Famurza had mentioned, anent the lamia who was said to haunt the necropolis. Famurza, he knew well, was no believer in such legendry, and had meant only to mock his fu-nereal mood. Yet, as a poet will, he began to play with the fancy of some presence, immortal, lovely and evil, that dwelt amid the antique marbles and would respond to the evocation of one who, without pos-itive belief, had longed vainly for visions from beyond mortality.

Through headstone aisles of moon-touched solitude, he came to a lofty mausoleum, still standing with few signs of ruin at the cemetery's center. Beneath it, he had been told, were extensive vaults housing the mummies of an extinct royal family that had ruled over the twin cities Umbri and Psiom in former centuries. The princess Morthylla had belonged to this family.

To his startlement a woman, or what appeared to be such, was sitting on a fallen shaft beside the mausoleum. He could not see her distinctly; the tomb's shadow still enveloped her from the shoulders downward. The face alone, glimmering wanly, was lifted to the rising moon. Its profile was such as he had seen on antique coins.

"Who are you?" he asked, with a curiosity that overpowered his courtesy.

"I am the lamia Morthylla," she replied, in a voice that left behind it a faint and elusive vibration like that of some briefly sounded harp. "Beware me—for my kisses are forbidden to those who would remain numbered among the living."

Valzain was startled by this answer that echoed his fantasies. Yet reason told him that the apparition was no spirit of the tombs but a living woman who knew the legend of Morthylla and wished to amuse herself by teasing him. And yet what woman would venture alone and at night to a place so desolate and eerie?

Most credibly, she was a wanton who had come out to keep a rendezvous amid the tombs. There were, he knew, certain perverse debauchees who required sepulchral surroundings and furnishings for the titillation of their desires.

"Perhaps you are waiting for someone," he suggested. "I do not wish to intrude, if such is the case."

"I wait only for him who is destined to come. And I have waited long, having had no lover for two hundred years. Remain, if you wish: there is no one to fear but me."

Despite the rational surmises he had formed, there crept along Valzain's spine the thrill of one who, without fully believing, suspects the presence of a thing beyond nature.... Yet surely it was all a game—a game that he too could play for the beguilement of his ennui.

"I came here hoping to meet you," he declared. "I am weary of mortal women, tired of every pleasure—tired even of poetry."

"I, too, am bored," she said, simply.

The moon had climbed higher, shining on the dress of antique mode that the woman wore. It was cut closely at waist and hips and bosom, with voluminous downward folds. Valzain had seen such costumes only in old drawings. The princess Morthylla, dead for three centuries, might well have worn a similar dress.

Whoever she might be, he thought, the woman was strangely beautiful, with a touch of quaintness in the heavily coiled hair whose color he could not decide in the moonlight. There was a sweetness about her mouth, a shadow of fatigue or sadness beneath her eyes. At the right corner of her lips he discerned a small mole.

Valzain's meeting with the self-named Morthylla was repeated nightly while the moon swelled like the rounding breast of a titaness and fell away once more to hollowness and senescence. Always she awaited him by the same mausoleum—which, she declared, was her dwelling place. And always she dismissed him when the east turned ashen with dawn, saying that she was a creature of the night.

Skeptical at first, he thought of her as a person with macabre leanings and fantasies akin to his own, with whom he was carrying on a flirtation of singular charm. Yet about her he could find no hint of the worldliness that he suspected: no seeming knowledge of present things, but a weird familiarity with the past and the lamia's legend. More and more she seemed a nocturnal being, intimate only with shadow and solitude.

Her eyes, her lips, appeared to withhold secrets forgotten and forbidden. In her vague, ambiguous answers to his questions, he read meanings that thrilled him with hope and fear.

"I have dreamed of life," she told him cryptically. "And I have dreamed also of death. Now, perhaps there is another dream—into which you have entered."

"I, too, would dream," said Valzain.

Night after night his disgust and weariness sloughed away from him, in a fascination fed by the spectral milieu, the environing silence of the dead, his withdrawal and separation from the carnal, garish city. By degrees, by alternations of unbelief and belief, he came to accept her as the actual lamia. The hunger that he sensed in her could be only the lamia's hunger; her beauty that of a being no longer human. It was like a dreamer's acceptance of things fantastic elsewhere than in sleep.

Together with his belief, there grew his love for her. The desires he had thought dead revived within him, wilder, more importunate.

She seemed to love him in return. Yet she betrayed no sign of the lamia's legendary nature, eluding his embrace, refusing him the kisses for which he begged.

"Sometime, perhaps," she conceded. "But first you must know me for what I am, must love me without illusion."

"Kill me with your lips, devour me as you are said to have devoured other lovers," beseeched Valzain.

"Can you not wait?" her smile was sweet—and tantalizing. "I do not wish your death so soon, for I love you too well. Is it not sweet to keep our tryst among the sepulchers? Have I not beguiled you from your boredom? Must you end it all?"

The next night he besought her again, imploring with all his ardor and eloquence the denied consummation.

She mocked him: "Perhaps I am merely a bodiless phantom, a spirit without substance. Perhaps you have dreamed me. Would you risk an awakening from the dream?"

Valzain stepped toward her, stretching out his arms in a passionate gesture. She drew back, saying:

"What if I should turn to ashes and moonlight at your touch? You would regret then your rash insistence."

"You are the immortal lamia," avowed Valzain. "My senses tell me that you are no phantom, no disembodied spirit. But for me you have turned all else to shadow."

"Yes, I am real enough in my fashion," she granted, laughing softly. Then suddenly she leaned toward him and her lips touched his throat. He felt their moist warmth a moment—and felt the sharp sting of her teeth that barely pierced his skin, withdrawing instantly. Before he could clasp her she eluded him again.

"It is the only kiss permitted to us at present," she cried, and fled swiftly with soundless footfalls among the gleams and shadows of the sepulchers.

On the following afternoon a matter of urgent and unwelcome business called Valzain to the neighboring city of Psiom: a brief journey, but one that he seldom took.

He passed the ancient necropolis, longing for that nocturnal hour when he could hasten once more to a meeting with Morthylla. Her poignant kiss, which had drawn a few drops of blood, had left him greatly fevered and distraught. He, like that place of tombs, was haunted; and the haunting went with him into Psiom.

He had finished his business, the borrowing of a sum of money from a usurer. Standing at the usurer's door, with that slightly obnoxious but necessary person beside him, he saw a woman passing on the street.

Her features, though not her dress, were those of Morthylla; and there was even the same tiny mole at one corner of her mouth. No phantom of the cemetery could have startled or dismayed him more profoundly.

"Who is that woman? he asked the money-lender. "Do you know her?"

"Her name is Beldith. She is well-known in Psiom, being rich in her own right and having had numerous lovers. I've had a little business with her, though she owes me nothing at present. Should you care to meet her? I can easily introduce you."

"Yes, I should like to meet her," agreed Valzain. "She looks strangely like someone that I knew a long time ago.

The usurer peered slyly at the poet. "She might not make too easy a conquest. It is said of late that she has withdrawn herself from the pleasures of the city. Some have seen her going out at night toward the old necropolis, or returning from it in the early dawn. Strange tastes, I'd say, for one who is little more than a harlot. But perhaps she goes out to meet some eccentric lover."

"Direct me to her house," Valzain requested. "I shall not need you to introduce me."

"As you like." The money-lender shrugged, looking a little disappointed. "It's not far, anyway."

Valzain found the house quickly. The woman Beldith was alone. She met him with a wistful and troubled smile that left no doubt of her identity.

"I perceive that you have learned the truth," she said. "I had meant to tell you soon, for the deception could not have gone on much longer. Will you not forgive me?"

"I forgive you," returned Valzain sadly. "But why did you deceive me?"

"Because you desired it. A woman tries to please the man whom she loves; and in all love there is more or less deception.

"Like you, Valzain, I had grown tired of pleasure. And I sought the solitude of the necropolis, so remote from carnal things. You too came, seeking solitude and peace—or some unearthly spectre. I recognized you at once. And I had read your poems. Knowing Morthylla's legend, I thought to play a game with you. Playing it, I grew to love you. . . . Valzain, you loved me as the lamia. Can you not now love me for myself?"

"It cannot be," averred the poet. "I fear to repeat the disappointment I have found in other women. Yet at least I am grateful for the hours you gave me. They were the best I have known—even though I have loved something that did not, and could not, exist. Farewell, Morthylla. Farewell, Beldith."

When he had gone, Beldith stretched herself face downward among the cushions of her couch. She wept a little; and the tears made a dampness that quickly dried. Later she arose briskly enough and went about her household business.

After a time she returned to the loves and revelries of Psiom. Perhaps, in the end, she found such peace as may be given to those who have grown too old for pleasure.

But for Valzain there was no peace, no balm for this last and most bitter of disillusionments. Nor could he return to the carnalities of his former life. So it was that he finally slew himself, stabbing his throat to its deepest vein with a keen knife in the same spot which the false lamia's teeth had bitten, drawing a little blood.

After his death, he forgot that he had died; forgot the immediate past with all its happenings and circumstances.

Following his talk with Famurza, he had gone forth from Famurza's house and from the city of Umbri and had taken the road that passed the abandoned cemetery. Seized by an impulse to visit it, he had climbed the slope toward the marbles under a swelling moon that rose behind him.

Gaining the flat, expansive ground of the summit, where dwarfish dying yews disputed with leafless briars the intervals of slabs blotched with lichen, he recalled the tale that Famurza had mentioned, anent the lamia who was said to haunt the necropolis. Famurza, he knew well, was no believer in such legendry, and had meant only to mock his funereal mood. Yet, as a poet will, he began to play with the thought of some presence, immortal, lovely and evil, that dwelt amid the antique marbles and would respond to the evocation of one who, without positive belief, had longed vainly for visions from beyond mortality.

Through headstone aisles of moon-touched solitude, he came to a lofty mausoleum, still standing with few signs of ruin at the cemetery's center. Beneath it, he had been told, were extensive vaults housing the mummies of an extinct royal family that had ruled over the twin cities Umbri and Psiom in former centuries. It was to this family that the princess Morthylla had belonged.

To his startlement a woman, or what appeared to be such, was sitting on a fallen shaft beside the mausoleum. He could not see her distinctly; the tomb's shadow still enveloped her from the shoulders downward. The face alone, glimmering wanly, was lifted to the rising moon. Its profile was such as he had seen on antique coins.

"Who are you?" he asked, with a curiosity that overpowered his courtesy.

"I am the lamia Morthylla," she replied.

LAMIA

Out of her desert lair the lamia came,
A lovely serpent, shaped as women are.
Meeting me there, she hailed me by the name

Beloved lips had used in days afar;
And when the lamia sang, it seemed I heard
The voice of love in some old avatar.

Her lethal beauty like a philtre stirred
Through all my blood and filled my heart with light:
I wedded her with ardor undeterred

By the strange mottlings of her body white,
By the things that crept across us in her den
And the dead who lay beside us through the night.

Colder her flesh than serpents of the fen,
Yet on her breast I lost mine ancient woe
And found the joy forbid to living men.

But, ah, it was a thousand years ago
I took the lovely lamia for bride. . .
And nevermore shall they that meet me know
It is a thousand years since I have died.

THE BLACK ABBOT OF PUTHUUM

Let the grape yield for us its purple flame,
And rosy love put off its maidenhood:
By blackening moons, in lands without a name,
We slew the Incubus and all his brood.

—*Song of King Hoaraph's Bowmen.*

Zobal the archer and Cushara the pike-bearer had poured many a libation to their friendship in the sanguine liquors of Yoros and the blood of the kingdom's enemies. In that long and lusty amity, broken only by such passing quarrels as concerned the division of a wineskin or the apportioning of a wench, they had served amid the soldiery of King Hoaraph for a strenuous decade. Savage warfare and wild, fantastic hazard had been their lot. The renown of their valor had drawn upon them, ultimately, the honor of Hoaraph's attention, and he had assigned them for duty among the picked warriors that guarded his palace in Faraad. And sometimes the twain were sent together on such missions as required no common hardihood and no disputable fealty to the king.

Now, in company with the eunuch Simban, chief purveyor to Hoaraph's well-replenished harem, Zobal and Cushara had gone on a tedious journey through the tract known as Izdrel, which clove the western part of Yoros asunder with its rusty-colored wedge of desolation. The king had sent them to learn if haply there abode any verity in certain travellers' tales, which concerned a young maiden of celestial beauty who had been seen among the pastoral peoples beyond Izdrel. Simban bore at his girdle a bag of gold coins with which, if the girl's pulchritude should be in any wise commensurate with the renown thereof, he was empowered to bargain for her purchase. The king had deemed that Zobal and Cushara should form an escort equal to all contingencies: for Izdrel was a land reputedly free of robbers, or, indeed, of any human inhabitants. Men said, however, that malign goblins, tall as giants and humped like camels, had oftentimes beset the wayfarers through Izdrel; that fair but ill-meaning lamiæ had lured them to an eldritch death. Simban, quaking corpulently in his saddle, rode with small willingness on that outward journey; but the archer and the pike-bearer, full of wholesome skepticism, divided their bawdy jests equally between the timid eunuch and the elusive demons.

Without other mishap than the rupturing of a wineskin from the force of the new vintage it contained, they came to the verdurous pasture-lands beyond that dreary desert. Here, in low valleys that held the middle meanderings of the river Vos, cattle and dromedaries were kept by a tribe of herders who sent biannual tribute to Hoaraph from their teeming droves. Simban and his companions found the girl, who dwelt with her grandmother in a village beside the Vos; and even the eunuch acknowledged that their journey was well rewarded.

Cushara and Zobal, on their part, were instantly smitten by the charms of the maiden, whose name was Rubalsa. She was slender and of queenly height, and her skin was pale as the petals of white poppies; and the undulant blackness of her heavy hair was full of sullen copper gleamings beneath the sun. While Simban haggled shrilly with the crone-like grandmother, the warriors eyed Rubalsa with circumspect ardor and addressed to her such gallantries as they deemed discreet within hearing of the eunuch.

At last the bargain was driven and the price paid, to the sore depletion of Simban's money-bag. Simban was now eager to return to Faraad with his prize, and he seemed to have forgotten his fear of the haunted desert. Zobal and Cushara were routed from their dreams by the impatient eunuch before dawn; and the three departed with the still drowsy Rubalsa ere the village could awaken about them.

Noon, with its sun of candent copper in a blackish-blue zenith, found them far amid the rusty sands and iron-toothed ridges of Izdrel. The route they followed was little more than a footpath: for, though Izdrel was but thirty miles in width at that point, few travellers would dare those fiend-infested leagues; and most preferred an immensely circuitous road, used by the herders, that ran to the southward of that evil desolation, following the Vos nearly to its debouchment in the Indaskian Sea.

Cushara, splendid in his plate-armor of bronze, on a huge piebald mare with a cataphract of leather scaled with copper, led the cavalcade. Rubalsa, who wore the red homespun of the herders' women, followed on a black gelding with silk and silver harness, which Hoaraph had sent for her use. Close behind her came the watchful eunuch, gorgeous in particolored sendal, and mounted ponderously, with swollen saddlebags all about him, on the grey ass of uncertain age which, through his fear of horses and camels, he insisted on riding at all times. In his hand he held the leading-rope of another ass which was nearly crushed to the ground by the wineskins, water-jugs and other provisions. Zobal guarded the rear, with unslung bow, slim and wiry in his suiting of light chain-mail, on a nervous red stallion that chafed incessantly at the rein. At his back he bore a quiver filled with arrows which the court-sorcerer, Amdok, had prepared with singular spells and dippings in doubtful fluids, for his possible use against demons. Zobal had accepted the arrows courteously but had satisfied himself later that their iron barbs were in no wise impaired by Amdok's treatment. A similarly ensorcelled pike had been offered by Amdok to Cushara, who had refused it bluffly, saying that his own well-tried weapon was equal to the spitting of any number of devils.

Because of Simban and the two asses, the party could make little speed. However, they hoped to cross the wilder and more desolate portion of Izdrel ere night. Simban, though he still eyed the dismal

waste dubiously, was plainly more concerned with his precious charge
than with the imagined imps and lamiæ. And Cushara and Zobal, both
rapt in amorous reveries that centered about the luscious Rubalsa, gave
only a perfunctory attention to their surroundings.

The girl had ridden all morning in demure silence. Now, suddenly,
she cried out in a voice whose sweetness was made shrill by alarm. The
others reined their mounts, and Simban babbled questions. To these
Rubalsa replied by pointing toward the southern horizon, where, as her
companions now saw, a peculiar pitch-black darkness had covered a
great portion of the sky and hills, obliterating them wholly. This darkness, which seemed due neither to cloud nor sandstorm, extended itself in a crescent on either hand, and came swiftly toward the
travellers. In the course of a minute or less, it had blotted the pathway
before and behind them like a black mist; and the two arcs of shadow,
racing northward, had flowed together, immuring the party in a circle.
The darkness then became stationary, its walls no more than a hundred
feet away on every side. Sheer, impenetrable, it surrounded the wayfarers, leaving above them a clear space from which the sun still glared
down, remote and small and discolored, as if seen from the bottom of
a deep pit.

"Ai! ai! ai!" howled Simban, cowering amid his saddle-bags. "I
knew well that some devilry would overtake us."

At the same moment the two asses began to bray loudly, and the
horses, with a frantic neighing and squealing, trembled beneath their
riders. Only with much cruel spurring could Zobal force his stallion
forward beside Cushara's mare.

"Mayhap it is only some pestilential mist," said Cushara.

"Never have I seen such mist," replied Zobal doubtfully. "And
there are no vapors to be met with in Izdrel. Methinks it is like the
smoke of the seven hells that men fable beneath Zothique."

"Shall we ride forward?" said Cushara. "I would learn whether or
not a pike can penetrate that darkness."

Calling out some words of reassurance to Rubalsa, the twain sought to spur their mounts toward the murky wall. But, after a few swerving paces, the mare and the stallion balked wildly, sweating and snorting, and would go no farther. Cushara and Zobal dismounted and continued their advance on foot.

Not knowing the source or nature of the phenomenon with which they had to deal, the two approached it warily. Zobal nocked an arrow to his string, and Cushara held the great bronze-headed pike before him as if charging an embattled foe. Both were more and more puzzled by the murkiness, which did not recede before them in the fashion of fog, but maintained its opacity when they were close upon it.

Cushara was about to thrust his weapon into the wall. Then, without the least prelude, there arose in the darkness, seemingly just before him, a horrible multitudinous clamor as of drums, trumpets, cymbals, jangling armor, jarring voices, and mailed feet that tramped to and fro on the stony ground with a mighty clangor. As Cushara and Zobal drew back in amazement, the clamor swelled and spread, till it filled with a babel of warlike noises the whole circle of mysterious night that hemmed in the travellers.

"Verily, we are sore beset," shouted Cushara to his comrade as they went back to their horses. "It would seem that some king of the north has sent his myrmidons into Yoros."

"Yea," said Zobal. . . . "But it is strange that we saw them not ere the darkness came. And the darkness, surely, is no natural thing."

Before Cushara could make any rejoinder, the martial clashings and shoutings ceased abruptly. All about it seemed that there was a rattling of innumerable sistra, a hissing of countless huge serpents, a raucous hooting of ill-omened birds that had foregathered by thousands. To these indescribably hideous sounds, the horses now added a continual screaming, and the asses a more frenzied braying, above which the outcries of Rubalsa and Simban were scarce audible.

Cushara and Zobal sought vainly to pacify their mounts and comfort the madly frightened girl. It was plain that no army of mortal men had beleaguered them: for the noises still changed from instant to instant, and they heard a most evil howling, and a roaring as of hell-born beasts that deafened them with its volume.

Naught, however, was visible in the gloom, whose circle now began to move swiftly, without widening or contracting. To maintain their position in its center, the warriors and their charges were compelled to leave the path and to flee northwardly amid the harsh ridges and hollows. All around them the baleful noises continued, keeping, as it seemed, the same interval of distance.

The sun, slanting westward, no longer shone into that eerily moving pit, and a deep twilight enveloped the wanderers. Zobal and Cushara rode as closely beside Rubalsa as the rough ground permitted, straining their eyes constantly for any visible sign of the cohorts that seemed to encompass them. Both were filled with the darkest misgivings, for it had become all too manifest that supernatural powers were driving them astray in the untracked desert.

Moment by moment the gross darkness seemed to close in; and there was a palpable eddying and seething as of monstrous forms behind its curtain. The horses stumbled over boulders and out-croppings of ore-sharp stone, and the grievously burdened asses were compelled to put forth an unheard-of speed to keep pace with the ever-shifting circle that menaced them with its horrid clamor. Rubalsa had ceased her outcries, as if overcome by exhaustion or resignation to the horror of her plight; and the shrill screeches of the eunuch had subsided into fearful wheezing and gasping.

Ever and anon, it seemed that great fiery eyes glared out of the gloom, floating close to earth or moving aloft at a gigantic height. Zobal began to shoot his enchanted arrows at these appearances, and the speeding of each bolt was hailed by an appalling outburst of Satanic laughters and ululations.

In such wise they went on, losing all measure of time and sense of orientation. The animals were galled and footsore. Simban was nigh dead from fright and fatigue; Rubalsa drooped in her saddle; and the warriors, awed and baffled by the predicament in which their weapons appeared useless, began to flag with a dull weariness.

"Never again shall I doubt the legendry of Izdrel," said Cushara gloomily.

"It is in my mind that we have not long either to doubt or believe," rejoined Zobal.

To add to their distress, the terrain grew rougher and steeper, and they climbed acclivitous hillsides and went down endlessly into drear valleys. Anon they came to a flat, open, pebbly space. There, all at once, it seemed that the pandemonium of evil noises drew back on every hand, receding and fading into faint, dubious whispers that died at a vast remove. Simultaneously, the circling night thinned out, and a few stars shone in the welkin, and the sharp-spined hills of the desert loomed starkly against a vermilion afterglow. The travellers paused and peered wonderingly at each other in a gloom that was no more than that of natural twilight.

"What new devilry is this?" asked Cushara, hardly daring to believe that the hellish leaguers had vanished.

"I know not," said the archer, who was staring into the dusk." "But here, mayhap, is one of the devils."

The others now saw that a muffled figure was approaching them, bearing a lit lantern made of some kind of translucent horn. At some distance behind the figure, lights appeared suddenly in a square dark mass which none of the party had discerned before. This mass was evidently a large building with many windows.

The figure, drawing near, was revealed by the dim yellowish lantern as a black man of immense girth and tallness, garbed in a voluminous robe of saffron such as was worn by certain monkish orders, and crowned with the two-horned purple hat of an abbot. He was indeed a singular and unlooked-for apparition: for if any monasteries existed amid the barren reaches of Izdrel, they were hidden and unknown to the world. Zobal, however, searching his memory, recalled a vague tradition he had once heard concerning a chapter of negro monks who had flourished in Yoros many centuries ago. The chapter had long been extinct, and the very site of its monastery was forgotten. Nowadays there were few blacks anywhere in the kingdom, other than those who did duty as eunuchs guarding the seraglios of nobles and rich merchants.

The animals began to display a certain uneasiness at the stranger's approach.

"Who art thou?" challenged Cushara, his fingers tightening on the haft of his weapon.

The black man grinned capaciously, showing great rows of discolored teeth whose incisors were like those of a wild dog. His enormous unctuous jowls were creased by the grin into folds of amazing number and volume; and his eyes, deeply slanted and close together, seemed to wink perpetually in pouches that shook like ebon jellies. His nostrils flared prodigiously; his purple, blubbery lips drooled and quivered, and he licked them with a fat, red, salacious tongue before replying to Cushara's question.

"I am Ujuk, abbot of the monastery of Puthuum," he said, in a thick voice of such extraordinary volume that it appeared almost to issue from the earth under his feet. "Methinks the night has overtaken you far from the route of travellers. I bid you welcome to our hospitality."

"Aye, the night took us betimes," Cushara returned dryly. Neither he nor Zobal was reassured by the look of lust in the abbot's obscenely twinkling eyes as he peered at Rubalsa. Moreover, they had now noted the excessive and disagreeable length of the dark nails on his huge hands and bare, splayed feet: nails that were curving, three-inch talons, sharp as those of some beast or bird of prey.

It seemed, however, that Rubalsa and Simban were less abhorrently impressed, or had not noticed these details: for both made haste to acknowledge the abbot's proffer of hospitality and to urge acceptance upon the visibly reluctant warriors. To this urging, Zobal and Cushara yielded, both inwardly resolving to keep a close watch on all the actions and movements of the abbot of Puthuum.

Ujuk, holding the horn lantern aloft, conducted the travellers to that massive building whose lights they had discerned at no great distance. A ponderous gate of dark wood swung open silently at their approach, and they entered a spacious courtyard cobbled with worn, greasy-looking stones, and dimly illumined by torches in rusty iron sockets. Several monks appeared with startling suddenness before the travellers, who had thought the courtyard vacant at first glance. They were all of unusual bulk and stature, and their features possessed an extraordinary likeness to those of Ujuk, from whom, indeed, they could hardly have been distinguished save by the yellow cowls which they wore in lieu of the abbot's horned purple hat. The similarity extended even to their curved and talon-like nails of inordinate length. Their movements were phantasmally furtive and silent. Without speaking, they took charge of the horses and asses. Cushara and Zobal relinquished their mounts to the care of these doubtful hostlers with a reluctance which, apparently, was not shared by Rubalsa or the eunuch.

The monks also signified a willingness to relieve Cushara of his heavy pike and Zobal of his ironwood bow and half-emptied quiver of ensorcelled arrows. But at this the warriors balked, refusing to let the weapons pass from their possession.

Ujuk led them to an inner portal which gave admission to the refectory. It was a large, low room, lit by brazen lamps of antique workmanship, such as ghouls might have recovered from a desert-sunken tomb. The abbot, with ogre-like grinnings, besought his guests to take their place at a long massive table of ebony with chairs and benches of the same material.

When they had seated themselves, Ujuk sat down at the table's head. Immediately, four monks came in, bearing platters piled with spicily smoking viands, and deep earthen flagons full of a dark amber-brown liquor. And these monks, like those encountered in the court-yard, were gross ebon-black simulacra of their abbot, resembling him precisely in every feature and member. Zobal and Cushara were chary of tasting the liquor, which, from its odor, appeared to be an excep-tionally potent kind of ale; for their doubts concerning Ujuk and his monastery grew graver every moment. Also, in spite of their hunger, they refrained from the food set before them, which consisted mainly of baked meats that neither could identify. Simban and Rubalsa, how-ever, addressed themselves promptly to the meal with appetites sharp-ened by long fasting and the weird fatigues of the day.

The warriors observed that neither food nor drink had been placed before Ujuk, and they conjectured that he had already dined. To their growing disgust and anger, he sat lolling obesely, with lustful eyes upon Rubalsa in a stare broken only by the nictations that accompanied his perpetual grinning. This stare soon began to abash the girl, and then to alarm and frighten her. She ceased eating; and Simban, who had been deeply preoccupied till then with his supper, was plainly perturbed when he saw the flagging of her appetite. He seemed for the first time to notice the abbot's unmonastic leering, and showed his disapproval by sundry horrible grimaces. He also remarked pointedly, in a loud, piercing voice, that the girl was destined for the harem of King Hoar-aph. But at this, Ujuk merely chuckled, as if Simban had uttered some exquisitely humorous jest.

Zobal and Cushara were hard put to repress their wrath, and both itched hotly for the fleshing of their weapons in the abbot's gross bulk. He, however, seemed to have taken Simban's hint, for he shifted his gaze from the girl. Instead, he began to eye the warriors with a curious and loathsome avidity, which they found little less insupportable than his ogling of Rubalsa. The well-nourished eunuch also came in for his share of Ujuk's regard, which seemed to have in it the hunger of a hyena gloating over his prospective prey.

Simban, obviously ill at ease, and somewhat frightened, now tried to carry on a conversation with the abbot, volunteering much information as to himself, his companions, and the adventures which had brought them to Puthuum. Ujuk seemed little surprised by this information; and Zobal and Cushara, who took no part in the conversation, became surer than ever that he was no true abbot.

"How far have we gone astray from the route to Faraad?" asked Simban.

"I do not consider that you have gone astray," rumbled Ujuk in his subterranean voice, "for your coming to Puthuum is most timely. We have few guests here, and we are loath to part with those who honor our hospitality."

"King Hoaraph will be impatient for our return with the girl," Simban quavered. "We must depart early tomorrow."

"Tomorrow is another matter," said Ujuk, in a tone half unctuous, half sinister. "Perhaps, by then, you will have forgotten this deplorable haste."

Little was said during the rest of the meal; and, indeed, little was drunk or eaten; for even Simban seemed to have lost his normally voracious appetite. Ujuk, still grinning as if at some uproarious jest known only to himself, was apparently not concerned with the urging of food upon his guests.

Certain of the monks came and went unbidden, removing the laden dishes, and as they departed, Zobal and Cushara perceived a strange thing: for no shadows were cast by the monks on the lamplit floor beside the moving adumbrations of the vessels they carried! From Ujuk, however, a heavy, misshapen umbrage fell and lay like a prone incubus beside his chair.

"Methinks we have come to a hatching-place of demons," whispered Zobal to Cushara. "We have fought many men, thou and I, but never such as wanted wholesome shadows."

"Aye," muttered the pike-bearer. . . . "But I like this abbot even less than his monks: though he alone is the caster of a shade."

Ujuk now rose from his seat, saying: "I trow that ye are all weary and would sleep betimes."

Rubalsa and Simban, who had both drunk a certain amount of the powerful ale of Puthuum, nodded a drowsy assent. Zobal and Cushara, noting their premature sleepiness, were glad they had declined the liquor.

The abbot led his guests along a corridor whose gloom was but little relieved by the flaring of torches in a strong draft that blew stealthily from an undetermined source, causing a rout of wild shadows to flitter beside the passers. On either hand there were cells with portals shut only by hangings of a coarse hempen fabric. The monks had all vanished, the cells were seemingly dark, and an air of age-old desolation pervaded the monastery, together with a smell as of mouldering bones piled in some secret catacomb.

Midway in the hall, Ujuk paused and held aside the arras of a doorway that differed in no wise from the rest. Within, a lamp burned, depending from an archaic chain of curiously linked and fretted metal. The room was bare but spacious, and a bed of ebony with opulent quiltings of an olden fashion stood by the farther wall under an open window. This chamber, the abbot indicated, was for the occupancy of Rubalsa; and he then offered to show the men and the eunuch their respective quarters.

Simban, seeming to wake all at once from his drowsiness, protested at the idea of being separated in such wise from his charge. As if Ujuk had been prepared for this, and had given orders accordingly, a monk appeared forthwith, bringing quilts which he laid on the flagged floor within the portals of Rubalsa's room. Simban stretched himself promptly on the improvised bed, and the warriors withdrew with Ujuk.

"Come," said the abbot, his wolfish teeth gleaming in the torchlight. "Ye will sleep soundly in the beds I have prepared."

Zobal and Cushara, however, had now assumed the position of guardsmen outside the doorway of Rubalsa's chamber. They told Ujuk curtly that they were responsible to King Hoaraph for the girl's safety and must watch over her at all times.

"I wish ye a pleasant vigil," said Ujuk, with a cachinnation like the laughter of hyenas in some underground tomb.

With his departure, it seemed that the black slumber of a dead antiquity settled upon all the building. Rubalsa and Simban, apparently, slept without stirring, for there was no sound from behind the hempen arras. The warriors spoke only in whispers, lest they should arouse the girl. Their weapons held ready for instant use, they watched the shadowy hall with a jealous vigilance: for they did not trust the quietude about them, being well assured that a host of foul cacodemons couched somewhere behind it, biding the time of assault.

Howbeit, nothing occurred to reconfirm them in such apprehensions. The draft that breathed furtively along the hall seemed to tell only of age-forgotten death and cyclic solitude. The two began to perceive signs of dilapidation in walls and floor that had heretofore escaped their notice. Eerie, phantastical thoughts came to them with insidious persuasion: it seemed that the building was a ruin that had lain uninhabited for a thousand years; that the black abbot Ujuk and his shadowless monks were mere imaginations, things that had never been; that the moving circle of darkness, the pandemonian voices, that had herded them toward Puthuum, were no more than a daymare whose memory was now fading in the fashion of dreams.

Thirst and hunger troubled them, for they had not eaten since early morn, and had snatched only a few hasty drafts of wine or water during the day. Both, however, began to feel the oncreeping of a sleepy hebetude which, under the circumstances, was most undesirable. They nodded, started and awoke recurrently to their peril. But still, like a siren voice in poppy-dreams, the silence seemed to tell them that all danger was a bygone thing, an illusion that belonged to yesterday.

Several hours passed, and the hall lightened with the rising of a late moon that shone through a window at its eastern end. Zobal, less bedrowsed than Cushara, was awakened to full awareness by a sudden commotion among the animals in the courtyard without. There were loud neighings that rose to a frenzied pitch, as if something had frightened the horses; and to these the asses began to add their heavy braying, till Cushara was also aroused.

"Make sure that thou drowsest not again," Zobal admonished the pike-bearer. "I shall go forth and inquire as to the cause of this tumult."

"'Tis a good thought," commended Cushara. "And while thou art gone, see to it that none has molested our provisions. And bring back with thee some apricots and cakes of sesame and a skin of ruby-red wine."

The monastery itself remained silent as Zobal went down the hall, his buskins of link-covered leather ringing faintly. At the hall's end an outer door stood open, and he passed through it into the courtyard. Even as he emerged, the animals ceased their clamor. He could see but dimly, for all the torches in the courtyard, save one, had burnt out or been extinguished; and the low gibbous moon had not yet climbed the wall. Nothing, to all appearance, was amiss: the two asses were standing quietly beside the mountainous piles of provisions and saddle-bags they had borne; the horses seemed to drowse amicably in a group. Zobal decided that perhaps there had been some temporary bickering between his stallion and Cushara's mare.

He went forward to make sure that there was no other cause of disturbance. Afterwards he turned to the wineskins, intending to refresh himself before rejoining Cushara with a supply of drinkables and comestibles. Hardly had he washed the dust of Izdrel from his throat with a long draught, when he heard an eerie, dry whispering whose source and distance he could not at once determine. Sometimes it seemed at his very ear, and then it ebbed away as if sinking into profound subterranean vaults. But the sound, though variable in this manner, never ceased entirely; and it seemed to shape itself into words that the listener almost understood: words that were fraught with the hopeless sorrow of a dead man who had sinned long ago, and had repented his sin through black sepulchral ages.

As he harkened to the sere anguish of that sound, the hair bristled on the archer's neck, and he knew such fear as he had never known in the thick of battle. And yet, at the same time, he was aware of deeper pity than the pain of dying comrades had ever aroused in his heart. And it seemed that the voice implored him for commiseration and succor, laying upon him a weird compulsion that he dared not disobey. He could not wholly comprehend the things that the whisperer besought him to do: but somehow he must ease that desolate anguish.

Still the whispering rose and fell; and Zobal forgot that he had left Cushara to a lone vigil beset with hellish dangers; forgot that the voice itself might well be only a device of demons to lure him astray. He began to search the courtyard, his keen ears alert for the source of the sound; and, after some dubitation, he decided that it issued from the ground in a corner opposite the gateway. Here, amid the cobbling, in the walls' angle, he found a large slab of syenite with a rusty metal ring in its center. He was quickly confirmed in his decision: for the whispering became louder and more articulate, and he thought that it said to him: "Lift the slab."

The archer grasped the rusty ring with both hands, and putting forth all his strength, he succeeded in tilting back the stone, albeit not without such exertion as made him feel that his very spine would crack. A dark opening was exposed, and from it surged a charnel stench so overpowering that Zobal turned his face away and was like to have vomited. But the whisper came with a sharp, woeful beseeching, out of the darkness below; and it said to him: "Descend."

Zobal wrenched from its socket the one torch that still burned in the courtyard. By its lurid flaring he saw a flight of worn steps that went down into the reeking sepulchral gloom; and resolutely he descended the steps, finding himself at their bottom in a hewn vault with deep shelves of stone on either hand. The shelves, running away into darkness, were piled with human bones and mummified bodies; and plainly the place was the catacomb of the monastery.

The whispering had ceased, and Zobal peered about in bewilderment not unmixed with horror.

"I am here," resumed the dry, susurrous voice, issuing from amid the heaps of mortal remnants on the shelf close beside him. Startled, and feeling again that crisping of the hairs on his neck, Zobal held his torch to the low shelf as he looked for the speaker. In a narrow niche between stacks of disarticulated bones, he beheld a half-decayed corpse about whose long, attenuate limbs and hollow body there clung a few rotten shreds of yellow cloth. These, he thought, were the remnants of a robe such as was worn by the monks of Puthuum. Then, thrusting his torch into the niche, he discerned the lean, mummy-like head, on which mouldered a thing that had once been the horned hat of an abbot. The corpse was black as ebony, and plainly it was that of a great negro. It bore an aspect of incredible age, as if it had lain there for centuries: but from it came the odor of newly ripe corruption that had sickened Zobal when he lifted the slab of syenite.

As he stood staring down, it seemed to Zobal that the cadaver stirred a little, as if fain to rise from its recumbent posture; and he saw a gleaming as of eyeballs in the deep-shadowed sockets; and the dolorously curling lips were retracted still farther; and from between the bared teeth there issued that awful whispering which had drawn him into the catacomb.

"Listen closely," said the whispering. "There is much for me to tell thee, and much for thee to do when the telling is done.

"I am Uldor, the abbot of Puthuum. More than a thousand years ago I came with my monks to Yoros from Ilcar, the black empire of the north. The emperor of Ilcar had driven us forth, for our cult of celibacy, our worship of the maiden goddess Ojhal, were hateful to him. Here amid the desert of Izdrel we built our monastery and dwelt unmolested.

"We were many in number at first; but the years went by, and one by one the Brothers were laid in the catacomb we had delved for our resting-place. They died with none to replace them. I alone survived in the end: for I had won such sanctity as ensures longeval days, and had also become a master of the arts of sorcery. Time was a demon that I held at bay, like one who stands in a charmed circle. My powers were still hale and unimpaired; and I lived on as an anchorite in the monastery.

"At first the solitude was far from irksome to me, and I was wholly absorbed in my study of the arcana of nature. But after a time it seemed that such things no longer sufficed. I grew aware of my loneliness, and was much beset by the demons of the waste, who had troubled me little heretofore. Succubi, fair but baneful, lamiæ with the round soft bodies of women, came to tempt me in the drear vigils of the night.

"I resisted. . . . But there was one she-devil, more cunning than the others, who crept into my cell in the semblance of a girl I had loved long ago, ere yet I had taken the vow of Ojhal. To her I succumbed; and of that unholy union was born the half-human fiend, Ujuk, who has since called himself the abbot of Puthuum.

"After that sin, I wished to die. . . . And the wish was manifoldly strengthened when I beheld the progeny of the sin. Too greatly, however, had I offended Ojhal; and a frightful penance was decreed for me. I lived. . . and daily I was plagued and persecuted by the monster, Ujuk, who grew lustily in the manner of such offspring. But when Ujuk had gained his full stature, there came upon me such weakness and decrepitude as made me hopeful of death. Scarce could I stir in my impotence, and Ujuk, taking advantage of this, bore me in his horrid arms to the catacomb and laid me among the dead. Here I have remained ever since, dying and rotting eternally—and yet eternally alive. For almost a millennium I have suffered unsleepingly the dire anguish of repentance that brings no expiation.

"Through the powers of saintly and sorcerous vision that never left me, I was doomed to watch the foul deeds, the hell-dark iniquities of Ujuk. Wearing the guise of an abbot, endowed with strange infernal powers together with a kind of immortality, he has presided over Puthuum through the centuries. His enchantments have kept the monastery hidden. . . save from those that he wishes to draw within reach of his ghoulish hunger, his incubus-like desires. Men he devours; and women are made to serve his lust. . . . And still I am condemned to see his turpitudes; and the seeing is my most grievous punishment."

The whisper sank away; and Zobal, who had listened in eldritch awe, as one who hears the speech of a dead man, was doubtful for a moment that Uldor still lived. Then the sere voice went on:

"Archer, I crave a boon from thee; and I offer in return a thing that will aid thee against Ujuk. In thy quiver thou bearest charmed arrows: and the wizardry of him that wrought them was good. Such arrows can slay the else-immortal powers of evil. They can slay Ujuk— and even such evil as endures in me and forbids me to die. Archer, grant me an arrow through the heart: and if that suffice not, an arrow through the right eye, and one through the left. And leave the arrows in their mark, for I deem that thou canst well spare so many. One alone is needed for Ujuk. As to the monks thou hast seen, I will tell thee a secret. They are twelve in number, but. . . . "

Zobal would scarcely have believed the thing that Uldor now unfolded, if the events of the day had not left him beyond all incredulity. The abbot continued:

"When I am wholly dead, take thou the talisman which depends about my neck. The talisman is a touchstone that will dissolve such ill enchantments as have a material seeming, if applied thereto with the hand."

For the first time, Zobal perceived the talisman, which was an oval of plain grey stone lying upon Uldor's withered bosom on a chain of black silver.

"Make haste, O archer," the whispering implored.

Zobal had socketed his torch in the pile of mouldering bones beside Uldor. With a sense of mingled compulsion and reluctance, he drew an arrow from his quiver, notched it, and aimed unflinchingly down at Uldor's heart. The shaft went straightly and deeply into its mark; and Zobal waited. But anon from the retracted lips of the black abbot there issued a faint murmuring: "Archer, another arrow!"

Again the bow was drawn, and a shaft sped unerringly into the hollow orbit of Uldor's right eye. And again, after an interval, there came the almost inaudible pleading: "Archer, still another shaft."

Once more the bow of ironwood sang in the silent vault, and an arrow stood in the left eye of Uldor, quivering with the force of its propulsion. This time there was no whisper from the rotting lips: but Zobal heard a curious rustling, and a sigh as of lapsing sand. Beneath his gaze the black limbs and body crumbled swiftly, the face and head fell in, and the three arrows sagged awry, since there was naught now but a pile of dust and parting bones to hold them embedded.

Leaving the arrows as Uldor had enjoined him to do, Zobal groped for the grey talisman that was now buried amid those fallen relics. Finding it, he hung it carefully at his belt beside the long straight sword which he carried. Perhaps, he reflected, the thing might have its use ere the night was over.

Quickly he turned away and climbed the steps to the courtyard. A saffron-yellow and lopsided moon was soaring above the wall, and he knew by this that he had been absent overlong from his vigil with Cushara. All, however, seemed tranquil: the drowsing animals had not stirred; and the monastery was dark and soundless. Seizing a full wineskin and a bag containing such edibles as Cushara had asked him to bring, Zobal hurried back to the open hall.

Even as he passed into the building, the arras-like silence before him was burst asunder by a frightful hubbub. He distinguished amid the clamor the screaming of Rubalsa, the screeching of Simban, and the furious roaring of Cushara: but above these, as if to drown them all, an obscene laughter mounted continually, like the welling forth of dark subterrene waters thick and foul with the fats of corruption.

Zobal dropped the wineskin and the sack of comestibles, and raced forward, unslinging his bow as he went. The outcries of his companions continued, but he heard them faintly now above the damnable incubus-like laughter that swelled as if to fill the whole monastery. As he neared the space before Rubalsa's chamber, he saw Cushara beating with the haft of his pike at a blank wall in which there was no longer a hempen-curtained doorway! Behind the wall the screeching of Simban ceased in a gurgling moan like that of some butchered steer; but the girl's terror-sharpened cries still mounted through the smothering cachinnation.

"This wall was wrought by demons," raged the pike-bearer as he smote vainly at the smooth masonry. "I kept a faithful watch—but they built it behind me in a silence as of the dead. And a fouler work is being done in that chamber."

"Master thy frenzy," said Zobal, as he strove to regain the command of his own faculties amid the madness that threatened to overwhelm him. At that instant he recalled the oval grey touchstone of Uldor, which hung at his baldric from its black silver chain; and it came to him that the closed wall was perhaps an unreal enchantment against which the talisman might serve even as Uldor had said.

Quickly he took the touchstone in his fingers and held it to the blank surface where the doorway had been. Cushara looked on with an air of stupefaction, as if deeming the archer demented. But even as the talisman clicked faintly against it, the wall seemed to dissolve, leaving only a rude arras that fell away in tatters as if it too had been no more than a sorcerous illusion. The strange disintegration continued to spread, the whole partition melted away to a few worn blocks, and the gibbous moon shone in as the abbey of Puthuum crumbled silently to a gapped and roofless ruin!

All this had occurred in a few moments; but the warriors found no room for wonder. By the livid light of the moon, which peered down like the face of a worm-gnawed cadaver, they looked upon a scene so hideous that it caused them to forget all else. Before them, on a cracked floor from whose interstices grew desert grasses, the eunuch Simban lay sprawled in death. His raiment was torn to a hundred streamers, and blood bubbled darkly from his mangled throat. Even the leather pouches which he bore at his girdle had been ripped open, and gold coins, vials of medicine and other oddments were scattered around him.

Beyond, by the half-crumbled outer wall, Rubalsa lay in a litter of rotted cloth and woodwork which had been the gorgeously quilted ebon bed. She was trying to fend off with her lifted hands the enormously swollen shape that hung horizontally above her, as if levitated by the floating wing-like folds of its saffron robe. This shape the warriors recognized as the abbot Ujuk.

The overwelling laughter of the black incubus had ceased, and he turned upon the intruders a face contorted by diabolic lust and fury. His teeth clashed audibly, his eyes glowed in their pouches like beads of red-hot metal, as he withdrew from his position over the girl and loomed monstrously erect before her amid the ruins of the chamber.

Cushara rushed forward with leveled pike ere Zobal could fit one of his arrows to the string. But even as the pike-bearer crossed the sill, it seemed that the foully bloated form of Ujuk multiplied itself in a dozen yellow-garmented shapes that surged to meet Cushara's onset. Appearing as if by some hellish legerdemain, the monks of Puthuum had mustered to assist their abbot.

Zobal cried out in warning, but the shapes were all about Cushara, dodging the thrusts of his weapon and clawing ferociously at his plate-armor with their terrific three-inch talons. Valiantly he fought them, only to go down after a little and disappear from sight as if whelmed by a pack of ravening hyenas.

Remembering the scarce-credible thing that Uldor had told him, Zobal wasted no arrows upon the monks. His bow ready, he waited for full sight of Ujuk beyond the seething rout that wrangled malignantly back and forth above the fallen pike-bearer. In an eddying of the pack he aimed swiftly at the looming incubus, who seemed wholly intent on that fiendish struggle, as if directing it in some wise without spoken word or ponderable gesture. Straight and true the arrow sped with an exultant singing; and good was the sorcery of Amdok, who had wrought it: for Ujuk reeled and went down, his horrid fingers tearing vainly at the shaft that was driven nigh to its fledging of eagle-quills in his body.

Now a strange thing occurred: for, as the incubus fell and writhed to and fro in his dying, the twelve monks all dropped away from Cushara, and lay tossing convulsively on the floor as if they were but shaken shadows of the thing that died. It seemed to Zobal that their forms grew dim and diaphanous, and he saw the cracks in the flag-stones beyond them; and their writhings lessened with those of Ujuk; and when Ujuk lay still at last, the faint outlines of the figures vanished as though erased from earth and air. Naught remained but the noisome bulk of that fiend who had been the progeny of the abbot Uldor and the lamia. And the bulk shrank visibly from instant to instant beneath its sagging garments, and a smell of ripe corruption arose, as if all that was human in the hellish thing were rotting swiftly away.

Cushara had scrambled to his feet and was peering about in a stunned fashion. His heavy armor had saved him from the talons of his assailants; but the armor itself was scored from greaves to helmet with innumerable scratches.

"Whither have the monks gone?" he inquired. "Methought they were all about me an instant ago, like so many wild dogs worrying a fallen aurochs."

"The monks were but emanations of Ujuk," said Zobal. "They were mere phantasms, multiple eidola, that he sent forth and withdrew into himself at will; and they had no real existence apart from him.

With Ujuk's death they have become less than shadows."

"Verily, such things are prodigious," opined the pike-bearer.

The warriors now turned their attention to Rubalsa, who had struggled to a sitting posture amid the downfallen wreckage of her bed. The tatters of rotten quilting which she clutched about her with shamefast fingers at their approach, served but little to conceal her well-rounded ivory nakedness. She wore an air of mingled fright and confusion, like a sleeper who has just awakened from some atrocious nightmare.

"Had the incubus harmed thee?" inquired Zobal anxiously. He was reassured by her faint, bewildered negative. Dropping his eyes before the piteous disarray of her girlish beauty, he felt in his heart a deeper enamorment than before, a passion touched with such tenderness as he had never known in the hot, brief loves of his hazard-haunted days. Eyeing Cushara covertly, he knew with dismay that this emotion was shared to the fullest by his comrade.

The warriors now withdrew to a little distance and turned their backs decorously while Rubalsa dressed.

"I deem," said Zobal in a low voice beyond overhearing of the girl, "that thou and I tonight have met and conquered such perils as were not contracted for in our service to Hoaraph. And I deem that we are of one mind concerning the maiden, and love her too dearly now to deliver her to the captious lust of a sated king. Therefore we cannot return to Faraad. If it please thee, we shall draw lots for the girl; and the loser will attend the winner as a true comrade till such time as we have made our way from Izdrel, and have crossed the border of some land lying beyond Hoaraph's rule."

To this Cushara agreed. When Rubalsa had finished her dressing, the two began to look about them for such objects as might serve in the proposed sortilege. Cushara would have tossed one of the gold coins, stamped with Hoaraph's image, which had rolled from Simban's torn money-bag. But Zobal shook his head at the suggestion, having

espied certain items which he thought even more exquisitely appropri-
ate than the coin. These objects were the talons of the incubus, whose
corpse had now dwindled in size and was horribly decayed, with a hideous wrinkling of the whole head and an actual shortening of the
members. In this process, the claws of hands and feet had all dropped
away and were lying loose on the pavement. Removing his helmet,
Zobal stooped down and placed within it the five hellish-looking talons of the right hand, among which that of the index finger was the
longest.

He shook the helmet vigorously, as one shakes a dice-box, and
there was a sharp clattering from the claws. Then he held the helmet
out to Cushara, saying: "He who draws the forefinger talon shall take
the girl."

Cushara put in his hand and withdrew it quickly, holding aloft the
heavy thumbnail, which was shortest of all. Zobal drew the nail of the
middle finger; and Cushara, at his second trial, brought forth the little
finger's claw. Then, to the deep chagrin of the pike-bearer, Zobal produced the dearly coveted index talon.

Rubalsa, who had been watching this singular procedure with open
curiosity, now said to the warriors: "What are ye doing?"

Zobal started to explain, but before he had finished, the girl cried
out indignantly: "Neither of ye has consulted my preference in this
matter." Then, pouting prettily, she turned away from the disconcerted
archer and proceeded to fling her arms about the neck of Cushara.

THE TOMB-SPAWN

Evening had come from the desert into Faraad, bringing the last stragglers of caravans. In a wine-shop near the northern gate, many travelling merchants from outer lands, parched and weary, were refreshing themselves with the famed vintages of Yoros. To divert them from their fatigue, a story-teller spoke amid the clinking of the wine-cups:

"Great was Ossaru, being both king and wizard. He ruled over half the continent of Zothique. His armies were like the rolling sands, blown by the simoom. He commanded the genii of storm and of darkness, he called down the spirits of the sun. Men knew his wizardry as the green cedars know the blasting of levin.

"Half immortal, he lived from age to age, waxing in his wisdom and power till the end. Thasaidon, black god of evil, prospered his every spell and enterprise. And during his latter years he was companioned by the monster Nioth Korghai, who came down to Earth from an alien world, riding a fire-maned comet.

"Ossaru, by his skill in astrology, had foreseen the coming of Nioth Korghai. Alone, he went forth into the desert to await the monster. In many lands people saw the falling of the comet, like a sun that came down by night upon the waste; but only King Ossaru beheld the arrival of Nioth Korghai. He returned in the black, moonless hours before dawn, when all men slept, bringing the strange monster to his palace, and housing him in a vault beneath the throne-room, which he had prepared for Nioth Korghai's abode.

"Dwelling always thereafter in the vault, the monster remained unknown and unbeheld. It was said that he gave advice to Ossaru, and instructed him in the lore of the outer planets. At certain periods of the stars, women and young warriors were sent down as a sacrifice to Nioth Korghai; and these returned never to give account of that which they had seen. None could surmise his aspect; but all who entered the palace heard ever in the vault beneath a muffled noise as of slow-beaten drums, and a regurgitation such as would be made by an under-ground fountain; and sometimes men heard an evil cackling as of a mad cockatrice.

"For many years King Ossaru was served by Nioth Korghai, and gave service to the monster in return. Then Nioth Korghai sickened with a strange malady, and men heard no more the cackling in the sunken vault; and the noises of drums and fountain-mouths grew fainter, and ceased. The spells of the wizard king were powerless to avert his death; but when the monster had died, Ossaru surrounded his body with a double zone of enchantment, circle by circle, and closed the vault. And later, when Ossaru died, the vault was opened from above, and the king's mummy was lowered therein by his slaves, to re-pose forever beside that which remained of Nioth Korghai.

"Cycles have gone by since then; and Ossaru is but a name on the lips of story-tellers. Lost now is the palace wherein he dwelt, and the city thereabout, some saying that it stood in Yoros, and some, in the empire of Cincor, where Yethlyreom was later built by the Nimboth dynasty. And this alone is certain, that somewhere still, in the sealed tomb, the alien monster abides in death, together with King Ossaru. And about them still is the inner circle of Ossaru's enchantment, ren-dering their bodies incorruptible throughout all the decay of cities and kingdoms; and around this is another circle, guarding against all intru-sion: since he who enters there by the tomb's door will die instantly and will putrefy in the moment of death, falling to dusty corruption ere he strike the ground.

"Such is the legend of Ossaru and Nioth Korghai. No man has ev-er found their tomb; but the wizard Namirrha, prophesying darkly, foretold many ages ago that certain travellers, passing through the desert, would some day come upon it unaware. And he said that these travellers, descending into the tomb by another way than the door, would behold a strange prodigy. And he spoke not concerning the nature of the prodigy, but said only that Nioth Korghai, being a creature from some far world, was obedient to alien laws in death as in life. And of that which Namirrha meant, no man has yet guessed the secret."

The brothers Milab and Marabac, who were jewel-merchants from Ustaim, had listened raptly to the story-teller.

"Now truly this is a strange tale," said Milab. "However, as all men know, there were great wizards in the olden days, workers of deep enchantment and wonder; and also there were true prophets. And the sands of Zothique are full of lost tombs and cities."

"It is a good story," said Marabac, "but it lacks an ending. Prithee, O teller of tales, canst tell us no more than this? Was there no treasure of precious metals and jewels entombed with the monster and the king? I have seen sepulchers where the dead were walled with gold ingots, and sarcophagi that poured forth rubies like the gouted blood of vampires."

"I relate the legend as my fathers told it," affirmed the story-teller. "They who are destined to find the tomb must tell the rest—if haply they return from the finding."

Milab and Marabac had traded their store of uncut jewels, of carven talismans and small jasper and carnelian idols, making a good profit in Faraad. Now, laden with rosy and purple-black pearls from the southern gulfs, and the black sapphires and winy garnets of Yoros, they were returning northward toward Tasuun with a company of other merchants on the long, circuitous journey to Ustaim by the orient sea.

The way had led through a dying land. Now, as the caravan approached the borders of Yoros, the desert began to assume a profounder desolation. The hills were dark and lean, like recumbent mummies of giants. Dry water-ways ran down to lake-bottoms leprous with salt. Billows of grey sand were driven high on the crumbling cliffs, where gentle waters had once rippled. Columns of dust arose and went by like fugitive phantoms. Over all, the sun was a monstrous ember in a charred heaven.

Into this waste, which was seemingly unpeopled and void of life, the caravan went warily. Urging their camels to a swift trot in the narrow, deep-walled ravines, the merchants made ready their spears and claymores and scanned the barren ridges with anxious eyes. For here, in hidden caves, there lurked a wild and half-bestial people, known as the Ghorii. Akin to the ghouls and jackals, they were eaters of carrion; and also they were anthropophagi, subsisting by preference on the bodies of travellers, and drinking their blood in lieu of water or wine. They were dreaded by all who had occasion to journey between Yoros and Tasuun.

The sun climbed to its meridian, searching with ruthless beams the nethermost umbrage of the strait, steep defiles. The fine ash-light sand was no longer stirred by any puff of wind. No lizards lifted or scurried on the rocks.

Now the road ran downward, following the course of some olden stream between acclivitous banks. Here, in lieu of former pools, there were pits of sand dammed up by riffles or boulders, in which the camels floundered knee-deep. And here, without the least warning, in a turn of the sinuous bed, the gully swarmed and seethed with the hideous earth-brown bodies of the Ghorii, who appeared instantaneously on all sides, leaping wolfishly from the rocky slopes or flinging themselves like panthers from the high ledges.

These ghoulish apparitions were unspeakably ferocious and agile. Uttering no sound, other than a sort of hoarse coughing and spitting, and armed only with their double rows of pointed teeth and their sickle-like talons, they poured over the caravan in a climbing wave. It seemed that there were scores of them to each man and camel. Several of the dromedaries were thrown to earth at once, with the Ghorii gnawing their legs and haunches and chines, or hanging dog-wise at their throats. They and their drivers were buried from sight by the ravenous monsters, who began to devour them immediately. Boxes of jewels and bales of rich fabrics were torn open in the melée, jasper and onyx idols were strewn ignominiously in the dust, pearls and rubies, unheeded, lay weltering in puddled blood; for these things were of no value to the Ghorii.

Milab and Marabac, as it happened, were riding at the rear. They had lagged behind, somewhat against their will, since the camel ridden by Milab had gone lame from a stone-bruise; and thus, by good fortune, they evaded the ghoulish onset. Pausing aghast, they beheld the fate of their companions, whose resistance was overcome with horrible quickness. The Ghorii, however, did not perceive Milab and Marabac, being wholly intent on devouring the camels and merchants they had dragged down, as well as those members of their own band that were wounded by the swords and lances of the travellers.

The two brothers, levelling their spears, would have ridden forward to perish bravely and uselessly with their fellows. But, terrified by the hideous tumult, by the odor of blood and the hyena-like scent of the Ghorii, their dromedaries balked and bolted, carrying them back along the route into Yoros.

During this unpremeditated flight they soon saw another band of the Ghorii, who had appeared far off on the southern slopes and were running to intercept them. To avoid this new peril Milab and Marabac turned their camels into a side ravine. Travelling slowly because of the lameness of Milab's dromedary, and thinking to find the swift Ghorii on their heels at any moment, they went eastward for many miles with the sun lowering behind them, and came at mid-afternoon to the low and rainless water-shed of that immemorial region.

Here they looked out over a sunken plain, wrinkled and eroded, where the white walls and domes of some innominate city gleamed. It appeared to Milab and Marabac that the city was only a few leagues away. Deeming they had sighted some hidden town of the outer sands, and hopeful now of escaping their pursuers, they began the descent of the long slope toward the plain.

For two days, on a powdery terrain that was like the bituminous dust of mummies, they travelled toward the ever-receding domes that had seemed so near. Their plight became desperate; for between them they possessed only a handful of dried apricots and a water-bag that was three-fourths empty. Their provisions, together with their stock of jewels and carvings, had been lost with the pack-dromedaries of the caravan. Apparently there was no pursuit from the Ghorii; but about them there gathered the red demons of thirst, the black demons of hunger. On the second morning Milab's camel refused to rise and would not respond either to the cursing of its master or the prodding of his spear. Thereafter, the two shared the remaining camel, riding together or by turns.

Often they lost sight of the gleaming city, which appeared and disappeared like a mirage. But an hour before sunset, on the second day, they followed the far-thrown shadows of broken obelisks and crumbling watch-towers into the olden streets.

The place had once been a metropolis; but now many of its lordly mansions were scattered shards or heaps of downfallen blocks. Great dunes of sand had poured in through proud triumphal arches, had filled the pavements and courtyards. Lurching with exhaustion, and sick at heart with the failure of their hope, Milab and Marabac went on, searching everywhere for some well or cistern that the long desert years had haply spared.

In the city's heart, where the walls of temples and lofty buildings of state still served as a barrier to the engulfing sand, they found the ruins of an old aqueduct, leading to cisterns dry as furnaces. There were dust-choked fountains in the market places; but nowhere was there anything to betoken the presence of water.

Wandering hopelessly on, they came to the ruins of a huge edifice which, it appeared, had been the palace of some forgotten monarch. The mighty walls, defying the erosion of ages, were still extant. The portals, guarded on either hand by green brazen images of mythic heroes, still frowned with unbroken arches. Mounting the marble steps, the jewelers entered a vast, roofless hall where cyclopean columns towered as if to bear up the desert sky.

The broad pavement flags were mounded with débris of arches and architraves and pilasters. At the hall's far extreme there was a dais of black-veined marble on which, presumably, a royal throne had once reared. Nearing the dais, Milab and Marabac both heard a low and indistinct gurgling as of some hidden stream or fountain, that appeared to rise from underground depths below the palace pavement.

Eagerly trying to locate the source of the sound, they climbed the dais. Here a huge block had fallen from the wall above, perhaps recently, and the marble had cracked beneath its weight, and a portion of the dais had broken through into some underlying vault, leaving a dark and jagged aperture. It was from this opening that the water-like regurgitation rose, incessant and regular as the beating of a pulse.

The jewelers leaned above the pit, and peered down into webby darkness shot with a doubtful glimmering that came from an indiscernible source. They could see nothing. A dank and musty odor touched their nostrils, like the breath of some long-sealed reservoir. It seemed to them that the steady fountain-like noise was only a few feet below in the shadows, a little to one side of the opening.

Neither of them could determine the depth of the vault. After a brief consultation they returned to their camel, which was waiting stolidly at the palace entrance; and removing the camel's harness they knotted the long reins and leather body-bands into a single thong that would serve them in lieu of rope. Going back to the dais, they secured one end of this thong to the fallen block, and lowered the other into the dark pit.

Milab descended hand over hand into the depths for ten or twelve feet before his toes encountered a solid surface. Still gripping the thong cautiously, he found himself on a level floor of stone. The day was fast waning beyond the palace walls; but a wan glimmer was afforded by the hole in the pavement above; and the outlines of a half-open door, sagging at a ruinous angle, were revealed at one side by the feeble twilight that entered the vault from unknown crypts or stairs beyond.

While Marabac came nimbly down to join him, Milab peered about for the source of the water-like noise. Before him in the undetermined shadows he discerned the dim and puzzling contours of an object that he could liken only to some enormous clepsydra or fountain surrounded with grotesque carvings.

The light seemed to fail momently. Unable to decide the nature of the object, and having neither torch nor candle, he tore a strip from the hem of his hempen burnoose, and lit the slow-burning cloth and held it aloft at arm's length before him. By the dull, smouldering luminance thus obtained, the jewelers beheld more clearly the thing that bulked prodigious and monstrous, rearing above them from the fragment-littered floor to the shadowy roof.

The thing was like some blasphemous dream of a mad devil. Its main portion or body was urn-like in form and was pedestaled on a queerly tilted block of stone at the vault's center. It was palish and pitted with innumerable small apertures. From its bosom and flattened base many arm-like and leg-like projections trailed in swollen nightmare segments to the ground; and two other members, sloping tautly, reached down like roots into an open and seemingly empty sarcophagus of gilded metal, graven with weird archaic ciphers, that stood beside the block.

The urn-shaped torso was endowed with two heads. One of these heads was beaked like a cuttle-fish and was lined with long oblique slits where the eyes should have been. The other head, in close juxtaposition on the narrow shoulders, was that of an aged man, dark and regal and terrible, whose burning eyes were like balas-rubies and whose grizzled beard had grown to the length of jungle moss on the loathsomely porous trunk. This trunk, on the side below the human head, displayed a faint outline as of ribs; and some of the members ended in human hands and feet, or possessed anthropomorphic jointings.

Through heads, limbs and body there ran recurrently the mysterious noise of regurgitation that had drawn Milab and Marabac to enter the vault. At each repetition of the sound a slimy dew exuded from the monstrous pores and rilled sluggishly down in endless drops.

The jewelers were held speechless and immobile by a clammy terror. Unable to avert their gaze, they met the baleful eyes of the human head, glaring upon them from its unearthly eminence. Then, as the hempen strip in Milab's fingers burned slowly away and failed to a red smoulder, and darkness gathered again in the vault, they saw the blind slits in the other head open gradually, pouring forth a hot, yellow, intolerably flaming light as they expanded to immense round orbits. At the same time they heard a singular drum-like throbbing, as if the heart of the huge monster had become audible.

They knew only that a strange horror not of earth, or but partially of earth, was before them. The sight deprived them of thought and memory. Least of all did they remember the story-teller in Faraad, and the tale he had told concerning the hidden tomb of Ossaru and Nioth Korghai, and the prophecy of the tomb's finding by those who should come to it unaware.

Swiftly, with a dreadful stretching and straightening, the monster lifted its foremost members, ending in the brown, shrivelled hands of an old man, and reached out toward the jewelers. From the cuttle-fish beak there issued a shrill demonian cackling; from the mouth of the kingly greybeard head a sonorous voice began to utter words of solemn cadence, like some enchanter's rune, in a tongue unknown to Milab and Marabac.

They recoiled before the abhorrently groping hands. In a frenzy of

fear and panic, by the streaming light of its incandescent orbs, they saw
the anomaly rise and lumber forward from its stone seat, walking
clumsily and uncertainly on its ill-assorted members. There was a
trampling of elephantine pads—and a stumbling of human feet inade-
quate to bear up their share of the blasphemous hulk. The two stiffly
sloping tentacles were withdrawn from the gold sarcophagus, their
ends muffled by empty, jewel-sewn cloths of a precious purple, such as
would be used for the winding of some royal mummy. With a ceaseless
and insane cackling, a malign thundering as of curses that broke to senile quavers, the double-headed horror leaned toward Milab and
Marabac.

Turning, they ran wildly across the roomy vault. Before them, illumined now by the pouring rays from the monster's orbits, they saw
the half-open door of somber metal whose bolts and hinges had rusted
away, permitting it to sag inward. The door was of cyclopean height
and breadth, as if designed for beings huger than man. Beyond it were
the dim reaches of a twilight corridor.

Five paces from the doorway there was a faint red line that followed the chamber's conformation on the dusty floor. Marabac, a little
ahead of his brother, crossed the line. As if checked in mid-air by some
invisible wall, he faltered and stopped. His limbs and body seemed to
melt away beneath the burnoose—the burnoose itself became tattered
as with incalculable age. Dust floated on the air in a tenuous cloud, and
there was a momentary gleaming of white bones where his outflung
hands had been. Then the bones too were gone—and an empty heap
of rags lay rotting on the floor.

A faint odor as of corruption rose to the nostrils of Milab. Un-
comprehending, he had checked his own flight for an instant. Then, on
his shoulders, he felt the grasp of slimy, withered hands. The cackling
and muttering of the heads was like a demon chorus behind him. The
drum-like beating, the noise of rising fountains, were loud in his ears.
With one swiftly dying scream he followed Marabac over the red line.

The enormity that was both man and star-born monster, the nameless amalgam of an unearthly resurrection, still lumbered on and did not pause. With the hands of that Ossaru who had forgotten his own enchantment, it reached for the two piles of empty rags. Reaching, it entered the zone of death and dissolution which Ossaru himself had established to guard the vault forever. For an instant, on the air, there was a melting as of misshapen cloud, a falling as of light ashes. After that the darkness returned, and with the darkness, silence.

Night settled above that nameless land, that forgotten city; and with its coming the Ghorii, who had followed Milab and Marabac over the desert plain. Swiftly they slew and ate the camel that waited patiently at the palace entrance. Later, in the old hall of columns, they found that opening in the dais through which the jewelers had descended. Hungrily they gathered about the hole, sniffing at the tomb beneath. Then, baffled, they went away, their keen nostrils telling them that the scent was lost, that the tomb was empty either of life or death.

THE GARDEN OF ADOMPHA

Lord of the sultry, red parterres
And orchards sunned by hell's unsetting flame!
Amid thy garden blooms the Tree which bears
Unnumbered heads of demons for its fruit;
And, like a slithering serpent, runs the root
That is called Baaras;
And there the forky, pale mandragoras,
Self-torn from out the soil, go to and fro,
Calling upon thy name:
Till men new-damned will deem that devils pass,
Crying in wrathful frenzy and strange woe.
      —*Ludar's Litany to Thasaidon.*

It was well known that Adompha, king of the wide orient isle of So-tar, possessed amid his far-stretching palace grounds a garden secret from all men except himself and the court magician, Dwerulas. The square-built granite walls of the garden, high and formidable as those of a prison, were plain for all to see, rearing above the stately beef-wood and camphor trees, and broad plots of multi-colored blossoms. But nothing had ever been ascertained regarding its interior: for such care as it required was given only by the wizard beneath Adompha's direction; and the twain spoke thereof in deep riddles that none could interpret. The thick brazen door responded to a mechanism whose mystery they shared with none other; and the king and Dwerulas, whether separately or together, visited the garden only at those hours when others were not abroad. And none could verily boast that he had

260

beheld even so much as the opening of the door.

Men said that the garden had been roofed over against the sun with great sheets of lead and copper, leaving no cranny through which the tiniest star could peer down. Some swore that the privacy of its masters during their visits was ensured by a lethean slumber which Dwerulas, through his magic art, was wont to lay at such times upon the whole vicinity.

A mystery so salient could hardly fail to provoke curiosity, and sundry different beliefs arose concerning the garden's nature. Some averred that it was filled with evil plants of nocturnal habit, that yielded their swift and mordant poisons for Adompha's use, along with more insidious and baleful essences employed by the warlock in the working of his enchantments. Such tales, it seemed, were perhaps not without authority: since, following the construction of the closed garden, there had been at the royal court numerous deaths attributable to poisoning, and disasters that were plainly the sendings of a wizard, together with the bodily vanishment of people whose mundane presence no longer pleased Adompha or Dwerulas.

Other tales, of a more extravagant kind, were whispered among the credulous. That legend of unnatural infamy, which had surrounded the king from childhood, assumed a more hideous tinge; and Dwerulas, who had reputedly been sold to the Archdemon before birth by his haggish mother, acquired a new blackness of renown as one exceeding all other sorcerers in the depth and starkness of his abandonment.

Waking from such slumber and such dreams as the juice of the black poppy had given him, King Adompha rose in the dead, stagnant hours between moonset and dawn. About him the palace lay hushed like a charnel-house, its occupants having yielded to their nightly sopor of wine, drugs and arrack. Around the palace, the gardens and the capital city of Loithé slept beneath the slow stars of windless southern heavens. At this time Adompha and Dwerulas were wont to visit the high-walled close with little fear of being followed or observed.

Adompha went forth, pausing but briefly to turn the covert eye of his black bronze lanthorn into the lampless chamber adjoining his own. The room had been occupied by Thuloneah, his favorite odalisque for the seldom-equalled period of eight nights; but he saw without surprise or disconcertion that the bed of disordered silks was now empty. By this, he felt sure that Dwerulas had preceded him to the garden. And he knew, moreover, that Dwerulas had not gone idly or unburdened.

The grounds of the palace, steeped everywhere in unbroken shadow, appeared to maintain that secrecy which the king preferred. He came to the shut brazen door in the blankly towering granite wall; emitting, as he approached it, a sharp sibilation like the hissing of a cobra. In response to the rising and falling of this sound, the door swung inward silently and closed silently behind him.

The garden, planted and tilled so privily, and sealed by its metal roof from the orbs of heaven, was illumined solely by a strange, fiery globe that hung in mid-air at the center. Adompha regarded this globe with awe, for its nature and purveyance were mysterious to him. Dwerulas claimed that it had risen from hell on a moonless midnight at his bidding, and was levitated by infernal power, and fed with the never-dying flames of that clime in which the fruits of Thasaidon swelled to unearthly size and enchanted savor. It gave forth a sanguine light, in which the garden swam and weltered as if seen through a luminous mist of blood. Even in the bleak nights of winter, the globe yielded a genial warmth; and it fell never from its weird suspension, though without palpable support; and beneath it the garden flourished balefully, lush and exuberant as some parterre of the nether circles.

Indeed, the growths of that garden were such as no terrestrial sun could have fostered, and Dwerulas said that their seed was of like origin with the globe. There were pale, bifurcated trunks that strained upward as if to disroot themselves from the ground, unfolding immense leaves like the dark and ribbed wings of dragons. There were amaranthine blossoms, broad as salvers, supported by arm-thick stems that trembled continually. . . . And there were many other weird plants, diverse as the seven hells, and having no common characteristics other than the scions which Dwerulas had grafted upon them here and there through his unnatural and necromantic art.

These scions were the various parts and members of human beings. Consummately, and with never-failing success, the magician had joined them to the half-vegetable, half-animate stocks, on which they lived and grew thereafter, drawing an ichor-like sap. Thus were preserved the carefully chosen souvenirs of a multitude of persons who had inspired Dwerulas and the king with distaste or ennui. On palmy boles, beneath feathery-tufted foliage, the heads of eunuchs hung in bunches, like enormous black drupes. A bare, leafless creeper was flowered with the ears of delinquent guardsmen. Misshapen cacti were fruited with the breasts of women, or foliated with their hair. Entire limbs or torsos had been united with monstrous trees. Some of the huge salver-like blossoms bore palpitating hearts, and certain smaller blooms were centered with eyes that still opened and closed amid their lashes. And there were other graftings, too obscene or repellent for narration.

Adompha went forward among the hybrid growths, which stirred and rustled at his approach. The heads appeared to crane toward him a little, the ears quivered, the breasts shuddered lightly, the eyes widened or narrowed as if watching his progress. These human remnants, he knew, lived only with the sluggish life of the plants, shared only in their sub-animal activity. He had regarded them with a curious and morbid aesthetic pleasure, had found in them the infallible attraction of things enormous and hypernatural. Now, for the first time, he passed among them with a languid interest. He began to apprehend that fatal hour when the garden, with all its novel thaumaturgies, would offer no longer a refuge from his inexorable ennui.

At the core of the strange pleasance, where a circular space was still vacant amid the crowding growths, Adompha came to a mound of loamy, fresh-dug earth. Beside it, wholly nude, and pale and supine as if in death, there lay the odalisque Thuloneah. Near her, various knives, and other implements, together with vials of liquid balsams and viscid gums that Dwerulas used in his grafting, had been emptied upon the ground from a leathern bag. A plant known as the *dedaim*, with a bulbous, pulpy, whitish-green bole from whose center rose and radiated several leafless reptilian boughs, dripped upon Thuloneah's bosom an occasional drop of yellowish-red ichor from incisions made in its smooth bark.

Behind the loamy mound, Dwerulas rose to view with the suddenness of a demon emerging from his subterrene lair. In his hands he held the spade with which he had just finished digging a deep and grave-like hole. Beside the regal stature and girth of Adompha, he seemed no more than a wizened dwarf. His aspect bore all the marks of immense age, as if dusty centuries had sered his flesh and sucked the blood from his veins. His eyes glowed in the bottom of pitlike orbits; his features were black and sunken as those of a long-dead corpse; his body was gnarled as some millennial desert cedar. He stooped incessantly so that his lank, knotty arms hung almost to the ground. Adompha marvelled, as always, at the well-nigh demoniac strength of those arms; marvelled that Dwerulas could have wielded the heavy shovel so expeditiously, could have carried to the garden on his back without human aid the burden of those victims whose members he had utilized in his experiments. The king had never demeaned himself to assist at such labors; but, after indicating from time to time the people whose disappearance would in no wise displease him, had done nothing more than watch and supervise the baroque gardening.

"Is she dead?" Adompha questioned, eyeing the luxurious limbs and body of Thuloneah without emotion.

"Nay," said Dwerulas, in a voice harsh as a rusty coffin-hinge, "but I have administered to her the drowsy and overpowering juice of the *dedaim*. Her heart beats impalpably, her blood flows with the sluggishness of that mingled ichor. She will not reawaken. . . save as a part of the garden's life, sharing its obscure sentience. I wait now your further instructions. What portion . . . or portions? . . ."

"Her hands were very deft," said Adompha, as if musing aloud, in reply to the half-uttered question. "They knew the subtle ways of love and were learned in all amorous arts. I would have you preserve her hands. . . but nothing else."

The singular and magical operation had been completed. The fair, slim, tapering hands of Thuloneah, severed cleanly at the wrists, were attached with little mark of suture to the pale and lopped extremities of the two topmost branches of the *dedaim*. In this process the magician had employed the gums of infernal plants, and had repeatedly invoked the curious powers of certain underground genii, as was his wont on such occasions. Now, as if in suppliance, the semi-vegetable arms reached out toward Adompha with their human hands. The king felt a revival of his old interest in Dwerulas' horticulture, a queer excitement woke within him before the mingled grotesquery and beauty of the grafted plant. At the same time there lived again in his flesh the subtle ardors of outworn nights. . . for the hands were filled with memories.

He had quite forgotten Thuloneah's body, lying close by with its maimed arms. Recalled from his reverie by the sudden movement of Dwerulas, he turned and saw the wizard stooping above the unconscious girl, who had not stirred during the whole course of the operation. Blood still flowed and puddled upon the dark earth from the stumps of her wrists. Dwerulas, with that unnatural vigor which informed all his movements, seized the odalisque in his pipy arms and swung her easily aloft. His air was that of a laborer resuming his unfinished task; but he seemed to hesitate before casting her into the hole that would serve as a grave; where, through seasons warmed and illumined by the hell-drawn globe, her hidden, decaying body would feed the roots of that anomalous plant which bore her own hands for scions. It was as if he were loath to relinquish his voluptuous burden. Adompha, watching him curiously, was aware as never before of the stark evil and turpitude that flowed like an overwhelming fetor from Dwerulas' hunched body and twisted limbs.

Deeply as he himself had gone into all manner of iniquities, the king felt a vague revulsion. Dwerulas reminded him of a loathsome insect that he had once surprised during its ghoulish activities. He remembered how he had crushed the insect with a stone... and remembering, he conceived one of those bold and sudden inspirations that had always impelled him to equally sudden action. He had not, he told himself, entered the garden with any such thought: but the opportunity was too urgent and too perfect to be overpassed. The wizard's back was turned to him for the nonce; the arms of the wizard were encumbered with their heavy and pulchritudinous load. Snatching up the iron spade, Adompha brought it down on the small, withered head of Dwerulas with a fair amount of warlike strength inherited from heroic and piratic ancestors. The dwarf, still carrying Thuloneah, toppled forward into the deep pit.

Poising the spade for a second blow if such should be necessary, the king waited; but there was neither sound nor movement from the grave. He felt a certain surprise at having overcome with such ease the formidable magician, of whose superhuman powers he was half convinced; a certain surprise, too, at his own temerity. Then, reassured by his triumph, the king bethought him that he might try an experiment of his own: since he believed himself to have mastered much of Dwerulas' peculiar skill and lore through observation. The head of Dwerulas would form a unique and suitable addition to one of the garden plants. However, upon peering into the pit, he was forced to relinquish this idea: for he saw that he had struck only too well and had reduced the sorcerer's head to a state in which it was useless for his experiment, since such graftings required a certain integrity of the human part or member.

Reflecting, not without disgust, on the unlooked-for frailty of the skulls of magicians, which were as easily squashed as emus' eggs, Adompha began to fill the pit with loam. The prone body of Dwerulas, the huddled form of Thuloneah beneath it, sharing the same inertness, were soon covered from view by the soft and dissolving clods. The king, who had grown to fear Dwerulas in his heart, was aware of a distinct relief when he had tamped the grave down very firmly and had levelled it smoothly with the surrounding soil. He told himself that he had done well: for the magician's stock of learning had come latterly to include too many royal secrets; and power such as his, whether drawn from nature or from occult realms, was never quite compatible with the secure dominion and prolonged empire of kings.

II

At King Adompha's court and throughout the sea-bordering city of Loithé, the vanishment of Dwerulas became the cause of much speculation but little inquiry. There was a division of opinion as to whether Adompha or the fiend Thasaidon could be thanked for so salutary a riddance; and in consequence, the king of Sotar and the lord of the seven hells were both feared and respected as never before. Only the most redoubtable of men or demons could have made away with Dwerulas, who was said to have lived through a whole millenium, never sleeping for one night, and crowding all his hours with iniquities and sorceries of a sub-tartarean blackness.

Following the inhumation of Dwerulas, a dim sentiment of fear and horror, for which he could not altogether account, had prevented the king from revisiting the sealed garden. Smiling impassively at the wild rumors of the court, he continued his search for novel pleasures and violent or rare sensations. In this, however, he met with small success: it seemed that every path, even the most outré and tortuous, led only to the hidden precipice of boredom. Turning from strange loves

and cruelties, from extravagant pomps and mad music; from the aphrodisiac censers of far-sought blossoms, the quaintly shapen breasts of
exotic girls, he recalled with new longing those semi-animate floral
forms that had been endowed by Dwerulas with the most provocative
charms of women.

So, on a latter night, at an hour midway between moonfall and sun-
rise, when all the palace and the city of Loithé were plunged in sodden
slumber, the king arose from beside his concubine and went forth to
the garden that was now secret from all men excepting himself.

In answer to the cobra-like sibilation, which alone could actuate its
cunning mechanism, the door opened to Adompha and closed behind
him. Even as it closed, he grew aware that a singular change had come
upon the garden during his absence. Burning with a bloodier light, a
more torrid radiation, the mysterious air-hung globe glared down as if
fanned by wrathful demons; and the plants, which had grown exces-
sively in height, and were muffled and hooded with a heavier foliage
than they had worn priorly, stood motionless amid an atmosphere that
was like the heated breath of some crimson hell.

Adompha hesitated, doubtful of the meaning of these changes.
For a moment he thought of Dwerulas, and recalled with a slight shiv-
er certain unexplained prodigies and necromantic feats performed by
the wizard. . . . But he had slain Dwerulas and had buried him with his
own royal hands. The waxing heat and radiance of that globe, the excessive growth of the garden, were no doubt due to some uncontrolled
natural process.

Held by a strong curiosity, the king inhaled the giddying perfumes
that came to assail his nostrils. The light dazzled his eyes, filling them
with queer, unheard-of colors; the heat smote upon him as if from a
nether solstice of infernal summer. He thought that he heard voices,
almost inaudible at first, but mounting anon to a half-articulate murmur that seduced his ear with unearthly sweetness. At the same time
he seemed to behold amid the stirless vegetation, in flashing glimpses,

the half-veiled limbs of dancing bayaderes: limbs that he could not identify with any of the graftings made by Dwerulas.

Drawn by the charm of mystery, and seized by a vague intoxication, the king went forward into the hell-born labyrinth. The plants recoiled gently when he neared them, and drew back on either side to permit his passage. As if in arboreal masquerade, they seemed to hide their human scions behind the mantles of their newly-grown leafage. Then, closing behind Adompha, they appeared to cast off their disguise, revealing wilder and more anomalous fusions than he had remembered. They changed about him from instant to instant like shapes of delirium, so that he was never quite sure how much of their semblance was tree and flower, how much was woman and man. By turns he beheld a swinging of convulsed foliage, a commotion of riotous limbs and bodies. Then, by some undiscerned transition, it seemed that they were no longer rooted in the ground but were moving about him on dim, fantastic feet, in ever-swiftening circles, like the dancers of some bewildering festival.

Around and around Adompha raced the forms that were both floral and human; till the dizzy madness of their motion swirled with an equal vertigo through his brain. He heard the soughing of a storm-driven forest, together with a clamoring of familiar voices that called him by name, that cursed or supplicated, mocked or exhorted, in myriad tones of warrior, councillor, slave, courtling, castrado or leman. Over all, the sanguine globe blazed down with an ever-brightening and more baleful effulgence, an ardor that became always more insupportable. It was as if the whole life of the garden turned and rose and flamed and swiftened ecstatically to some infernal culmination.

King Adompha had lost all memory of Dwerulas and his dark magic. In his senses burned the ardor of the hell-risen orb, and he seemed to share the delirious motion and ecstasy of those obscure shapes by which he was surrounded. A mad ichor mounted in his blood; before him hovered the vague images of pleasures he had never

known or suspected: pleasures in which he would pass far beyond the
ordained limits of mortal sensation.

Then, amid that whirling phantasmagoria, he heard the screeching
of a voice that was harsh as some rusty hinge on the lifted lid of a sarcophagus. He could not understand the words: but, as if a spell of stillness had been uttered, the whole garden resumed immediately a hushed
and hooded aspect. The king stood in a very stupor: for the voice had
been that of Dwerulas! He looked about him wildly, bemazed and bewildered, seeing only the still plants with their mantling of profuse leafage. Before him towered a growth which he somehow recognized as
the *dedaim,* though its bulb-shaped bole and elongated branches had
put forth a matted-mass of dark, hairlike filaments.

Very slowly and gently, the two topmost branches of the *dedaim*
descended till their tips were level with Adompha's face. The slender,
tapering hands of Thuloneah emerged from their foliage and began to
caress the king's cheeks with that loverlike adroitness which he still
remembered. At the same moment, he saw the thick hairy matting fall
apart upon the broad and flattish top of the *dedaim's* bole; and from it,
as if rearing from hunched shoulders, the small, wizened head of
Dwerulas rose up to confront him. . . .

Still gazing in vacuous horror at the crushed and blood-clotted
cranium, at the features sered and blackened as if by centuries, at the
eyes that glowed in dark pits like embers blown by demons, Adompha
had the confused impression of a multitude of people that hurled
themselves upon him from every side. There were no longer any trees
in that garden of mad minglings and sorcerous transformations. About
him in the fiery air swam faces that he recalled only too well: faces now
contorted with malign rage, and the lethal lust of revenge. Through an
irony which Dwerulas alone could have conceived, the soft fingers of
Thuloneah continued to caress him, while he felt the clutching of
numberless hands that tore all his garments into rags and shredded all
his flesh with their nails

The Voyage of King Euvoran

The crown of the kings of Ustaim was fashioned only from the rarest materials that could be procured anywhere. The magically graven gold of its circlet had been mined from a huge meteor that fell in the southern isle of Cyntrom, shaking the isle from shore to shore with calamitous earthquake; and the gold was harder and brighter than any native gold of Earth, and was changeable in color from a flamelike red to the yellow of young moons. It was set with thirteen jewels, every one of which was unique and without fellow even in fable. These jewels were a wonder to behold, starring the circlet with strange unquiet fires and fulgurations terrible as the eyes of the cockatrice. But more wonderful than all else was the stuffed gazolba-bird which formed the superstructure of the crown, gripping the circlet with its steely claws above the wearer's brow, and towering royally with resplendent plumage of green, violet and vermilion. Its beak was the hue of burnished brass, its eyes were like small dark garnets in bezels of silver; and seven lacy, carmine quills arose from its ebon-dappled head, and a white tail fell down in a straightly spreading fan like the beams of some white sun behind the circle. The gazolba-bird was the last of its kind, according to the mariners who had slain it in an almost legendary isle beyond Sotar, far to the east of Zothique. For nine generations it had decked the crown of Ustaim, and the kings looked upon it as the sacred emblem of their fortunes, and a talisman inseparable from their royalty, whose loss would be followed by grave disaster.

Euvoran, the son of Karpoom, was the ninth wearer of the crown. Superbly and magnificently he had worn it for two years and ten months, following the death of Karpoom from a surfeit of stuffed eels and jellied salamanders' eggs. On all state occasions, levees, and daily grantings of public audience and administerings of justice, it had graced the brow of the young king and had conferred upon him a dreadful majesty in the eyes of the beholders. Also, it had served to conceal the lamentable increase of an early baldness.

It came to pass, in the late autumn of the third year of his reign, that King Euvoran rose from a goodly breakfast of twelve courses and twelve wines, and went forth as was his custom to the hall of justice, which occupied an entire wing of his palace in the city of Aramoam, looking down in several-colored marble from its palmy hills to the rippled lazuli of the orient ocean.

Being well fortified by his breakfast, Euvoran felt himself prepared to unravel the most involute skeins of legality and crime, and was likewise ready for the meting of swift punishment to all malefactors. And beside him, at the right arm of his kraken-sculptured throne of ivory, there stood an executioner leaning on a huge mace with a leaden head that was tempered to the hardness of iron. Full often, with this mace, the bones of the more flagitious offenders were broken immediately, or their brains were split in the king's presence on a floor that was strewn with black sand. And beside the left arm of the throne, a professional torturer busied himself continually with the screws and pulleys of certain fearsome instruments of torture, as a warning of their fate to all evil-doers. And not always idle were the turnings of these screws and the tightenings of these pulleys, and not always empty were the metal beds of the machines.

Now, on that morning, the constables of the city brought before King Euvoran only a few petty thieves and suspicious vagrants; and there were no cases of felony such as would have warranted the wielding of the mace or the use of the torture-implements. So the king, who had looked forward to a pleasurable session, was somewhat balked and disappointed; and he questioned with much severity the minor culprits before him, trying to extort from each of them, in turn, an admission of some graver crime than that whereof he was accused. But it seemed that the pilferers were innocent of aught but pilfering; and the vagrants were guilty of naught worse than vagrancy; and Euvoran began to think that the morning would offer scant entertainment. For the bastinado was the heaviest punishment that he could legally impose on such misdemeanants.

"Away with these mackerel!" he roared to the officers, and his crown shook with indignation, and the tall gazolba-bird on the crown appeared to nod and bow. "Away with them, for they pollute my presence. Give each of them a hundred strokes with the hardwood briar on the bare sole of each foot, and forget not the heels. Then drive them forth from Aramoam toward the public refuse-grounds, and prod them with red-hot tridents if they linger in their crawling."

Then, ere the officers could obey him, there entered the hall of justice two belated constables, haling between them a peculiar and most unsavory individual with the long-handled, many-pointed hooks that were used in Aramoam for the apprehending of malefactors and suspects. And though the hooks were seemingly embedded in his flesh as well as in the filthy rags that served him for raiment, the prisoner bounded perpetually aloft in the manner of a goat, and his captors were obliged to follow in these lively and undignified saltations, so that the three presented the appearance of tumblers. With a final volitation in which the officers were drawn through the air like the tails of a kite, the incredible personage came to a pause before Euvoran. The king regarded him in amazement, blinking rapidly, and was not prepossessed by the singular suppleness with which he louted to the very floor, upsetting the scarce-recovered equilibrium of the officers, and causing them to sprawl at full length in the royal presence.

"Ha! what have we now?" said the king in an ominous voice.

"Sire, 'tis another vagabond," replied the breathless officers, when they had regained a more respectfully inclined position. "He would have passed through Aramoam by the main avenue in the fashion that you behold, without stopping, and without even lessening the altitude of his saltations, if we had not arrested him."

"Such behavior is highly suspicious," growled Euvoran hopefully. "Prisoner, declare your name, your nativity and occupation, and the infamous crimes of which, beyond doubt, you are guilty."

The captive, who was cross-eyed, appeared to regard Euvoran, the royal mace-wielder, and the royal torturer and his instruments all in a single glance. He was ill-favored to an extravagant degree, his nose, ears and other features were all possessed of unnatural mobility, and he grimaced perpetually in a manner that caused his unclean beard to toss and curl like sea-weed on a boiling whirlpool.

"I have many names," he replied, in an insolent voice whose pitch was peculiarly disagreeable to Euvoran, setting his teeth on edge like the grating of metal upon glass. "As for my nativity and occupation, the knowledge of these, O king, would profit you little."

"Sirrah, you are malapert. Give answer, or tongues of red-hot iron shall question you," roared Euvoran.

"Be it known to you, then, that I am a necromancer, and was born in the realm where the dawn and the sunset come together and the moon is equal in brightness to the sun."

"Ha! a necromancer!" snorted the king. "Know you not that necromancy is a capital crime in Ustaim? Verily, we shall find means to dissuade you from the practice of such infamies."

At a sign from Euvoran, the officers drew their captive toward the instruments of torture. Much to their surprise, in view of his former ebullience, he allowed himself to be chained supinely on the iron bed that produced a remarkable elongation of the limbs of its occupants. The official engineer of these miracles began to work the levers, and the bed lengthened little by little with a surly grating, till it seemed that the prisoner's joints would be torn apart. Inch by inch was added to his stature; and though, after a time, he had gained more than a half-cubit from the stretching, he appeared to experience no discomfort whatever; and to the stupefaction of all present, it became plain that the elasticity of his arms, legs and body was beyond the extensibility of the rack itself; for the latter was now drawn to its limit.

All were silent, viewing this prodigy; and Euvoran rose from his seat and went over to the rack, as if doubtful of his own eyes that testified to a thing so enormous. And the prisoner said to him:

"It were well to release me, O King Euvoran."

"Say you so?" the king cried out in a rage. "However, it is not thus that we deal with felons in Ustaim." And he made a private sign to the executioner, who came forward quickly, rearing his massive, leaden-headed mace aloft.

"On your own head be it," said the necromancer, and he rose instantly from the iron bed, breaking the bonds that held him, as if they had been chains of grass. Then, towering to a terrible height, which the wrenchings of the rack had given him, he pointed his long forefinger, dark and sere as that of a mummy, at the king's crown; and simultaneously he uttered a foreign word that was shrill and eldritch as the crying of migrant fowl that pass over toward unknown shores in the night. And lo! as if in answer to that word, there was a loud, sudden flapping of wings above Euvoran's head and the king felt that his brow was lightened of the crown's goodly and well-accustomed weight. A shadow fell upon him, and he, and all who were present, beheld above them in the air the stuffed gazolba-bird, which had been slain more than two hundred years before by sea-faring men in a remote isle. The wings of the bird, a living splendor, were outspread as if for flight, and it carried still in its steely claws the rare circlet of the crown. Librating, it hung for a little over the throne, while the king watched it in wordless awe and consternation. Then, with metallic whirring, its white tail deployed like the beams of a flying sun, it flew swiftly through the open portals, and passed seaward from Aramoam into the morning light.

After it, with great bounds and goatish leapings, the necromancer followed; and no man tried to deter him. But those who saw him depart from the city swore that he went north along the ocean-strand, while the bird flew directly eastward, as if homing to the half-fabulous isle of its nativity. Thereafter, as if he had gone at a single bound into alien realms, the necromancer was not seen in Ustaim. But the crew of a merchant galley from Sotar, landing later in Aramoam, told how the gazolba-bird had passed over them in mid-main, a several-colored glory still flying toward the sources of the dayspring. And they said that the crown of changeable gold, with its thirteen fellowless gems, was still carried by the bird. And though they had trafficked long in the archipelagoes of wonder, and had seen many prodigies, they deemed this thing a most rare and unexampled portent.

King Euvoran, so strangely reft of that avian headgear, with his baldness rudely bared to the gaze of thieves and vagrants in the hall of justice, was as one on whom the gods have sent down a sudden bolt. If the sun had turned black in heaven, or his palace walls had crumbled about him, his dumbfoundment would hardly have been more excessive. For it seemed to him that his royalty had flown with that crown which was the emblem and the talisman of his fathers. And, moreover, the thing was wholly against nature, and the laws of god and man were annulled thereby: since never before, in all history or fable, had a dead bird taken flight from the kingdom of Ustaim.

Indeed, the loss was a dire calamity, and Euvoran, having donned a voluminous turban of purple samite, held council with his sagest ministers regarding the state dilemma that had thus arisen. The ministers were no less troubled and perplexed than the king: for the bird and the circlet were both irreplaceable. And in the meanwhile, the rumor of this misfortune was borne abroad through Ustaim, and the land became filled with lamentable doubt and confusion, and some of the people began to murmur covertly against Euvoran, saying that no man could be the rightful ruler of that country without the gazolba-crown.

Then, as was the custom of the kings in a time of national exigence, Euvoran repaired to the temple in which dwelt the god Geol, who was a terrestrial god and the chief deity of Aramoam. Alone, with bare head and unshod feet, as was ordained by hierarchal law, he entered the dim adytum where the image of Geol, pot-bellied, and wrought of earth-brown faience, reclined eternally on its back and regarded the motes in a narrow beam of sunlight from the slotted wall. And, falling prone in the dust that had gathered around the idol through ages, the king gave homage to Geol and implored an oracle to illuminate and guide him in his need. And after an interim, a voice issued from the god's navel, as if a subterrene rumbling had become articulate. And the voice said to King Euvoran:

"Go forth and seek the gazolba in those isles that lie beneath the orient sun. There, O king, on the far coasts of dawn, thou shalt again behold the living bird which is the symbol and the fortune of thy dynasty; and there, with thine own hand, thou shalt slay the bird."

Euvoran was much comforted by this oracle, since the utterances of the god were deemed infallible. And it seemed to him that the oracle implied in plain terms that he should recover the lost crown of Ustaim, which had the reanimated bird for its superstructure. So, returning to the royal palace, he sent for the captains of his proudest argosies of war, which lay then at anchor in the tranquil harbor of Aramoam, and ordered them to make immediate provision for a long voyage into the east and among the archipelagoes of morning.

When all was made ready, King Euvoran went aboard the flagship of the fleet, which was a towering quadrireme with oars of beef-wood and sails of stout-woven byssus dyed in yellowish scarlet, and a long gonfalon at the mast-head, bearing the gazolba bird in its natural colors on a field of heavenly cobalt. The rowers and sailors of the quadrireme were mighty negroes from the north; and the soldiers who manned it were fierce mercenaries from Xylac in the west; and with him, going aboard, the king took certain of his concubines and jesters and other ministrants, as well as an ample store of liquors and rare viands, so that he should lack for nothing during the voyage. And, mindful of the prophecy of Geol, the king armed himself with a longbow and a quiver filled with parrot-feathered arrows; and he also carried a sling of lion-leather and a blow-gun of black bamboo from which tiny poisoned darts were discharged.

It seemed that the gods favored the voyage; for a wind blew strongly from the west on the morning of departure; and the fleet, which numbered fifteen vessels, was borne with bellying sails toward the sea-risen sun. And the farewell clamors and shoutings of Euvoran's people on the wharves were soon stilled by distance; and the marble houses of Aramoam on its four palmy hills were drowned in that swift-ly foundering bank of azure which was the shoreline of Ustaim. And thereafter, for many days, the iron-wood beaks of the galleys clove a softly weltering sea of indigo that rose unbroken on all sides to a cloudless, dark-blue heaven.

Trusting in the oracle of Geol, that earthen god who had never failed his fathers, the king made merry as was his wont; and reclining beneath a saffron canopy on the poop of the quadrireme, he swilled from an emerald beaker the wines and brandies that had lain in his pal-ace-vaults, storing the warmth of elder, ardent suns whereon oblivion's black rime was fallen. And he laughed at the ribaldries of his fools, at unquenchable ancient bawdries that had won the laughter of other kings in the sea-lost continents of yore. And his women diverted him with harlotries that were older than Rome or Atlantis. And ever he kept at hand, beside his couch, the weapons wherewith he hoped to hunt and slay again the gazolba-bird, according to the oracle of Geol.

The winds were unfailing and auspicious, and the fleet sped on-ward, with the great black oarsmen singing gaily at their oars, and the gorgeous sail-cloths flapping loudly, and the long banners floating on the air like straight-blown flames. After a fortnight they came to Sotar, whose low-lying coast of cassia and sago barred the sea for a hundred leagues from north to south; and in Loithe, the chief port, they paused to inquire for the gazolba-bird. There were rumors that the bird had passed above Sotar; and some of the people said that a cunning sorcerer of that isle, named Iffibos, had drawn it down through his sorcery and had closed it in a cage of sandalwood. So the king landed in Loithe, deeming his quest perhaps already nigh to its end, and went with certain of his captains and soldiers to visit Iffibos, who dwelt in a retired vale among the mountains at the island's core.

It was a tedious journey, and Euvoran was much annoyed by the huge and vicious gnats of Sotar, which were no respecters of royalty, and were always insinuating themselves under his turban. And when, after some delay and divagation in the deep jungle, he came to the house of Iffibos on a high, precarious crag, he found that the bird was merely one of the bright-plumaged vultures peculiar to the region, which Iffibos had tamed for his own amusement. So the king returned to Loithe, after declining somewhat rudely the invitation of the sorcerer, who wished to show him the unusual feats of falconry to which he had trained the vulture. And in Loithe the king tarried no longer than was needful for the laying aboard of fifty jars of the sovereign arrack in which Sotar excels all other orient lands.

Then, coasting the southern cliffs and promontories, where the sea bellowed prodigiously in mile-deep caverns, the ships of Euvoran sailed beyond Sotar, and Tosk, whose people were more akin to apes and lemurs than to men. And Euvoran asked the people for news of the gazolba, and received only a chattering as of apes in answer. So the king ordered his men-at-arms to catch a number of these savage islanders and crucify them on the coco-palms for their incivility. And the men-at-arms pursued the nimble people of Tosk for a full day among the trees and boulders in which the isle abounded, but without catching a single one of them. So the king contented himself by crucifying several of the men-at-arms for their failure to obey him and sailed on to the seven atolls of Yumatot, whose inhabitants were mostly cannibals. And beyond Yumatot, which was the usual limit of eastern voyaging from Ustaim, the vessels entered the Ilozian Sea, and began to touch at partly mythic shores and islands charted only in story.

It were tedious to relate the full particulars of that voyage, in which Euvoran and his captains went ever toward the sources of the dawn. Various and without number were the strange marvels they found in the archipelagoes beyond Yumatot; but nowhere could they find a single feather such as had formed part of the gazolba's plumage; and the quaint people of those isles had never seen the bird.

Howbeit, the king beheld many a flock of unknown, fiery-winged fowl that went over the galleys in mid-sea, passing between the unmapped islets. And, landing often, he practiced his archery on lorikeets and lyrebirds and boobies, or stalked the golden cockatoos with his blowgun. And he chased the dodo and dinornis on shores that were otherwise unpeopled. And once, in a sea of high-beetling barren rocks, the fleet was assailed by mighty griffins that flew down from their crag-built eyries, with wings shining like feathery brass under the meridian sun, and making a harsh clangor as of shields shaken in battle. And the griffins, being both ferocious and pertinacious, were driven away with much difficulty by boulders hurled from the catapults of the vessels.

Everywhere, as the ships drove eastward, there were multitudes of fowl. But at the sunset of a day in the fourth moon following their departure from Aramoam, the vessels approached a nameless isle that towered mile-high with cliffs of black, naked basalt, around whose base the sea cried with baffled anger, and about whose precipices there were no wings nor voices of birds. The isle was topped with gnarly cypresses that might have grown in a windy graveyard; and sullenly it took the afterglow, as if drenched with a gore of darkening blood. Far up in the cliffs there were strange columned eaves like the dwellings of forgotten troglodytes, but seemingly inaccessible to men; and the caves to all appearances were unoccupied by any kind of life, though pitting the face of the isle for leagues. And Euvoran ordered his captains to drop anchor, meaning to search for a landing-place on the morrow: since, in his anxiety to retrieve the gazolba, he would pass no isle of the dawnward main, not even the unlikeliest, without due inquiry and examination.

Quickly fell the darkness, without moon, till the close-anchored ships were visible to each other only by their lanterns. And Euvoran sat at supper in his cabin, sipping the golden arrack of Sotar between mouthfuls of mango-jelly and phenicopter's meat. And, saving a small watch on each of the vessels, the sailors and men-at-arms were all at evening mess; and the rowers ate their figs and lentils in the oar-decks. Then, from the watches, there was a wild shouting of alarm, and the shouting ceased in a moment, and each of the great vessels rocked and sagged in the water, as if a monstrous weight had settled upon it. No man knew the thing that had happened, but everywhere there was turmoil and confusion, some saying that the fleet was attacked by pirates. Those who peered from the ports and oar-holes saw that the lanterns of their neighbors had been quenched, and perceived a milling and seething as of low-driven clouds in the darkness, and saw that foul black creatures, large as men and winged like oupires, were clinging to the ranged oars in myriads. And those who dared to approach the open hatches found that the decks, the rigging and the masts were crowded with similar creatures, who, it seemed, were of nocturnal habit and had come down in the manner of bats from their caves in the island.

Then, like things of nightmare, the monsters began to invade the hatches and assail the ports, clawing with hellish talons at the men who opposed them. And, being somewhat hampered by their wings, they were driven back with spears and arrows, but returned again and again in a thickening press without number, cheeping with a faint and bat-like sound. It was plain that they were vampires, for whenever they had dragged a man down, as many of them as could gain mouthhold would fasten upon him incontinently, and suck his blood till little more re-

mained than a skinful of bones. The upper oar-decks, being half open
to the sky, were quickly usurped, and their crews overcome with a hideous swarming; and the rowers in the orlops cried that the sea-water
was pouring in through the oar-holes as the ships sank deeper beneath
an ever-gathering weight.

All night, at the ports and hatches, the men of Euvoran fought the
vampires, taking turns in shifts when they wearied. Many of them were
seized and their blood sucked before the eyes of their fellows as the
night wore on; and the vampires, it seemed, were not to be slain by
mortal weapons, though the blood they had gorged came forth in
spouting rills from their wounded bodies. And thicklier they clustered
upon the fleet, till the biremes began to founder, and the rowers were
drowned in the sunken lower decks of certain triremes and quadri-
remes.

King Euvoran was wroth at this unseemly turmoil that had interrupted his supper; and when the golden arrack was spilt and the dishes
of rare meat were emptied on the floor by the vessel's violent rocking,
he would have issued from his cabin, fully armed, to try conclusions
with these piacular miscreants. But, even as he turned to fling wide the
cabin-door, there was a soft infernal pittering at the port-holes behind
him; and the women who were with him began to shriek, and the fools
cried out in terror. And the king saw in the lamplight a grisly face with
the teeth and nostrils of a flittermouse, that leaned in through one of
the cabin-ports. He sought to repel the face, and thereafter, till dawn,
he fought the vampires with those very weapons he had designed for
the slaying of the gazolba; and the ship's captain, who was with him at
supper, guarded a second port with his claymore; and the others were
held by two of the king's eunuchs, armed with scimitars. In this warfare they were favored by the smallness of the ports, which could hardly in any case have allowed the free passage of their winged assailants.
And, after lightless hours of tedious, horrid struggle, the darkness became thinned with brown twilight, and the vampires lifted from the

vessels in a black cloud and returned to their caves in the mile-high cliffs of that unnamed island.

Heavy was the heart of Euvoran within him when he surveyed the damage done to his proud argosies of war: for, among the fifteen vessels, seven had sunk in the night, borne under and swamped by those obscenely clinging hordes of oupires; and the decks of the others were bloody as abattoirs; and half of their sailors and rowers and men-at-arms were lying flat and flaccid as empty wineskins after the greedy drinking of the great bats. And the sails and banners were shredded into rags; and everywhere, from beak to rudder of Euvoran's galleys, there was the stain and reek of a Stymphalian foulness. So, lest another eve should find them within wing-shot of that accursed isle, the king ordered his remaining captains to weigh anchor: and the other ships, with sea-water still awash in their orlops, and some with drowned rowers still at the oars of their nether banks, drew slowly and heavily to eastward, till the pitted walls of the isle began to sink beneath the main. At eve there was no land in sight anywhere; and after two days, still unharried by the vampires, they came to a coral island, low in the wave, with a calm lagoon that was haunted only by ocean-fowl. And there, for the first time, Euvoran paused to repair his tattered sails, and pump the sea from his holds, and clean the blood and vileness from his decks.

However, in spite of this disaster, the king abated not in any degree his purpose, to sail ever on toward the fountains of the day, until, as Geol had predicted, he should come again on the flown gazolba and slay it with his own royal hand. So, for another moon, they passed amid other and stranger archipelagoes, and penetrated deeplier into the regions of myth and story.

Bravely they drove into mornings of amaranth crossed by gilded lories, and noontides of darkly ardent sapphire where the rose flamingoes went before them to lost, inviolate strands. The stars changed above them, and under the alien-figured Signs they heard the wild, melancholy crying of swans that flew southward fleeing the winter of realms indiscoverable, and seeking the summer in trackless worlds. And they held speech with fabulous men who wore for mantles the ell-wide pennons of the roc, trailing far on the earth behind them; and men who arrayed themselves in aepyornis plumes. And they spoke also with antic people whose bodies were covered with a down like that of new-hatched fowl, and others whose flesh was studded as if with pin-feathers. But nowhere could they learn aught of the gazolba.

At mid-forenoon, early in the sixth month of the voyage, a new and unheard-of shore ascended from the deep, curving for many miles, from north-east to south-west, with sheltered harbors, and cliffs and pinnacled crags that were interspaced with low-lying verdurous dales. As the galleys hove toward it, Euvoran and his captains saw that towers were builded on certain of the highmost crags; but in the haven below them there were no ships at anchor nor boats moving; and the shore of the haven was a wilderness of green trees and grass. And, sailing still nearer, and entering the harbor, they descried no evident sign of man, other than the crag-reared towers.

The place, however, was full of an extraordinary number and variety of birds, ranging in size from little tits and passerines to creatures of greater wing-spread than eagle or condor. They circled over the ships in coveys and great, motley flocks, seeming to be both curious and wary; and Euvoran saw that a winged concourse, as it were, went to and fro above the woods and about the cliffs and towers. He bethought him that here was a likely haunt in which to track down the gazolba; so, arming himself for the chase, he went ashore in a small boat with several of his men.

The birds, even the largest, were patently timid and inoffensive; for when the king landed on the beach, the very trees appeared to take flight, so numerous were the fowl that soared and flew inland, or sought the crags and pinnacles that rose beyond bow-shot. None remained of the multitude visible shortly before; and Euvoran marvelled at such cunning; and moreover he was somewhat exasperated, for he wished not to depart without bringing down a trophy of his skill, even though he should fail to find the gazolba itself. And he deemed the behavior of the birds all the more curious because of the island's solitude: for here there were no paths other than would be made by forest animals; and the woods and meadows were wholly wild and incult; and the towers were seemingly desolate, with sea-fowl and land-fowl flying in and out of their empty windows.

The king and his men combed the deserted woods along the shore, and came to a steep slope of bushes and dwarf cedars, whose upper incline approached the tallest tower at one side. Here, at the slope's bottom, Euvoran saw a small owl that slept in one of the cedars, as if wholly unaware of the commotion made by the other birds in their flight. And Euvoran trained an arrow and shot down the owl, though ordinarily he would have spared a prey so paltry. And he was about to pick up the fallen owl, when one of the men who accompanied him cried out as if in alarm. Then, turning his head as he stooped beneath the foliage of the cedar, the king beheld a brace of colossal birds, larger than any he had yet descried on that isle, who came down from the tower like falling thunderbolts. Before he could fit another arrow to the string, they were upon him, making a loud roar with the drumming of their mighty vans, and beating him instantly to the ground, so that he was aware of them only as a storm of dreadfully rushing plumes and a hurlyburly of cruel beaks and talons. And, before his men could rally to assist him, one of the birds fastened its huge claws in the shoulder-cape of the king's mantle, not sparing the flesh beneath in its fell clutch, and carried him away to the tower on the crag as easily as a ger-falcon would have carried a small leveret. The king was wholly helpless, and he had dropped his longbow beneath the onset of the birds, and his blowgun had been shaken loose from the girdle at which it depended, and all his darts and arrows were spilled. And he had no weapon remaining, other than a sharp misericordia; and this he could not use to any purpose against his captor in mid-air.

Swiftly he neared the tower, with a flock of lesser fowl circling about him and shrieking as if with derision till he was deafened by their din. And a sickness came upon him because of the height to which he had been carried and the violence of his ascent; and giddily he saw the walls of the tower sink past him with wide and portal-like windows. Then, as he began to retch in his sickness, he was borne in through one of the windows and was dropped rudely on the floor of a high and spacious chamber.

He sprawled at full length on his face and lay vomiting for awhile, heedless of his surroundings. Then, recovering somewhat, he raised himself to a sitting position, and beheld before him, above a sort of dais, an enormous perch of red gold and yellow ivory wrought in the form of a new crescent arching upward. The perch was supported between posts of black jasper flecked as if with blood, and upon it there sat a most gigantic and uncommon bird, eyeing Euvoran with a grim and dreadful and austere mien, as an emperor might eye the gutter-scum that his guards have haled before him for some obscene offense. The plumage of the bird was Tyrian purple, and his beak was like a mighty pickaxe of pale bronze that darkened greenly toward the point, and he clutched the perch with iron talons that were longer than the mailed fingers of a warrior. His head was adorned with quills of turquoise blue and amber yellow, like a many pointed crown; and about his long, unfeathered throat, rough as the scaled skin of a dragon, he wore a singular necklace composed of human heads, and the heads of various ferine beasts such as the weasel, the wildcat, the stoat and the fox, all of which had been reduced to a common size and were no larger than groundnuts.

Euvoran was terrified by the aspect of this fowl; and his alarm was not lessened when he saw that many other birds of a size inferior only to his were sitting about the chamber on less costly and less elevated perches, even as grandees of the realm might sit in the presence of their sovereign. And behind Euvoran, like guards, there stood together with its fellow the creatures that had rapt him to the tower.

Now, to his utter confounding, the great Tyrian-feathered bird addressed him in human speech. And the bird said to him in a harsh but magniloquent and majestic voice:

"Too hardily, O filth of mankind, thou hast intruded on the peace of Ornava, isle that is sacred to the birds, and wantonly thou hast slain one of my subjects. For know that I am the monarch of all birds that fly, walk, wade or swim on this terraqueous globe of Earth; and in Ornava is my seat and my capital. Verily, justice shall be done upon thee for thy crime. But if thou hast aught to say in thy defense, I will give thee hearing now, for I would not that even the vilest of earthly vermin, and the most pernicious, should accuse me of inequity or tyranny."

Then, blustering somewhat, though sorely afraid at heart, Euvoran gave answer to the bird, and said:

"I came hither seeking the gazolba, which adorned my crown in Ustaim, and was feloniously reft from me together with the crown through the spell of a lawless necromancer. And know that I am Euvoran, King of Ustaim, and I bow me to no bird, not even the mightiest of that species."

Thereat the ruler of the birds, as if amazed and more indignant than before, made question of Euvoran and interrogated him sharply concerning the gazolba. And, learning that this bird had been slain by sailors and afterwards stuffed, and that the whole purpose of Euvoran in his voyage was to catch and kill it a second time and re-stuff it if necessary, the ruler cried in a great and wrathful voice:

"This helpeth not thy case, but showeth thee guilty of a twofold crime and a triple infamy: for thou hast owned a most abominable thing, and one that subverteth nature. In this my tower, as is right and proper, I keep the bodies of men that my taxidermists have stuffed for me; but truly, it is not allowable nor sufferable that man should do thus to birds. So, for the sake of justice and retribution, I shall presently commit thee to the care of my taxidermists. Indeed, methinks that a stuffed king (since even the vermin have kings) will serve to enhance my collection."

After that, he addressed Euvoran's guards and enjoined them: "Away with this vileness. Confide it to the man-cage, and maintain a strict watch before it."

Euvoran, urged and directed by the pecking of his guards, was compelled to climb a sort of sloping ladder with broad rungs of teak, that led from the chamber to one above it in the tower's top. In the center of this room there was a bamboo cage of capacity more than ample for the housing of six men. The king was driven into the cage, and the birds bolted the door upon him with their claws, which seemed to have the deftness of fingers. Thereafter one of them remained beside the cage, eyeing Euvoran vigilantly through the spaces of the bars; and the other flew away through a great window and did not return.

The king sat down on a litter of straw, since the cage contained no better provision for his comfort. Despair was heavy upon him, and it seemed that his plight was both dreadful and ignominious. And sorely was he astonished, that a bird should speak with human speech, insulting and reviling humankind; and he deemed it an equally monstrous thing that a bird should dwell in royal state, with servitors to do his will, and the pomp and power of a king. And, pondering these unholy prodigies, Euvoran waited for his doom in the man-cage; and after awhile, water and raw grain were brought to him in earthen vessels; but he could not eat the grain. And still later, as the day drew toward afternoon, he heard a shouting of men and a shrieking of birds below the tower; and above these noises, anon, there were clashings as of weapons and thuddings as of boulders loosened from the crag. So Euvoran knew that his sailors and soldiers, having seen him borne into captivity in the tower, were assailing the place in an effort to succor him. And the noises waxed, mounting to a most tremendous and atrocious din, and there were cries as of people mortally wounded, and a vengeful shrilling as of harpies in battle. Then, presently, the clamor ebbed away, and the shoutings grew faint, and Euvoran knew that his men had failed to take the tower. And hope waned within him, dying in a darker murk of despair.

So the afternoon went over, declining seaward, and the sun touched Euvoran with its level beams through a western window and colored the bars of his cage with a mockery of gold. Presently the light flowed from the room, and after awhile the twilight rose, weaving a tremulous phantom web on the pale air. And between the sunset and the darkness, a night-guard came in to relieve the day-flying fowl who warded the captive king. The newcomer was a nyctalops with glowing yellow eyes, and he stood taller than Euvoran himself, and was formed and feathered somewhat in the burly fashion of an owl, and he had the stout legs of a megapode. Euvoran was uncomfortably aware of the bird's eyes, which burned upon him with a brighter bale as the dusk deepened. Hardly could he sustain that ever vigilant scrutiny. But anon the moon rose, being but little past the full, and poured a spectral quicksilver into the room, and paled the eyes of the bird; and Euvoran conceived a desperate plan.

His captors, deeming all his weapons lost, had neglected to remove from his girdle the misericordia, which was long and double-edged and needle-sharp at the tip. And stealthily he gripped the hilt of the misericordia under his mantle, and feigned a sudden illness with groanings and tossings and convulsions that threw him against the bars. And, even as he had schemed, the great nyctalops came nearer, curious to learn what ailed the king; and stooping, he leaned his owl-like head between the bars above Euvoran. And the king, pretending a more violent convulsion, drew the misericordia from its sheath and struck quickly at the outstretched throat of the bird.

Shrewdly the thrust went home, piercing the deepest veins, and the squawking of the bird was choked by his own blood; and he fell, flapping noisily, so that Euvoran feared that all the occupants of the tower would be awakened by the sound. But it seemed that his fears were bootless; for none came to the chamber; and soon the flappings ceased, and the nyctalops lay still in a great heap of ruffled feathers. Thereupon the king proceeded with his plan, and shot back the bolts of the wide-latticed bamboo door with small difficulty. Then, going to the head of the teak-wood ladder which ran to the room beneath, he looked down and beheld the ruler of the birds asleep in the moonlight on his chryselephantine perch, with his terrible pickaxe beak under his wing. And Euvoran was afraid to descend into the chamber, lest the ruler should awake and see him. And also, it occurred to him that the lower stories of the tower might well be guarded by such fowl as the nocturnal creature he had slain.

Again his despair returned upon him; but being of a sleightful and crafty bent, Euvoran bethought him of another scheme. With much labor, using the misericordia, he skinned the mighty nyctalops, and cleaned the blood from its plumage as best he could. Then Euvoran wrapped himself in the skin, with the head of the nyctalops rearing above his own head, and eyeholes in its burly throat through which he could look out amid the feathers. And the skin fitted him well enough because of his pigeon-breast and his potbelly; and his spindle shanks were hidden behind the heavy shanks of the bird as he walked.

Then, imitating the gait and carriage of this fowl, the king descended the ladder, treading cautiously to avoid a fall and making little noise, lest the ruler of the birds should awaken and detect his imposture. And the ruler was all alone, and he slept without stirring while Euvoran reached the floor and crossed the chamber stealthily to another ladder, leading to the next room below.

In this room there were many great birds asleep on perches, and the king was nigh to perishing with terror as he passed among them. Some of the birds moved a little and chirped drowsily, as if aware of his presence; but none challenged him. And he went down to a third room, and was startled to see therein the standing figures of many men, some in the garb of sailors, and others clad like merchants, and others nude and ruddled with bright ores like savages. And the men were still and stark as if enchanted; and the king feared them little less than he had feared the birds. But, remembering that which the ruler had told him, he divined that these were persons who had been captured even as he himself, and had been slain by the birds and preserved through the art of an avian taxidermy. And, trembling, he passed down to another room, which was full of stuffed cats and tigers and serpents and various other enemies of bird-kind. And the room below this was the ground story of the tower, and its windows and portals were guarded by several gigantic night-fowl similar to those whose skin was worn by the king. Here, indeed, was his greatest peril and the supreme trial of his courage; for the birds eyed him alertly with their fiery golden orbs, and they greeted him with a soft whoo-whooing as of owls. And the knees of Euvoran knocked together behind the bird-shanks; but, imitating the sound in reply, he passed among the guards and was not molested by them. And, reaching an open portal of the tower, he saw the moonlit rock of the crag lying at a distance of no more than two cubits below him; and he hopped from the door-sill in the manner of a fowl, and found his way precariously from ledge to ledge along the crag, till he reached the upper beginning of that declivity at whose bottom he had slain the little owl. Here his descent was easier, and he came anon to the woods around the harbor.

But, ere he could enter the woods, there was a shrill singing of arrows about him, and the king was wounded slightly by one of the arrows, and he roared out in anger, and dropped the mantling bird-skin. Thereby, no doubt, he was saved from death at the hands of his own men, who were coming through the wood with intent to assail the tower at night. And, learning this, the king forgave the jeopardy in which their arrows had placed him. But he thought it best to refrain from attacking the tower, and to quit the isle with all dispatch. So, returning to his flagship, he ordered all his captains to set sail immediately; for, knowing the baleful power of the bird-monarch, he was more than apprehensive of pursuit; and he deemed it well to place a wide interval of sea between his vessels and that isle ere dawn. So the galleys drew from the tranquil harbor, and rounding a north-eastern promontory, they went due east in a course contrary to the moon. And, Euvoran, sitting in his cabin, regaled himself with a variety and plenitude of viands to make up for his fasting in the man-cage; and he drank a whole gallon of palm-wine and added thereto a jarful of the puissant pale-gold arrack of Sotar.

Halfway betwixt midnight and morn, when the isle of Ornava was left far behind, the steersmen of the vessels beheld a wall of ebon cloud that rose swiftly athwart the lowering moon. Higher it climbed upon the heavens, spreading and toppling in towers of thunder, till the storm overtook Euvoran's fleet and drove it on as if with the loosed hurricanes of hell through a weltering of unstarred chaos. The ships were sundered in the gloom and were borne far apart; and at daybreak the king's quadrireme was alone in a prone-rushing tumult of mingled wave and cloud; and the mast was shattered, along with most of the beef-wood oars; and the vessel was a toy for the demons of the tempest.

For three days and nights, with no glimmer of sun or star discerned through the ever-boiling murk, the vessel was hurled onward as if caught in a cataract of elements pouring to some bottomless gulf beyond the verges of the world. And early on the fourth day the clouds were somewhat riven; but a wind still blew like the breath of perdition. Then, lifting darkly through the spray and vapor, a half-seen land arose before the prow, and the helmsman and the rowers were wholly helpless to turn the doomed ship from its course. And shortly after, with a great crashing of its carven beak, and a terrible rending of timbers, the vessel struck on a low reef hidden by the flying foam, and its lower decks were flooded quickly. And the vessel began to founder, with the poop tilting sharply and more sharply, and the water frothing at the lee bulwarks.

Gaunt and cragged and austere was the shore beyond the reef, beheld only through the veils of the sea's foaming fury. And scant, it seemed, was the hope of reaching land. But, ere the wrecked argosy had gone beneath him, Euvoran lashed himself with ropes of coir to an empty wine-barrel, and cast himself from the sloping deck. And those of his men who were not already drowned in the hold or swept overboard by the typhoon, leapt after him into that high wallowing sea, some trusting only to their might as swimmers and others clinging to casks or broken spars or planks. And most were drawn under in the seething maelstroms or were beaten to death on the rocks; and of all the ship's company, the king alone survived and was cast ashore with the breath of life unquenched within him by the bitter sea.

Half-drowned and senseless, he lay where the surf had spewed him on a shelving beach. Soon the gale forgot its violence, and the billows came in with falling crests, and the clouds went over in a rack of pearl, and the sun, climbing above the rocks, shone down upon Euvoran from a deep immaculate azure. And the king, still dazed from the buffeting rudeness of the sea, heard dimly and as if in dream the shrilling of an unknown bird. Then, opening his eyes, he beheld betwixt himself and the sun, librating on spread wings, that various-colored glory of plumes and feathers which he knew as the gazolba. Crying again with a voice that was harsh and shrill as that of the peafowl, the bird hung above him for a moment, and then flew inland through a rift among the crags.

Forgetful of all his hardships and the loss of his proud galleys of war, the king unbound himself in haste from the empty barrel; and, rising giddily, he followed the bird. And, though he was now weaponless, it seemed to him that the fulfillment of the oracle of Geol was at hand. And hopefully he armed himself with a great cudgel of driftwood and gathered heavy pebbles from the beach as he pursued the gazolba.

Beyond the cleft in the high and rugged crags, he found a sheltered valley with quiet-flowing springs, and woods of exotic leaf, and fragrant orient shrubs in blossom. Here, from bough to bough before his astounded eyes, there darted great numbers of fowl that wore the gaudy plumage of the gazolba; and among them he was unable to distinguish the one he had followed, deeming it the avian garniture of his lost crown. The multitude of these birds was a thing beyond his comprehension: since he and all his people had thought the stuffed fowl unique and fellowless throughout the world, even as the other components of the crown of Ustaim. And it came to him that his fathers had been deceived by the mariners who had slain the birds in a remote isle, swearing later that it was the last of its kind.

However, though wrath and confusion were in his heart, Euvoran bethought him that a single bird from out the flock would still stand as the emblem and the talisman of his royalty in Ustaim, and would vindicate his quest among the isles of dawn. So, with a valiant hurling of sticks and stones, he tried to bring down one of the gazolbas. And ever before him as he chased them, the birds flew from tree to tree with a horrid shrieking, and a flurry of plumes that wrought an imperial splendor on the air. And at length, by his own good aim or the cast of chance, Euvoran slew him a gazolba.

As he went to retrieve the fallen bird, he saw a man in tattered raiment of an uncouth cut, armed with a rude bow, and carrying over his shoulder a brace of gazolbas tied together at the feet with tough grass. And the man wore in lieu of other headgear the skin and feathers of the same fowl. He came toward Euvoran, shouting indistinctly through his matted beard; and the king beheld him with surprise and anger, and cried loudly:

"Vile serf, how darest thou to kill the bird that is sacred to the kings of Ustaim? And knowest thou not that only the kings may wear the bird for headgear? I, who am King Euvoran, shall hold you to a dire accounting of these deeds."

At this, eyeing Euvoran strangely, the man laughed a long and derisive laugh, as if he deemed the king a person somewhat addled in his wits. And he seemed to find much merriment in the aspect of the king, whose garments were draggled and were stiff and stained with the drying sea-water, and whose turban had been snatched away by the felon waves, leaving his baldness without disguise. And when he had done laughing, the man said:

"Verily, this is the first and only jest that I have heard in nine years, and my laughter must be forgiven. For nine years agone I was shipwrecked on this isle, being a sea-captain from the far southwestern land of Ullotroi, and the sole member of my ship's company that survived and came safe to shore. In all those years I have held speech with no other man, since the isle is remote from the maritime routes, and has no people other than the birds. And as for your questions, they are readily answered: I kill these fowl to avert the pangs of famine, since there is little else on the isle for sustenance, apart from roots and berries. And I wear on my head the skin and feathers of the fowl because my tarboosh was stolen by the sea whenas it flung me rudely upon this strand. And I wot not of the strange laws that you mention; and moreover, your kingship is a matter that concerns me little, since the isle is kingless, and you and I are alone thereon, and I am the stronger of us twain and the better armed. Therefore be well advised, O King Euvoran; and since you have slain yourself a bird, I counsel you to pick up the bird and come with me. Truly, it may be that I can help you in the matter of spitting and broiling this fowl: for I must deem that you are more familiar with the products of the culinary art than with the practice."

Now, hearing all this, the wrath of Euvoran sank within him like a flame that fails for oil. Clearly he saw the plight to which his voyage had brought him in the end; and bitterly he discerned the irony that was hidden in the true oracle of Geol. And he knew that the wreckage of his fleet of war was scattered among lost islands or blown into seas unvoyageable. And it came to him that never again should he see the marble houses of Aramoam, nor live in pleasant luxury, nor administer the dooms of law between the torturer and the executioner in the hall of justice, nor wear the gazolba-crown amid the plaudits of his people. So, not being utterly bereft of reason, he bowed him to his destiny. And he said to the sea-captain:

"There is sense in what you say. Therefore, lead on."

Then, laden with the spoils of the chase, Euvoran and the captain, whose name was Naz Obbamar, repaired companionably to a cave in the rocky hill-slope of the isle's interior, which Naz Obbamar had chosen for his abode. Here the captain made a fire of dry cedar boughs, and showed the king the proper manner in which to pluck his fowl and broil it over the fire, turning it slowly on a spit of green camphor-wood. And Euvoran, being famished, found the meat of the gazolba far from unpalatable, though somewhat lean and strongly flavored. And after they had eaten, Naz Obbamar brought out from the cave a rough jar of the island clay containing a wine he had made from certain berries; and he and Euvoran drank from the jar by turns, and told each other the tale of their adventures, and forgot for awhile the rudeness and desolation of their plight.

Thereafter they shared the isle of gazolbas, killing and eating the birds as their hunger ordained. Sometimes, for a great delicacy, they slew and ate some other fowl that was more rarely met on the isle, though common enough, perhaps in Ustaim or Ullotroi. And King Euvoran made him a headdress from the skin and plumes of the gazolba, even as Naz Obbamar had done. And this was the fashion of their days till the end.

A Phantasy

I have dreamt of an unknown land—a land remote in ulterior time, and alien space not ascertainable; the desert of a long-completed past, upon which has settled the bleak, irrevocable silence of infinitude; where all is ruined save the stone of tombs and cenotaphs; and where the sole peoples are the kingless, uncounted tribes of the subterranean dead.

Above this land of my dream, citied with tombs and cenotaphs, a red and smouldering sun maintains a spectral day, in alternation with an ashen moon through the black ether where the stars have long since perished. And through the hush of the consummation of time, above the riven monuments and crumbled records of alien history, flit in the final twilight the mysterious wings of seraphim, sent to fulfill ineffable errands, or confer with demons of the abyss; and black, gigantic angels, newly returned from missions of destruction, pause amid the sepulchers to sift from their gloomy and tremendous vans the pale ashes of annihilated stars.

THE ISLE OF THE TORTURERS

B etween the sun's departure and return, the Silver Death had fallen upon Yoros. Its advent, however, had been foretold in many prophecies, both immemorial and recent. Astrologers had said that this mysterious malady, heretofore unknown on earth, would descend from the great star, Achernar, which presided balefully over all the lands of the southern continent of Zothique; and having sealed the flesh of a myriad men with its bright, metallic pallor, the plague would still go onward in time and space, borne by the dim currents of ether to other worlds.

Dire was the Silver Death; and none knew the secret of its contagion or the cure. Swift as the desert wind, it came into Yoros from the devastated realm of Tasuun, overtaking the very messengers who ran by night to give warning of its nearness. Those who were smitten felt an icy, freezing cold, an instant rigor, as if the outermost gulf had breathed upon them. Their faces and bodies whitened strangely, gleaming with a wan luster, and became stiff as long-dead corpses, all in an interim of minutes.

In the streets of Silpon and Siloar, and in Faraad, the capital of Yoros, the plague passed like an eerie, glittering light from countenance to countenance under the golden lamps; and the victims fell where they were stricken; and the deathly brightness remained upon them.

The loud, tumultuous public carnivals were stilled by its passing, and the merry-makers were frozen in frolic attitudes. In proud mansions, the wine-flushed revelers grew pale amid their garish feasts, and reclined in their opulent chairs, still holding the half-emptied cup with rigid fingers. Merchants lay in their counting-houses on the heaped coins they had begun to reckon; and thieves, entering later, were unable to depart with their booty. Diggers died in the half completed graves they had dug for others; but no one came to dispute their possession.

There was no time to flee from the strange, inevitable scourge. Dreadfully and quickly, beneath the clear stars, it breathed upon Yoros; and few were they who awakened from slumber at dawn. Fulbra, the young king of Yoros, who had but newly succeeded to the throne, was virtually a ruler without a people.

Fulbra had spent the night of the plague's advent on a high tower of his palace above Faraad: an observatory tower, equipped with astronomical appliances. A great heaviness had lain on his heart, and his thoughts were dulled with an opiate despair; but sleep was remote from his eye-lids. He knew the many predictions that foretold the Silver Death; and moreover he had read its imminent coming in the stars, with the aid of the old astrologer and sorcerer, Vemdeez. This latter knowledge he and Vemdeez had not cared to promulgate, knowing full well that the doom of Yoros was a thing decreed from all time by infinite destiny; and that no man could evade the doom, unless it were written that he should die in another way than this.

Now Vemdeez had cast the horoscope of Fulbra; and though he found therein certain ambiguities that his science could not resolve, it was nevertheless written plainly that the king would not die in Yoros. Where he would die, and in what manner, were alike doubtful. But Vemdeez, who had served Altath the father of Fulbra, and was no less devoted to the new ruler, had wrought by means of his magical art an enchanted ring that would protect Fulbra from the Silver Death in all times and places. The ring was made of a strange red metal, darker than ruddy gold or copper, and was set with a black and oblong gem, not known to terrestrial lapidaries, that gave forth eternally a strong aromatic perfume. The sorcerer told Fulbra never to remove the ring from the middle finger on which he wore it—not even in lands afar from Yoros and in days after the passing of the Silver Death: for if once the plague had breathed upon Fulbra, he would bear its subtle contagion always in his flesh; and the contagion would assume its wonted virulence with the ring's removal. But Vemdeez did not tell the origin of the red metal and the dark gem, nor the price at which the protective magic had been purchased.

With a sad heart, Fulbra had accepted the ring and had worn it; and so it was that the Silver Death blew over him in the night and harmed him not. But waiting anxiously on the high tower, and watching the golden lights of Faraad rather than the white, implacable stars, he felt a light, passing chillness that belonged not to the summer air. And even as it passed the gay noises of the city ceased; and the moaning lutes faltered strangely and expired. A stillness crept on the carnival; and some of the lamps went out and were not re-lit. In the palace beneath him there was also silence; and he heard no more the laughter of his courtiers and chamberlains. And Vemdeez came not, as was his custom, to join Fulbra on the tower at midnight. So Fulbra knew himself for a realmless king; and the grief that he still felt for the noble Altath was swollen by a great sorrow for his perished people.

Hour by hour he sat motionless, too sorrowful for tears. The stars changed above him; and Achernar glared down perpetually like the bright, cruel eye of a mocking demon; and the heavy balsam of the black-jeweled ring arose to his nostrils and seemed to stifle him. And once the thought occurred to Fulbra, to cast the ring away and die as his people had died. But his despair was too heavy upon him even for this; and so, at length, the dawn came slowly in heavens pale as the Silver Death, and found him still on the tower.

In the dawn, King Fulbra rose and descended the coiled stairs of porphyry into his palace. And midway on the stairs he saw the fallen corpse of the old sorcerer Vemdeez, who had died even as he climbed to join his master. The wrinkled face of Vemdeez was like polished metal, and was whiter than his beard and hair; and his open eyes, which had been dark as sapphires, were frosted with the plague. Then, grieving greatly for the death of Vemdeez, whom he had loved as a foster-father, the king went slowly on. And in the suites and halls below, he found the bodies of his courtiers and servants and guardsmen. And none remained alive, excepting three slaves who warded the green, brazen portals of the lower vaults, far beneath the palace.

Now Fulbra bethought him of the counsel of Vemdeez, who had urged him to flee from Yoros and to seek shelter in the southern isle of Cyntrom, which paid tribute to the kings of Yoros. And though he had no heart for this, nor for any course of action, Fulbra bade the three remaining slaves to gather food and such other supplies as were necessary for a voyage of some length, and to carry them aboard a royal barge of ebony that was moored at the palace porticoes on the river Voum,

Then, embarking with the slaves, he took the helm of the barge, and directed the slaves to unfurl the broad amber sail. And past the stately city of Faraad, whose streets were thronged with the silvery dead, they sailed on the widening jasper estuary of the Voum, and into the amaranth-colored gulf of the Indaskian Sea.

A favorable wind was behind them, blowing from the north over desolate Tasuun and Yoros, even as the Silver Death had blown in the night. And idly beside them, on the Voum, there floated seaward many vessels whose crews and captains had all died of the plague. And Faraad was still as a necropolis of old time; and nothing stirred on the estuary shores, excepting the plumy, fan-shapen palms that swayed southward in the freshening wind. And soon the green strand of Yoros receded, gathering to itself the blueness and the dreams of distance.

Creaming with a winy foam, full of strange murmurous voices and vague tales of exotic things, the halcyon sea was about the voyagers now beneath the high-lifting summer sun. But the sea's enchanted voices and its long languorous, immeasurable cradling could not

soothe the sorrow of Fulbra; and in his heart a despair abided, black as
the gem that was set in the red ring of Vemdeez.

Howbeit, he held the great helm of the ebon barge, and steered as
straightly as he could by the sun toward Cyntrom. The amber sail was
taut with the favoring wind; and the barge sped onward all that day,
cleaving the amaranth waters with its dark prow that reared in the
carven form of an ebony goddess. And when the night came with familiar austral stars, Fulbra was able to correct such errors as he had
made in reckoning the course.

For many days they flew southward; and the sun lowered a little in
its circling behind them; and new stars climbed and clustered at evening about the black goddess of the prow. And Fulbra, who had once
sailed to the isle of Cyntrom in boyhood days with his father Altath,
thought to see ere long the lifting of its shores of camphor and sandalwood from the winy deep. But in his heart there was no gladness;
and often now he was blinded by wild tears, remembering that other
voyage with Altath.

Then, suddenly and at high noon, there fell an airless calm, and the
waters became as purple glass about the barge. The sky changed to a
dome of beaten copper, arching close and low; and as if by some evil
wizardry, the dome darkened with untimely night, and a tempest rose
like the gathered breath of mighty devils and shaped the sea into vast
ridges, and abysmal valleys. The mast of ebony snapped like a reed in
the wind, and the sail was torn asunder, and the helpless vessel pitched
headlong in the dark troughs and was hurled upward through veils of
blinding foam to the giddy summits of the billows.

Fulbra clung to the useless helm, and the slaves, at his command,
took shelter in the forward cabin. For countless hours they were borne
onward at the will of the mad hurricane; and Fulbra could see naught
in the lowering gloom, except the pale crests of the beetling waves; and
he could tell no longer the direction of their course.

Then, in that lurid dusk, he beheld at intervals another vessel that rode the storm-driven sea, not far from the barge. He thought that the vessel was a galley such as might be used by merchants that voyaged among the southern isles, trading for incense and plumes and vermilion; but its oars were mostly broken, and the toppled mast and sail hung forward on the prow.

For a time the ships drove on together; till Fulbra saw, in a rifting of the gloom, the sharp and somber crags of an unknown shore, with sharper towers that lifted palely above them. He could not turn the helm; and the barge and its companion vessel were carried toward the looming rocks, till Fulbra thought that they would crash thereon. But, as if by some enchantment, even as it had risen, the sea fell abruptly in a windless calm; and quiet sunlight poured from a clearing sky; and the barge was left on a broad crescent of ochre-yellow sand between the crags and the lulling waters, with the galley beside it.

Dazed and marvelling, Fulbra leaned on the helm, while his slaves crept timidly forth from the cabin, and men began to appear on the decks of the galley. And the king was about to hail these men, some of whom were dressed as humble sailors and others in the fashion of rich merchants. But he heard a laughter of strange voices, high and shrill and somehow evil, that seemed to fall from above; and looking up he saw that many people were descending a sort of stairway in the cliffs that enclosed the beach.

The people drew near, thronging about the barge and the galley. They wore fantastic turbans of blood-red, and were clad in closely fitting robes of vulturine black. Their faces and hands were yellow as saffron; their small and slaty eyes were set obliquely beneath lashless lids; and their thin lips, which smiled eternally, were crooked as the blades of scimitars.

They bore sinister and wicked-looking weapons, in the form of saw-toothed swords and doubled-headed spears. Some of them bowed low before Fulbra and addressed him obsequiously, staring upon him all the while with an unblinking gaze that he could not fathom. Their speech was no less alien than their aspect; it was full of sharp and hissing sounds; and neither the king nor his slaves could comprehend it. But Fulbra bespoke the people courteously, in the mild and mellow-flowing tongue of Yoros, and inquired the name of this land whereon the barge had been cast by the tempest.

Certain of the people seemed to understand him, for a light came in their slaty eyes at his question; and one of them answered brokenly in the language of Yoros, saying that the land was the Isle of Uccastrog. Then, with something of covert evil in his smile, this person added that all shipwrecked mariners and seafarers would receive a goodly welcome from Ildrac, the king of the Isle.

At this, the heart of Fulbra sank within him; for he had heard numerous tales of Uccastrog in bygone years; and the tales were not such as would reassure a stranded traveller. Uccastrog, which lay far to the east of Cyntrom, was commonly known as the Isle of the Torturers; and men said that all who landed upon it unaware, or were cast thither by the seas, were imprisoned by the inhabitants and were subjected later to unending curious tortures whose infliction formed the chief delight of these cruel beings. No man, it was rumored, had ever escaped from Uccastrog; but many had lingered for years in its dungeons and hellish torture chambers, kept alive for the pleasure of King Ildrac and his followers. Also, it was believed that the Torturers were great magicians who could raise mighty storms with their enchantments, and could cause vessels to be carried far from the maritime routes, and then fling them ashore upon Uccastrog.

Seeing that the yellow people were all about the barge, and that no escape was possible, Fulbra asked them to take him at once before King Ildrac. To Ildrac he would announce his name and royal rank; and it seemed to him, in his simplicity, that one king, even though cruel-hearted, would scarcely torture another or keep him captive. Also, it might be that the inhabitants of Uccastrog had been somewhat maligned by the tales of travellers.

So Fulbra and his slaves were surrounded by certain of the throng and were led toward the palace of Ildrac, whose high, sharp towers crowned the crags beyond the beach, rising above those clustered abodes in which the island people dwelt. And while they were climbing the hewn steps in the cliff, Fulbra heard a loud outcry below and a clashing of steel against steel; and looking back, he saw that the crew of the stranded galley had drawn their swords and were fighting the islanders. But being outnumbered greatly, their resistance was borne down by the swarming Torturers; and most of them were taken alive. And Fulbra's heart misgave him sorely at this sight; and more and more did he mistrust the yellow people.

Soon he came into the presence of Ildrac, who sat on a lofty brazen chair in a vast hall of the palace. Ildrac was taller by half a head than any of his followers; and his features were like a mask of evil wrought from some pale, gilded metal; and he was clad in vestments of a strange hue, like sea-purple brightened with fresh-flowing blood. About him were many guardsmen, armed with terrible scythe-like weapons; and the sullen, slant-eyed girls of the palace, in skirts of vermilion and breast-cups of lazuli, went to and fro among huge basaltic columns. About the hall stood numerous engineries of wood and stone and metal such as Fulbra had never beheld, and having a formidable aspect with their heavy chains, their beds of iron teeth and their cords and pulleys of fish-skin.

The young king of Yoros went forward with a royal and fearless bearing, and addressed Ildrac, who sat motionless and eyed him with a level, unwinking gaze. And Fulbra told Ildrac his name and station, and the calamity that had caused him to flee from Yoros; and he mentioned also his urgent desire to reach the Isle of Cyntrom.

"It is a long voyage to Cyntrom," said Ildrac, with a subtle smile. "Also, it is not our custom to permit guests to depart without having fully tasted the hospitality of the Isle of Uccastrog. Therefore, King

Fulbra, I must beg you to curb your impatience. We have much to show you here, and many diversions to offer. My chamberlains will now conduct you to a room befitting your royal rank. But first I must ask you to leave with me the sword that you carry at your side; for swords are often sharp—and I do not wish my guests to suffer injury by their own hand."

So Fulbra's sword was taken from him by one of the palace guardsmen; and a small ruby-hilted dagger that he carried was also removed. Then several of the guards, hemming him in with their scythed weapons, led him from the hall and by many corridors and downward flights of stairs into the solid rock beneath the palace. And he knew not whither his three slaves were taken, or what disposition was made of the captured crew of the galley. And soon he passed from the daylight into cavernous halls illumed by sulfur-colored flames in copper cressets; and all around him, in hidden chambers, he heard the sound of dismal moans and loud, maniacal howlings that seemed to beat and die upon adamantine doors.

In one of these halls, Fulbra and his guardsmen met a young girl, fairer and less sullen of aspect than the others; and Fulbra thought that the girl smiled upon him compassionately as he went by; and it seemed that she murmured faintly in the language of Yoros: "Take heart, King Fulbra, for there is one who would help you." And her words, apparently, were not heeded or understood by the guards, who knew only the harsh and hissing tongue of Uccastrog.

After descending many stairs, they came to a ponderous door of bronze; and the door was unlocked by one of the guards, and Fulbra was compelled to enter; and the door clanged dolorously behind him.

The chamber into which he had been thrust was walled on three sides with the dark stone of the island, and was walled on the fourth with heavy, unbreakable glass. Beyond the glass he saw the blue-green, glimmering waters of the undersea, lit by the hanging cressets of the chamber; and in the waters were great devil-fish whose tentacles writhed along the wall; and huge pythonomorphs with fabulous golden coils receding in the gloom; and the floating corpses of men that stared in upon him with eyeballs from which the lids had been excised.

There was a couch in one corner of the dungeon, close to the wall of glass; and food and drink had been supplied for Fulbra in vessels of wood. The king laid himself down, weary and hopeless, without tasting the food. Then, lying with close-shut eyes while the dead men and sea-monsters peered in upon him by the glare of the cressets, he strove to forget his griefs and the dolorous doom that impended. And through his clouding terror and sorrow, he seemed to see the comely face of the girl who had smiled upon him compassionately, and who, alone of all that he had met in Uccastrog, had spoken to him with words of kindness. The face returned ever and anon, with a soft haunting, a gentle sorcery; and Fulbra felt, for the first time in many suns, the dim stirring of his buried youth and the vague, obscure desire of life. So, after a while, he slept; and the face of the girl came still before him in his dreams.

The cressets burned above him with undiminished flames when he awakened; and the sea beyond the wall of glass was thronged with the same monsters as before, or with others of like kind. But amid the floating corpses he now beheld the flayed bodies of his own slaves, who, after being tortured by the island people, had been cast forth into the submarine cavern that adjoined his dungeon, so that he might see them on awakening.

He sickened with new horror at the sight; but even as he stared at the dead faces, the door of bronze swung open with a sullen grinding, and his guards entered. Seeing that he had not consumed the food and water provided for him, they forced him to eat and drink a little, menacing him with their broad, crooked blades till he complied. And then they led him from the dungeon and took him before King Ildrac, in the great hall of tortures.

Fulbra saw, by the level golden light through the palace windows

and the long shadows of the columns and machines of torment, that
the time was early dawn. The hall was crowded with the Torturers and
their women; and many seemed to look on while others, of both sexes,
busied themselves with ominous preparations. And Fulbra saw that a
tall brazen statue, with cruel and demonian visage, like some implacable god of the underworld, was now standing at the right hand of Ildrac where he sat aloft on his brazen chair.

Fulbra was thrust forward by his guards, and Ildrac greeted him
briefly, with a wily smile that preceded the words and lingered after
them. And when Ildrac had spoken, the brazen image also began to
speak, addressing Fulbra in the language of Yoros, with strident and
metallic tones, and telling him with full and minute circumstance the
various infernal tortures to which he was to be subjected on that day.

When the statue had done speaking, Fulbra heard a soft whisper in
his ear, and saw beside him the fair girl whom he had previously met in
the nether corridors. And the girl, seemingly unheeded by the Torturers, said to him: "Be courageous, and endure bravely all that is inflicted; for I shall effect your release before another day, if this be
possible."

Fulbra was cheered by the girl's assurance; and it seemed to him
that she was fairer to look upon than before; and he thought that her
eyes regarded him tenderly; and the twin desires of love and life were
strangely resurrected in his heart, to fortify him against the tortures of
Ildrac.

Of that which was done to Fulbra for the wicked pleasure of King
Ildrac and his people, it were not well to speak fully. For the islanders
of Uccastrog had designed innumerable torments, curious and subtle,
wherewith to harry and excruciate the five senses; and they could harry
the brain itself, driving it to extremes more terrible than madness; and
could take away the dearest treasures of memory and leave unutterable
foulness in their place.

On that day, however, they did not torture Fulbra to the uttermost. But they racked his ears with cacophonous sounds; with evil flutes that chilled the blood and curdled it upon his heart; with deep drums that seemed to ache in all his tissues; and thin tabors that wrenched his very bones. Then they compelled him to breathe the mounting fumes of braziers wherein the dried gall of dragons and the adipocere of dead cannibals were burned together with a fetid wood. Then, when the fire had died down, they freshened it with the oil of vampire bats; and Fulbra swooned, unable to bear the fetor any longer.

Later, they stripped away his kingly vestments and fastened about his body a silken girdle that had been freshly dipt in an acid corrosive only to human flesh; and the acid ate slowly, fretting his skin with infinite pangs.

Then, after removing the girdle lest it slay him, the Torturers brought in certain creatures that had the shape of ell-long serpents, but were covered from head to tail with sable hairs like those of a caterpillar. And these creatures twined themselves tightly about the arms and legs of Fulbra; and though he fought wildly in his revulsion, he could not loosen them with his hands; and the hairs that covered their constringent coils began to pierce his limbs like a million tiny needles, till he screamed with the agony. And when his breath failed him and he could scream no longer, the baby serpents were induced to relinquish their hold by a languorous piping of which the islanders knew the secret. They dropped away and left him; but the mark of their coils was imprinted redly about his limbs; and around his body there burned the raw branding of the girdle.

King Ildrac and his people looked on with a dreadful gloating; for in such things they took their joy, and strove to pacify an implacable obscure desire. But seeing now that Fulbra could endure no more, and wishing to wreak their will upon him for many future days, they took him back to his dungeon.

Lying sick with remembered horror, feverish with pain, he longed not for the clemency of death, but hoped for the coming of the girl to release him as she had promised. The long hours passed with a half-delirious tedium; and the cressets, whose flames had been changed to crimson, appeared to fill his eyes with flowing blood; and the dead men and the sea-monsters swam as if in blood beyond the wall of glass. And the girl came not; and Fulbra had begun to despair. Then, at last, he heard the door open gently and not with the harsh clangor that had proclaimed the entrance of his guards.

Turning, he saw the girl, who stole swiftly to his couch with a lifted fingertip, enjoining silence. She told him with soft whispers that her plan had failed; but surely on the following night she would be able to drug the guards and obtain the keys of the outer gates; and Fulbra could escape from the palace to a hidden cove in which a boat with water and provisions lay ready for his use. She prayed him to endure for another day the torments of Ildrac; and to this, perforce, he consented. And he thought that the girl loved him; for tenderly she caressed his feverous brow, and rubbed his torture-burning limbs with a soothing ointment. He deemed that her eyes were soft with a compassion that was more than pity. So Fulbra believed the girl and trusted her, and took heart against the horror of the coming day. Her name, it seemed, was Ilvaa; and her mother was a woman of Yoros who had married one of the evil islanders, choosing this repugnant union as an alternative to the flaying-knives of Ildrac.

Too soon the girl went away, pleading the great danger of discovery, and closed the door softly upon Fulbra. And after a while the king slept; and Ilvaa returned to him amid the delirious abominations of his dreams, and sustained him against the terror of strange hells.

At dawn the guards came with their hooked weapons, and led him again before Ildrac. And again the brazen, demoniac statue, in a strident voice, announced the fearful ordeals that he was to undergo. And this time he saw that other captives, including the crew and merchants of the galley, were also awaiting the malefic ministrations of the Torturers in the vast hall.

Once more in the throng of watchers the girl Ilvaa pressed close to him, unreprimanded by his guards, and murmured words of comfort; so that Fulbra was enheartened against the enormities foretold by the brazen oracular image. And indeed a bold and hopeful heart was required to endure the ordeals of that day . . . .

Among other things less goodly to be mentioned, the Torturers held before Fulbra a mirror of strange wizardry, wherein his own face was reflected as if seen after death. The rigid features, as he gazed upon them, became marked with the green and bluish marbling of corruption; and the withering flesh fell in on the sharp bones, and displayed the visible fretting of the worm. Hearing meanwhile the dolorous groans and agonizing cries of his fellow captives all about the hall, he beheld other faces, dead, swollen, lidless, and flayed, that seemed to approach him from behind and to throng about his own face in the mirror. Their locks were dank and dripping, like the hair of corpses recovered from the sea; and sea-weed was mingled with the locks. Then, turning at a cold and clammy touch, he found that these faces were no illusion but the actual reflection of cadavers drawn from the under-sea by a malign sorcery, that had entered the hall of Ildrac like living men and were peering over his shoulder.

His own slaves, with flesh that the sea-things had gnawed even to the bone, were among them. And the slaves came toward him with glaring eyes that saw only the voidness of death. And beneath the sorcerous control of Ildrac, their evilly animated corpses began to assail Fulbra, clawing at his face and raiment with half-eaten fingers. And Fulbra, faint with loathing, struggled against his dead slaves, who knew not the voice of their master and were deaf as the wheels and racks of torment used by Ildrac. . . .

Anon the drowned and dripping corpses went away; and Fulbra was stripped by the Torturers and was laid supine on the palace floor, with iron rings that bound him closely to the flags at knee and wrist, at elbow and ankle. Then they brought in the disinterred body of a woman, nearly eaten, in which a myriad maggots swarmed on the uncovered bones and tatters of dark corruption; and this body they placed on the right hand of Fulbra. And also they fetched the carrion of a black goat that was newly touched with beginning decay; and they laid it down beside him on the left hand. Then, across Fulbra, from right to left, the hungry maggots crawled in a long and undulant wave . . . .

After the consummation of this torture, there came many others that were equally ingenious and atrocious, and were well designed for the delectation of King Ildrac and his people. And Fulbra endured the tortures valiantly, upheld by the thought of Ilvaa.

Vainly, however, on the night that followed this day, he waited in his dungeon for the girl. The cressets burned with a bloodier crimson; and new corpses were among the flayed and floating dead in the sea-cavern; and strange double-bodied serpents of the nether deep arose with an endless squirming; and their horned heads appeared to bloat immeasurably against the crystal wall. Yet the girl Ilvaa came not to free him as she had promised; and the night passed. But though despair resumed its old dominion in the heart of Fulbra, and terror came with talons steeped in fresh venom, he refused to doubt Ilvaa, telling himself that she had been delayed or prevented by some unforeseen mishap.

At dawn of the third day, he was again taken before Ildrac. The brazen image, announcing the ordeals of the day, told him that he was to be bound on a wheel of adamant; and, lying on the wheel, was to drink a drugged wine that would steal away his royal memories for ever, and would conduct his naked soul on a long pilgrimage through monstrous and infamous hells before bringing it back to the hall of Ildrac and the broken body on the wheel.

Then certain women of the Torturers, laughing obscenely, came forward and bound King Fulbra to the adamantine wheel with thongs of dragon-gut. And after they had done this, the girl Ilvaa, smiling with the shameless exultation of open cruelty, appeared before Fulbra and stood close beside him, holding a golden cup that contained the drugged wine. She mocked him for his folly and credulity in trusting her promises; and the other women and the male Torturers, even to Ildrac on his brazen seat, laughed loudly and evilly at Fulbra, and praised Ilvaa for the perfidy she had practiced upon him.

So Fulbra's heart grew sick with a darker despair then any he had yet known. The brief, piteous love that had been born amid sorrow and agony perished within him, leaving but ashes steeped in gall. Yet, gazing at Ilvaa with sad eyes, he uttered no word of reproach. He wished to live no longer; and yearning for a swift death, he bethought him of the wizard ring of Vemdeez and of that which Vemdeez had said would follow its removal from his finger. He still wore the ring which the Torturers had deemed a bauble of small value. But his hands were bound tightly to the wheel, and he could not remove it. So, with a bitter cunning, knowing full well that the islanders would not take away the ring if he should offer it to them, he feigned a sudden madness and cried wildly:

"Steal my memories, if ye will, with your accursed wine—and send me through a thousand hells and bring me back again to Uccastrog: but take not the ring that I wear on my middle finger; for it is more precious to me than many kingdoms or the pale breasts of love."

Hearing this, King Ildrac rose from his brazen seat; and bidding Ilvaa to delay the administration of the wine, he came forward and inspected curiously the ring of Vemdeez, which gleamed darkly, set with its rayless gem, on Fulbra's finger. And all the while, Fulbra cried out against him in a frenzy, as if fearing that he would take the ring.

So Ildrac, deeming that he could plague the prisoner thereby and could heighten his suffering a little, did the very thing for which Fulbra had planned. And the ring came easily from the shrunken finger; and Ildrac, wishing to mock the royal captive, placed it on his own middle digit.

Then, while Ildrac regarded the captive with a more deeply graven smile of evil on the pale, gilded mask of his face, there came to King Fulbra of Yoros the dreadful and longed-for thing. The Silver Death, that had slept so long in his body beneath the magical abeyance of the ring of Vemdeez, was made manifest even as he hung on the adamantine wheel. His limbs stiffened with another rigor than that of agony; and his face shone brightly with the coming of the Death; and so he died.

Then, to Ilvaa and to many of the Torturers who stood wondering about the wheel, the chill and instant contagion of the Silver Death was communicated. They fell even where they had stood; and the pestilence remained like a glittering light on the faces and the hands of the men and shone forth from the nude bodies of the women. And the plague passed along the immense hall; and the other captives of King Ildrac were released thereby from their various torments; and the Torturers found surcease from the dire longing that they could assuage only through the pain of their fellowmen. And through all the palace, and throughout the Isle of Uccastrog, the Death flew swiftly, visible in those upon whom it had breathed, but otherwise unseen and impalpable.

But Ildrac, wearing the ring of Vemdeez, was immune. And guessing not the reason for his immunity, he beheld with consternation the doom that had overtaken his followers, and watched in stupefaction the freeing of his victims. Then, fearful of some inimic sorcery, he rushed from the hall; and standing in the early sun on a palace-terrace above the sea, he tore the ring of Vemdeez from his finger and hurled it to the foamy billows far below, deeming in his terror that the ring was perhaps the source or agent of the unknown hostile magic.

So Ildrac, in his turn, when all the others had fallen, was smitten by the Silver Death; and its peace descended upon him where he lay in his robes of blood-brightened purple, with features shining palely to the unclouded sun. And oblivion claimed the Isle of Uccastrog; and the Torturers were one with the tortured.

IN THE BOOK OF VERGAMA

It was said of Vergama, in the lattermost ages, that he had existed immortally ever since the lifting of Zothique from the foundered ruins of continents that history had forgotten. Always, throughout the wide realms and empires of the continent, there had been rumors of Vergama, and various beliefs about his identity, his essence, his birth-place and dwelling-place. The sages disputed learnedly whether he was demon, god, sorcerer, phantom, or a being from worlds whose inhab-itants were not akin to any of these. Likewise they debated whether he dwelt in mummy-peopled Cincor, or amid the stark fearful mountains of northern Xylac, or in Naat, isle of evil gramaries lying shrouded with the mist and foam of the sunset ocean, or in some other kingdom or sea-lost island.

No idols were wrought in the image of Vergama, no altars were dedicated to him: yet sometimes he was addressed in prayer by savage peoples, or was called upon with dark runic formulæ by the more ven-turous wizards. Some claimed that the prayers and the incantations were answered; but this, like all else that concerned Vergama, was a matter of much doubt. Curious and almost omnipotent powers were ascribed to him, and attributes of tremendous bale and benignity; but there was no virtual proof of their manifestation at any time. In a land of murky enchantments, of multiform mysteries, Vergama resided un-known, occult, and apart. It was believed that vast multitudes of peo-ple had entered his secret house through the centuries and milleniums; but none had returned therefrom to declare the actual nature of Ver-gama and the situation of his abode. Certain prophets, appearing in the ultimate years, avowed that he was coeval with life and death, and was the first and the last of the uncreated gods.

Even till the ending of time, weird legends gathered about Vergama; and there were diverse tales of the destinies of them that passed into his shadowy mansion; and much was fabled concerning a volume called the Book of Hieroglyphics, which belonged to this inscrutable entity. Among such tales and fablings, there is the story of what happened to Nushain, the astrologer.

THE LAST HIEROGLYPH

The world itself, in the end, shall be turned to a round cipher.
—*Old prophecy of Zothique.*

Nushain the astrologer had studied the circling orbs of night from many far-separated regions, and had cast, with such skill as he was able to command, the horoscopes of a myriad men, women and children. From city to city, from realm to realm he had gone, abiding briefly in any place: for often the local magistrates had banished him as a common charlatan; or elsewise, in due time, his consultants had discovered the error of his predictions and had fallen away from him. Sometimes he went hungry and shabby; and small honor was paid to him anywhere. The sole companions of his precarious fortunes were a wretched mongrel dog that had somehow attached itself to him in the desert town of Zul-Bha-Sair, and a mute, one-eyed negro whom he had bought very cheaply in Yoros. He had named the dog Ansarath, after the canine star, and had called the negro Mouzda, which was a word signifying darkness.

In the course of his prolonged itinerations, the astrologer came to Xylac and made his abode in its capital, Ummaos, which had been built above the shards of an elder city of the same name, long since destroyed by a sorcerer's wrath. Here Nushain lodged with Ansarath and Mouzda in a half-ruinous attic of a rotting tenement; and from the tenement's roof, Nushain was wont to observe the positions and movements of the sidereal bodies on evenings not obscured by the fumes of the city. At intervals some housewife or jade, some porter or huckster or petty merchant, would climb the decaying stairs to his chamber, and would pay him a small sum for the nativity which he plotted with immense care by the aid of his tattered books of astrological science.

When, as often occurred, he found himself still at a loss regarding the significance of some heavenly conjunction or opposition after poring over his books, he would consult Ansarath, and would draw profound auguries from the variable motions of the dog's mangy tail or his actions in searching for fleas. Certain of these divinations were fulfilled, to the considerable benefit of Nushain's renown in Ummaos. People came to him more freely and frequently, hearing that he was a soothsayer of some note; and, moreover, he was immune from prosecution, owing to the liberal laws of Xylac, which permitted all the sorcerous and mantic arts.

It seemed, for the first time, that the dark planets of his fate were yielding to auspicious stars. For this fortune, and the coins which accrued thereby to his purse, he gave thanks to Vergama who, throughout the whole continent of Zothique, was deemed the most powerful and mysterious of the genii, and was thought to rule over the heavens as well as the earth.

On a summer night, when the stars were strewn thickly like a fiery sand on the black azure vault, Nushain went up to the roof of his lodging-place. As was often his custom, he took with him the negro Mouzda, whose one eye possessed a miraculous sharpness and had served well, on many occasions, to supplement the astrologer's own rather near-sighted vision. Through a well codified system of signs and gestures, the mute was able to communicate the result of his observations to Nushain.

On this night the constellation of the Great Dog, which had presided over Nushain's birth, was ascendant in the east. Regarding it closely, the dim eyes of the astrologer were troubled by a sense of something unfamiliar in its configuration. He could not determine the precise character of the change till Mouzda, who evinced much excitement, called his attention to three new stars of the second magnitude which had appeared in close proximity to the Dog's hindquarters. These remarkable novæ, which Nushain could discern only as three reddish blurs, formed a small equilateral triangle. Nushain and Mouzda were both certain that they had not been visible on any previous evening.

"By Vergama, this is a strange thing," swore the astrologer, filled with amazement and dumbfoundment. He began to compute the problematic influence of the novæ on his future reading of the heavens, and perceived at once that they would exert, according to the law of astral emanations, a modifying effect on his own destiny, which had been so largely controlled by the Dog.

He could not, however, without consulting his books and tables, decide the particular trend and import of this supervening influence; though he felt sure that it was most momentous, whether for his bale or welfare. Leaving Mouzda to watch the heavens for other prodigies, he descended at once to his attic. There, after collating the opinions of several old-time astrologers on the power exerted by novæ, he began to re-cast his own horoscope. Painfully and with much agitation he labored throughout the night, and did not finish his figurings till the dawn came to mix a deathly greyness with the yellow light of the candles.

There was, it seemed, but one possible interpretation of the altered heavens. The appearance of the triangle of novæ in conjunction with the Dog signified clearly that Nushain was to start ere long on an unpremeditated journey which would involve the transit of no less than three elements. Mouzda and Ansarath were to accompany him; and three guides, appearing successively, at the proper times, would lead him toward a destined goal. So much his calculations had revealed, but no more: there was nothing to foretell whether the journey would prove auspicious or disastrous, nothing to indicate its bourn, purpose or direction.

The astrologer was much disturbed by this somewhat singular and equivocal augury. He was ill pleased by the prospect of an imminent journey, for he did not wish to leave Ummaos, among whose credulous people he had begun to establish himself not without success. Moreover, a strong apprehension was roused within him by the oddly manifold nature and veiled outcome of the journey. All this, he felt, was suggestive of the workings of some occult and perhaps sinister providence; and surely it was no common travelling which would take him through three elements and would require a triple guidance.

During the nights that followed, he and Mouzda watched the mysterious novæ as they went over toward the west behind the bright-flaming Dog. And he puzzled interminably over his charts and volumes, hoping to discover some error in the reading he had made. But always, in the end, he was compelled to the same interpretation.

More and more, as time went on, he was troubled by the thought of that unwelcome and mysterious journey which he must make. He continued to prosper in Ummaos, and it seemed that there was no conceivable reason for his departure from that city. He was as one who awaited a dark and secret summons, not knowing whence it would come, nor at what hour. Throughout the days, he scanned with fearful anxiety the faces of his visitors, deeming that the first of the three star-predicted guides might arrive unheralded and unrecognized among them.

Mouzda and the dog Ansarath, with the intuition of dumb things, were sensible of the weird uneasiness felt by their master. They shared it palpably, the negro showing his apprehension by wild and demoniac grimaces, and the dog crouching under the astrologer's table or prowling restlessly to and fro with his half-hairless tail between his legs. Such behavior, in its turn, served to reconfirm the inquietude of Nushain, who deemed it a bad omen.

On a certain evening, Nushain pored for the fiftieth time over his horoscope, which he had drawn with sundry-colored inks on a sheet of papyrus. He was much startled when, on the blank lower margin of the sheet, he saw a curious character which was no part of his own scribbling. The character was a hieroglyph written in dark bituminous brown, and seeming to represent a mummy whose shroudings were loosened about the legs and whose feet were set in the posture of a long stride. It was facing toward that quarter of the chart where stood the sign indicating the Great Dog, which, in Zothique, was a House of the Zodiac.

Nushain's surprise turned to a sort of trepidation as he studied the hieroglyph. He knew that the margin of the chart had been wholly clear on the previous night; and during the past day he had not left the attic at any time. Mouzda, he felt sure, would never have dared to touch the chart; and, moreover, the negro was little skilled in writing. Among the various inks employed by Nushain, there was none that resembled the sullen brown of the character, which seemed to stand out in a sad relief on the white papyrus.

Nushain felt the alarm of one who confronts a sinister and unexplainable apparition. No human hand, surely, had inscribed the mummy-shapen character, like the sign of a strange outer planet about to invade the Houses of his horoscope. Here, as in the advent of the three novæ, an occult agency was suggested. Vainly, for many hours, he sought to unriddle the mystery: but in all his books there was naught to enlighten him; for this thing, it seemed, was wholly without precedent in astrology.

During the next day he was busied from morn till eve with the plotting of those destinies ordained by the heavens for certain people of Ummaos. After completing the calculations with his usual toilsome care, he unrolled his own chart once more, albeit with trembling fingers. An eeriness that was nigh to panic seized him when he saw that the brown hieroglyph no longer stood on the margin, but was now placed like a striding figure in one of the lower Houses, where it still fronted toward the Dog, as if advancing on that ascendant sign.

Henceforth the astrologer was fevered with the awe and curiosity

of one who watches a fatal but inscrutable portent. Never, during the
hours that he pondered above it, was there any change in the intruding
character; and yet, on each successive evening when he took out the
chart, he saw that the mummy had strode upward into a higher House,
drawing always nearer to the House of the Dog. . . .

There came a time when the figure stood on the Dog's threshold.
Portentous with mystery and menace that were still beyond the astrologer's divining, it seemed to wait while the night wore on and was shot
through with the grey wefting of dawn. Then, overworn with his prolonged studies and vigils, Nushain slept in his chair. Without the troubling of any dream he slept; and Mouzda was careful not to disturb him;
and no visitors came to the attic on that day. So the morn and the noon
and the afternoon went over, and their going was unheeded by Nushain.

He was awakened at eve by the loud and dolorous howling of Ansarath, which appeared to issue from the room's farthest corner. Confusedly, ere he opened his eyes, he became aware of an odor of bitter
spices and piercing natron. Then, with the dim webs of sleep not wholly swept from his vision, he beheld, by the yellowy tapers that Mouzda
had lighted, a tall, mummy-like form that waited in silence beside him.
The head, arms and body of the shape were wound closely with bitu-
men-colored cerements; but the folds were loosened from the hips
downward, and the figure stood like a walker, with one brown, withered foot in advance of its fellow.

Terror quickened in Nushain's heart, and it came to him that the
shrouded shape, whether lich or phantom, resembled the weird, invasive
hieroglyph that had passed from House to House through the chart of
his destiny. Then, from the thick swathings of the apparition, a voice issued indistinctly, saying: "Prepare yourself, O Nushain, for I am the
first guide of that journey which was foretold to you by the stars."

Ansarath, cowering beneath the astrologer's bed, was still howling
his fear of the visitant; and Nushain saw that Mouzda had tried to conceal himself in company with the dog. Though a chill as of imminent

death was upon him, and he deemed the apparition to be death itself, Nushain arose from his chair with that dignity proper to an astrologer, which he had maintained through all the vicissitudes of his lifetime. He called Mouzda and Ansarath from their hiding-place, and the two obeyed him, though with many cringings before the dark, muffled mummy.

With the comrades of his fortunes behind him, Nushain turned to the visitant. "I am ready," he said, in a voice whose quavering was almost imperceptible. "But I would take with me certain of my belongings."

The mummy shook his mobled head. "It were well to take with you nothing but your horoscope: for this alone shall you retain in the end."

Nushain stooped above the table on which he had left his nativity. Before he began to roll the open papyrus, he noticed that the hieroglyph of the mummy had vanished. It was as if the written symbol, after moving athwart his horoscope, had materialized itself in the figure that now attended him. But on the chart's nether margin, in remote opposition to the Dog, was the sea-blue hieroglyph of a quaint merman with carp-like tail and head half human, half apish; and behind the merman was the black hieroglyph of a small barge.

Nushain's fear, for a moment, was subdued by wonder. But he rolled the chart carefully, and stood holding it in his right hand.

"Come," said the guide. "Your time is brief, and you must pass through the three elements that guard the dwelling-place of Vergama from unseasonable intrusion."

These words, in a measure, confirmed the astrologer's divinations. But the mystery of his future fate was in no wise lightened by the intimation that he must enter, presumably at the journey's end, the dim House of that being called Vergama, whom some considered the most secret of all the gods, and others, the most cryptical of demons. In all the lands of Zothique, there were rumors and fables regarding Vergama; but these were wholly diverse and contradictory, except in their common attribution of almost omnipotent powers to this entity. No man knew the situation of his abode; but it was believed that vast multitudes of people had entered it during the centuries and millenniums, and that none had returned therefrom.

Ofttimes had Nushain called upon the name of Vergama, swearing or protesting thereby as men are wont to do by the cognomens of their shrouded lords. But now, hearing the name from the lips of his macabre visitor, he was filled with the darkest and most eerie apprehensions. He sought to subdue these feelings, and to resign himself to the manifest will of the stars. With Mouzda and Ansarath at his heels, he followed the striding mummy, which seemed little hampered, if at all, by its trailing cerements.

With one regretful backward glance at his littered books and papers, he passed from the attic room and down the tenement stairs. A wannish light seemed to cling about the swathings of the mummy; but, apart from this, there was no illumination; and Nushain thought that the house was strangely dark and silent, as if all its occupants had died or had gone away. He heard no sound from the evening city; nor could he see aught but close-encroaching darkness beyond the windows that should have gazed on a litten street. Also, it seemed that the stairs had changed and lengthened, giving no more on the courtyard of the tenement, but plunging deviously into an unsuspected region of stifling vaults and foul, dismal, nitrous corridors.

Here the air was pregnant with death, and the heart of Nushain failed him. Everywhere, in the shadow-curtained crypts and deep-shelved recesses, he felt the innumerable presence of the dead. He thought that there was a sad sighing of stirred cerements, a breath exhaled by long-stiffened cadavers, a dry clicking of lipless teeth beside him as he went. But darkness walled his vision, and he saw nothing save the luminous form of his guide, who stalked onward as if through a natal realm.

It seemed to Nushain that he passed through boundless catacombs in which were housed the mortality and corruption of all the ages. Behind him still he heard the shuffling of Mouzda, and at whiles the low, frightened whine of Ansarath; so he knew that the twain were faithful to him. But upon him, with a chill of lethal damps, there grew the horror of his surroundings; and he shrank with all the repulsion of living flesh from the shrouded thing that he followed, and those other things that mouldered round about in the fathomless gloom.

Half thinking to hearten himself by the sound of his own voice, he began to question the guide; though his tongue clove to his mouth as if palsied. "Is it indeed Vergama, and none other, who has summoned me forth upon this journey? For what purpose has he called me? And in what land is his dwelling?"

"Your fate has summoned you," said the mummy. "In the end, at the time appointed and no sooner, you shall learn the purpose. As to your third question, you would be no wiser if I should name the region in which the house of Vergama is hidden from mortal trespass: for the land is not listed on any terrene chart, nor map of the starry heavens."

These answers seemed equivocal and disquieting to Nushain, who was possessed by frightful forebodings as he went deeper into the subterranean charnels. Dark, indeed, he thought, must be the goal of a journey whose first stage had led him so far amid the empire of death and corruption; and dubious, surely, was the being who had called him forth and had sent to him as the first guide a sere and shrunken mummy clad in the tomb's habiliments.

Now, as he pondered these matters almost to frenzy, the shelfy walls of the catacomb before him were outlined by a dismal light, and he came after the mummy into a chamber where tall candles of black pitch in sockets of tarnished silver burned about an immense and solitary sarcophagus. Upon the blank lid and sides of the sarcophagus, as Nushain neared it, he could see neither runes nor sculptures nor hieroglyphs engraven; but seemed, from the proportions, that a giant must lie within.

The mummy passed athwart the chamber without pausing. But

Nushain, seeing that the vaults beyond were full of darkness, drew back with a reluctance that he could not conquer; and though the stars had decreed his journey, it seemed to him that human flesh could go no farther. Prompted by a sudden impulse, he seized one of the heavy yard-long tapers that burned stilly about the sarcophagus; and, holding it in his left hand, with his horoscope still firmly clutched in the right, he fled with Mouzda and Ansarath on the way he had come, hoping to retrace his footsteps through the gloomy caverns and return to Ummaos by the taper's light.

He heard no sound of pursuit from the mummy. But ever, as he fled, the pitch candle, flaring wildly, revealed to him the horrors that darkness had curtained from his eyes. He saw the bones of men that were piled in repugnant confusion with those of fell monsters, and the riven sarcophagi from which protruded the half-decayed members of innominate beings; members which were neither heads nor hands nor feet. And soon the catacomb divided and redivided before him, so that he must choose his way at random, not knowing whether it would lead him back to Ummaos or into the untrod depths.

Presently he came to the huge, browless skull of an uncouth creature, which reposed on the ground with upward-gazing orbits; and beyond the skull was the monster's mouldy skeleton, wholly blocking the passage. Its ribs were cramped by the narrowing walls, as if it had crept there and had died in the darkness, unable to withdraw or go forward. White spiders, demon-headed and large as monkeys, had woven their webs in the hollow arches of the bones; and they swarmed out interminably as Nushain approached; and the skeleton seemed to stir and quiver as they seethed over it abhorrently and dropped to the ground before the astrologer. Behind them others poured in a countless army, crowding and mantling every ossicle. Nushain fled with his companions; and running back to the forking of the caverns, he followed another passage.

Here he was not pursued by the demon spiders. But, hurrying on lest they or the mummy overtake him, he was soon halted by the rim of a great pit which filled the catacomb from wall to wall and was overwide for the leaping of man. The dog Ansarath, sniffing certain odors that arose from the pit, recoiled with a mad howling; and Nushain, holding the taper outstretched above it, discerned far down a glimmer of ripples spreading circle-wise on some unctuous black fluid; and two blood-red spots appeared to swim with a weaving motion at the center. Then he heard a hissing as of some great cauldron heated by wizard fires; and it seemed that the blackness boiled upward, mounting swiftly and evilly to overflow the pit; and the red spots, as they neared him, were like luminous eyes that gazed malignantly into his own. . . .

So Nushain turned away in haste; and, returning upon his steps, he found the mummy awaiting him at the junction of the catacombs.

"It would seem, O Nushain, that you have doubted your own horoscope," said the guide, with a certain irony. "However, even a bad astrologer, on occasion, may read the heavens aright. Obey, then, the stars that decreed your journey."

Henceforward, Nushain followed the mummy without recalcitrance. Returning to the chamber in which stood the immense sarcophagus, he was enjoined by his guide to replace in its socket the black taper he had stolen. Without other light than the phosphorescence of the mummy's cerements, he threaded the foul gloom of those profounder ossuaries which lay beyond. At last, through caverns where a dull dawning intruded upon the shadows, he came out beneath shrouded heavens, on the shore of a wild sea that clamored in mist and cloud and spindrift. As if recoiling from the harsh air and light, the mummy drew back into the subterrane, and it said:

"Here my dominion ends, and I must leave you to await the second guide."

Standing with the poignant sea-salt in his nostrils, with his hair and garments outblown on the gale, Nushain heard a metallic clangor, and

saw that a door of rusty bronze had closed in the cavern-entrance. The
beach was walled by unscalable cliffs that ran sheerly to the wave on
each hand. So perforce the astrologer waited; and from the torn surf
he beheld erelong the emergence of a sea-blue merman whose head
was half human, half apish; and behind the merman there hove a small
black barge that was not steered or rowed by any visible being. At this,
Nushain recalled the hieroglyphs of the sea-creature and the boat
which had appeared on the margin of his nativity; and unrolling the
papyrus, he saw with wonderment that the figures were both gone; and
he doubted not that they had passed, like the mummy's hieroglyph,
through all the zodiacal Houses, even to that House which presided
over his destiny; and thence, mayhap, they had emerged into material
being. But in their stead now was the burning hieroglyph of a fire-
colored salamander, set opposite to the Great Dog.

The merman beckoned to him with antic gestures, grinning deeply,
and showing the white serrations of his shark-like teeth. Nushain went
forward and entered the barge in obedience to the signs made by the
sea-creature; and Mouzda and Ansarath, in faithfulness to their master,
accompanied him. Thereupon the merman swam away through the
boiling surf; and the barge, as if oared and ruddered by mere enchantment, swung about forthwith, and warring smoothly against the wind
and wave, was drawn straightly over that dim, unnamable ocean.

Half-seen amid rushing foam and mist, the merman swam steadily
on before. Time and space were surely outpassed during that voyage;
and as if he had gone beyond mortal existence, Nushain experienced
neither thirst nor hunger. But it seemed that his soul drifted upon seas
of strange doubt and direst alienation; and he feared the misty chaos
about him even as he had feared the nighted catacombs. Often he tried
to question the mer-creature concerning their destination, but received
no answer. And the wind blowing from shores unguessed, and the tide
flowing to unknown gulfs, were alike filled with whispers of awe and
terror.

Nushain pondered the mysteries of his journey almost to madness; and the thought came to him that, after passing through the region of death, he was now traversing the grey limbo of uncreated things; and, thinking this, he was loath to surmise the third stage of his journey; and he dared not reflect upon the nature of its goal.

Anon, suddenly, the mists were riven, and a cataract of golden rays poured down from a high-seated sun. Near at hand, to the lee of the driving barge, a tall island hove with verdurous trees and light, shell-shaped domes and blossomy gardens hanging far up in the dazzlement of noon. There, with a sleepy purling, the surf was lulled on a low, grassy shore that had not known the anger of storm; and fruited vines and full-blown flowers were pendent above the water. It seemed that a spell of oblivion and slumber was shed from the island, and that any who landed thereon would dwell inviolable forever in sun-bright dreams. Nushain was seized with a longing for its green, bowery refuge; and he wished to voyage no farther into the dreadful nothingness of the mist-bound ocean. And between his longing and his terror, he quite forgot the terms of that destiny which had been ordained for him by the stars.

There was no halting nor swerving of the barge; but it drew still nearer to the isle in its coasting; and Nushain saw that the intervening water was clear and shallow, so that a tall man might easily wade to the beach. He sprang into the sea, holding his horoscope aloft, and began to walk toward the island; and Mouzda and Ansarath followed him, swimming side by side.

Though hampered somewhat by his long wet robes, the astrologer thought to reach that alluring shore; nor was there any movement on the part of the merman to intercept him. The water was midway between his waist and his armpits; and now it lapped at his girdle; and now at the knee-folds of his garment; and the island vines and blossoms drooped fragrantly above him.

Then, being but a step from that enchanted beach, he heard a great

hissing, and saw that the vines, the boughs, the flowers, the very grasses, were intertwined and mingled with a million serpents, writhing endlessly to and fro in hideous agitation. From all parts of that lofty island
the hissing came, and the serpents, with foully mottled volumes,
coiled, crept and slithered upon it everywhere; and no single yard of its
surface was free from their defilement, or clear for human treading.

Turning seaward in his revulsion, Nushain found the merman and
the barge waiting close at hand. Hopelessly he re-entered the barge
with his followers, and the magically driven boat resumed its course.
And now, for the first time, the merman spoke, saying over his shoulder in a harsh, half-articulate voice, not without irony: "It would seem,
O Nushain, that you lack faith in your own divinations. However, even
the poorest of astrologers may sometimes cast a horoscope correctly.
Cease, then, to rebel against that which the stars have written."

The barge drove on, and the mists closed heavily about it, and the
noon-bright island was lost to view. After a vague interim the muffled
sun went down behind inchoate waters and clouds; and a darkness as
of primal night lay everywhere. Presently, through the torn rack,
Nushain beheld a strange heaven whose signs and planets he could not
recognize; and at this there came upon him the black horror of utmost
dereliction. Then the mists and clouds returned, veiling that unknown
sky from his scrutiny. And he could discern nothing but the merman,
who was visible by a wan phosphor that clung always about him in his
swimming.

Still the barge drove on; and in time it seemed that a red morning
rose stifled and conflagrant behind the mists. The boat entered the
broadening light, and Nushain, who had thought to behold the sun
once more, was dazzled by a strange shore where flames towered in a
high unbroken wall, feeding perpetually, to all appearances, on bare
sand and rock. With a mighty leaping and a roar as of blown surf the
flames went up, and a heat like that of many furnaces smote far on the
sea. Swiftly the barge neared the shore; and the merman, with uncouth

gestures of farewell, dived and disappeared under the waters.

Nushain could scarcely regard the flames or endure their heat. But the barge touched the strait tongue of land lying between them and the sea; and before Nushain, from the wall of fire, a blazing salamander emerged, having the form and hue of that hieroglyph which had last appeared on his horoscope. And he knew, with ineffable consternation, that this was the third guide of his threefold journey.

"Come with me," said the salamander, in a voice like the crackling of fagots. Nushain stepped from the barge to that strand which was hot as an oven beneath his feet; and behind him, though with palpable reluctance, Mouzda and Ansarath still followed. But, approaching the flames behind the salamander, and half swooning from their ardor, he was overcome by the weakness of mortal flesh; and seeking again to evade his destiny, he fled along the narrow scroll of beach between the fire and the water. But he had gone only a few paces when the salamander, with a great fiery roaring and racing, intercepted him; and it drove him straight toward the fire with terrible flailings of its dragon-like tail, from which showers of sparks were emitted. He could not face the salamander, and he thought the flames would consume him like paper as he entered them: but in the wall there appeared a sort of opening, and the fires arched themselves into an arcade, and he passed through with his followers, herded by the salamander, into an ashen land where all things were veiled with low-hanging smoke and steam. Here the salamander observed with a kind of irony: "Not wrongly, O Nushain, have you interpreted the stars of your horoscope. And now your journey draws to an end, and you will need no longer the services of a guide." So saying, it left him, going out like a quenched fire on the smoky air.

Nushain, standing irresolute, beheld before him a white stairway that mounted amid the veering vapors. Behind him the flames rose unbroken, like a topless rampart; and on either hand, from instant to instant, the smoke shaped itself into demon forms and faces that menaced him. He began to climb the stairs, and the shapes gathered below and about, frightful as a wizard's familiars, and keeping pace with him as he went upward, so that he dared not pause or retreat. Far up he climbed in the fumy dimness, and came unaware to the open portals of a house of grey stone rearing to unguessed height and amplitude.

Unwillingly, but driven by the thronging of the smoky shapes, he passed through the portals with his companions. The house was a place of long, empty halls, tortuous as the folds of a sea-conch. There were no windows, no lamps; but it seemed that bright suns of silver had been dissolved and diffused in the air. Fleeing from the hellish wraiths that pursued him, the astrologer followed the winding halls and emerged ultimately in an inner chamber where space itself was immured. At the room's center a cowled and muffled figure of colossal proportions sat upright on a marble chair, silent, unstirring. Before the figure, on a sort of table, a vast volume lay open.

Nushain felt the awe of one who approaches the presence of some high demon or deity. Seeing that the phantoms had vanished, he paused on the room's threshold: for its immensity made him giddy, like the void interval that lies between the worlds. He wished to withdraw; but a voice issued from the cowled being, speaking softly as the voice of his own inmost mind:

"I am Vergama, whose other name is Destiny; Vergama, on whom you have called so ignorantly and idly, as men are wont to call on their hidden lords; Vergama, who has summoned you on the journey which all men must make at one time or another, in one way or another way. Come forward, O Nushain, and read a little in my book."

The astrologer was drawn as by an unseen hand to the table. Leaning above it, he saw that the huge volume stood open at its middle pages, which were covered with a myriad signs written in inks of various colors, and representing men, gods, fishes, birds, monsters, animals, constellations and many other things. At the end of the last column of the right-hand page, where little space was left for other inscriptions, Nushain beheld the hieroglyphs of an equal-sided triangle of stars, such as had lately appeared in proximity to the Dog; and, following these, the hieroglyphs of a mummy, a merman, a barge and a salamander, resembling the figures that had come and gone on his horoscope, and those that had guided him to the house of Vergama.

"In my book," said the cowled figure, "the characters of all things are written and preserved. All visible forms, in the beginning, were but symbols written by me; and at the last they shall exist only as the writing of my book. For a season they issue forth, taking to themselves that which is known as substance. . . . It was I, O Nushain, who set in the heavens the stars that foretold your journey; I, who sent the three guides. And these things, having served their purpose, are now but infoliate ciphers, as before."

Vergama paused, and an infinite silence returned to the room, and a measureless wonder was upon the mind of Nushain. Then the cowled being continued:

"Among men, for a while, there was that person called Nushain the astrologer, together with the dog Ansarath and the negro Mouzda, who followed his fortunes. . . . But now, very shortly, I must turn the page, and before turning it, must finish the writing that belongs thereon."

Nushain thought that a wind arose in the chamber, moving lightly with a weird sigh, though he felt not the actual breath of its passing. But he saw that the fur of Ansarath, cowering close beside him, was ruffled by the wind. Then, beneath his marvelling eyes, the dog began to dwindle and wither, as if seared by a lethal magic; and he lessened to the size of a rat, and thence to the smallness of a mouse and the lightness of an insect, though preserving still his original form. After that, the tiny thing was caught up by the sighing air, and it flew past Nushain as a gnat might fly; and, following it, he saw that the hieroglyph of a dog was inscribed suddenly beside that of the salamander, at the bottom of the right-hand page. But, apart from this, there remained no trace of Ansarath.

Again a wind breathed in the room, touching not the astrologer, but fluttering the ragged raiment of Mouzda, who crouched near to his master, as if appealing for protection. And the mute became shrunken and shrivelled, turning at the last to a thing light and thin as the black, tattered wing-shard of a beetle, which the air bore aloft. And Nushain saw that the hieroglyph of a one-eyed negro was inscribed following that of the dog; but, aside from this, there was no sign of Mouzda.

Now, perceiving clearly the doom that was designed for him, Nushain would have fled from the presence of Vergama. He turned from the outspread volume and ran toward the chamber door, his worn, tawdry robes of an astrologer flapping about his thin shanks. But softly in his ear, as he went, there sounded the voice of Vergama:

"Vainly do men seek to resist or evade that destiny which turns them to ciphers in the end. In my book, O Nushain, there is room even for a bad astrologer."

Once more the weird sighing arose, and a cold air played upon Nushain as he ran; and he paused midway in the vast room as if a wall had arrested him. Gently the air breathed on his lean, gaunt figure, and it lifted his greying locks and beard, and it plucked softly at the roll of papyrus which he still held in his hand. To his dim eyes, the room seemed to reel and swell, expanding infinitely. Borne upward, around and around, in a swift vertiginous swirling, he beheld the seated shape as it loomed ever higher above him in cosmic vastness. Then the god was lost in light; and Nushain was a weightless and exile thing, the withered skeleton of a lost leaf, rising and falling on the bright whirlwind.

In the book of Vergama, at the end of the last column of the right-hand page, there stood the hieroglyph of a gaunt astrologer, carrying a furled nativity.

Vergama leaned forward from his chair, and turned the page.

CYCLES

The sorcerer departs . . . and his high tower is drowned
Slowly by low flat communal seas that level all . . .
While crowding centuries retreat, return and fall
Into the cyclic gulf that girds the cosmos round,
Widening, deepening ever outward without bound. . . .
Till the oft-rerisen bells from young Atlantis call;
And again the wizard-mortised tower upbuilds its wall
Above a re-beginning cycle, turret-crowned.

New-born, the mage re-summons stronger spells, and spirits
With dazzling darkness clad about, and fiercer flame
Renewed by aeon-curtained slumber. All the powers
Of genii and Solomon the sage inherits;
And there, to blaze with blinding glory the bored hours,
He calls upon Shem-hamphorash, the nameless Name.

EPILOGUE

The Final Cycle

The Zothique story cycle of the far future depicts the last days of the earth and human civilization, so is quite final in this respect. However, the title, or term, "The Final Cycle" is by definition an oxymoron and readers may well ask, How can a cycle be final? I'd like to think that Klarkash-Ton himself would approve of this paradox, not to mention its lyrical qualities. The concluding poem in this collection is another example of a Final Cycle. The sonnet "Cycles" was commissioned from Smith by Donald Sidney-Fryer for his bio-bibliography *Emperor of Dreams* and would be Smith's last poem, written only a few months before his death in 1961. It deals with new beginnings and describes how all things are subject to a cyclic rebirth in the fullness of time, a theme he returns to over and over during his literary career. It is hoped that in this same spirit his fans and acolytes will often revisit the world of Zothique, and that with each re-reading will continue to discover the deeper meanings and subtle ironies that are such integral aspects of the literary legacy of the Bard of Auburn.

ACKNOWLEDGMENTS

"The Black Abbot of Puthuum." *Weird Tales* 27, No. 3 (March 1936): 308–22. In *Genius Loci* (Arkham House, 1948). Text taken from *The Last Hieroglyph* (Night Shade Books, 2010).

"The Charnel God." *Weird Tales* 23, No. 3 (March 1934): 316–30. In *Genius Loci* (Arkham House, 1948). Text taken from *The Maze of the Enchanter* (Night Shade Books, 2009).

"The Corpse and the Skeleton." In *Poems in Prose* (Arkham House, 1965).

"Cycles." Glendale, CA: Roy A. Squires, March 1963. In Jack L. Chalker, ed., *In Memoriam: Clark Ashton Smith* ("Anthem"/Jack L. Chalker and Associates, 1963).

"The Dark Eidolon." *Weird Tales* 25, No. 1 (January 1935): 93–111. In *Out of Space and Time* (Arkham House, 1942). Text taken from *The Maze of the Enchanter* (Night Shade Books, 2009).

The Dead Will Cuckold You. In Jack L. Chalker, ed., *In Memoriam: Clark Ashton Smith* ("Anthem"/Jack L. Chalker and Associates, 1963). Text taken from *The Miscellaneous Writings of Clark Ashton Smith* (Night Shade Books, 2011).

"The Death of Illalotha." *Weird Tales* 30, No. 3 (September 1937): 323–30. In *Out of Space and Time* (Arkham House, 1942). Text taken from *The Last Hieroglyph* (Night Shade Books, 2010)

"The Empire of the Necromancers." *Weird Tales* 20, No. 3 (September 1932): 338–44. In *Lost Worlds* (Arkham House, 1944). Text taken from *A Vintage from Atlantis* (Night Shade Books, 2007).

"The Garden of Adompha." *Weird Tales* 31, No. 6 (June 1938): 393–400. In *Genius Loci* (Arkham House, 1948). Text taken from *The Last Hieroglyph* (Night Shade Books, 2010).

"In the Book of Vergama." In *Strange Shadows* (Greenwood Press, 1989).

"The Isle of the Torturers." *Weird Tales* 21, No. 3 (March 1933): 362–72. In *Lost Worlds* (Arkham House, 1944). Text taken from *The Maze of the Enchanter* (Night Shade Books, 2009).

"Lamia." *Arkham Sampler* 1, No. 1 (Winter 1948): 20. In *The Dark Chateau* (Arkham House, 1951).

"The Last Hieroglyph." *Weird Tales* 25, No. 4 (April 1935): 466–77. In *Out of Space and Time* (Arkham House, 1942). Text taken from *The Last Hieroglyph* (Night Shade Books, 2010).

"The Master of the Crabs." *Weird Tales* 40, No. 3 (March 1948): 64–71. In *The Abominations of Yondo* (Arkham House, 1960). Text taken from *The Last Hieroglyph* (Night Shade Books, 2010).

"Morthylla." *Weird Tales* 25, No. 4 (April 1935): 466–77. In *Tales of Science and Sorcery* (Arkham House, 1964). Text taken from *The Last Hieroglyph* (Night Shade Books, 2010).

"Nada." *Lyric* 37, No. 2 (Spring 1957): 42. In *Spells and Philtres* (Arkham House, 1958).

"Necromancy in Naat." *Weird Tales* 28, No. 1 (July 1936): 2–15. In *Lost Worlds* (Arkham House, 1944). Text taken from *The Last Hieroglyph* (Night Shade Books, 2010).

"A Phantasy." In *Ebony and Crystal* (Auburn Journal Press, 1922).

"The Tomb-Spawn." *Weird Tales* 23, No. 5 (May 1934): 634–40. In *Tales of Science and Sorcery* (Arkham House, 1964). Text taken from *The Last Hieroglyph* (Night Shade Books, 2010).

"The Traveller." In *Ebony and Crystal* (Auburn Journal Press, 1922).

"The Voyage of King Euvoran." In *The Double Shadow and Other Fantasies*. In *The Abominations of Yondo*. *Weird Tales* 39, No. 12 (September 1947): 4–13 (as "Quest of the Gazolba"; abridged). Text taken from *The Maze of the Enchanter* (Night Shade Books, 2009).

"The Weaver in the Vaults." *Weird Tales* 23, No. 1 (January 1934): 85–93. In *Genius Loci* (Arkham House, 1948). Text taken from *The Maze of the Enchanter* (Night Shade Books, 2009).

"The Witchcraft of Ulua." *Weird Tales* 23, No. 2 (February 1934): 253–59. In *The Abominations of Yondo* (Arkham House, 1960). Text taken from *The Last Hieroglyph* (Night Shade Books, 2010).

"Xeethra." *Weird Tales* 24, No. 6 (December 1934): 726–38. In *Lost Worlds* (Arkham House, 1944). Text taken from *The Last Hieroglyph* (Night Shade Books, 2010).

"Zothique." In *The Dark Chateau* (Arkham House, 1951).

CPSIA information can be obtained
at www.ICGtesting.com
Printed in the USA
BVHW031158190722
642428BV00016B/406